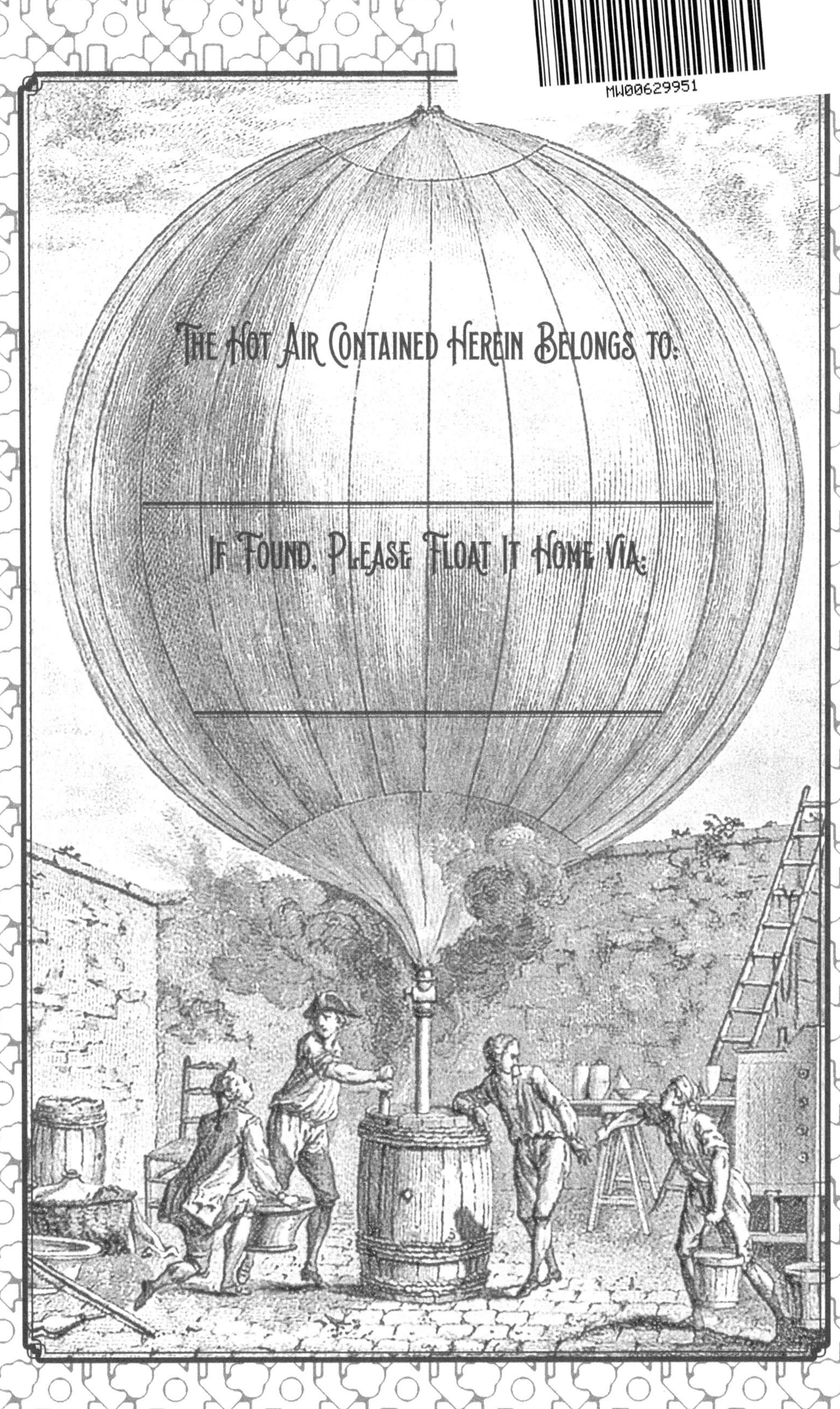
The Hot Air Contained Herein Belongs to:
If Found, Please Float It Home via:

BOOKS IN THIS SERIES:

The Politically Incorrect Real Estate Agent Handbook
A Serious How-to Manual with a Sense of Humor

The Politically Incorrect Real Estate Agent Logbook
A Daily Journal, Activity Tracker & Stats Generator

THE POLITICALLY INCORRECT REAL ESTATE AGENT LOG-BOOK

Daily Journal, Activity Tracker & Stats Generator

PETER F. PORCELLI JR.

BACKYARD BOOKWORKS
MARIETTA, GA

The Politically Incorrect Real Estate Agent Logbook

This publication is designed to provide accurate and authoritative information in regard to the subject matter covered. It is sold with the understanding that the publisher is not engaged in rendering legal, accounting, or other professional service. If legal advice or other expert assistance is required, the services of a competent professional should be sought. —From a *Declaration of Principles* jointly adopted by a committee of the American Bar Association and a committee of publishers and associations.

This book is an abridged compendium of the real estate sales process. For obvious reasons, the author, publisher, and editors disclaim any liability, in part or in whole, arising from the information contained herein. The reader is urged to independently verify the reference material prior to any detrimental reliance thereupon. The real estate sales industry is regulated by Federal, State, and local laws, ordinances, and regulations—and is ever changing. Act accordingly.

IMAGE CREDITS:
All images contained herein were procured via the Library of Congress, Prints & Photographs Division, and have been digitally-modified to remove blemishes, enhanced for contrast, and (at times) tweaked to fit content. Digital modifications were painstakingly performed by the author, with love.

Primarily set in Harriet Text and garnished with Playfair Display.

Backyard Bookworks
Marietta, GA
backyardbookworks.com

RealEstateAgentBook.com/Logbook

ISBN: 978-0-9989608-1-4

BISAC: BUS054000

Printed in the United States of America

3 5 7 9 0 8 6 4 2

FIRST EDITION

DEDICATED:

To those in pursuit of
fiscal insight,
purposeful action,
and personal growth.

Even if you're on the right track, you'll get run over if you just sit there.

—Will Rogers

CONTENTS

INTRODUCTION

How-to Maximize this Book . . . viii
How-to Use this Book (Step by Step) . . . ix
An Introduction to Your Stats & Their Formulas . . . x
Examples & Explanations
- JOURNAL PAGE & DAILY ACTIVITY TRACKER . . . xii
- ACTIVITY LOG . . . xiv
- TRANSACTION DATA & MARKET COMPARISON . . . xv
- CONVERSION RATIOS, TURNOVER RATES & OTHER METRICS . . . xvi
- LEVERAGE LOG . . . xvii
- QUARTERLY BUSINESS PLAN . . . xviii
- MONTHLY ACTIVITY TRACKER . . . xix
- DATABASE & REFERRAL METRICS . . . xx
- REFERRAL LOG . . . xxi

Ode to Momentum . . . xxiii

JOURNAL PAGES & DAILY ACTIVITY TRACKERS

January . . . 01-31
February . . . 01-29
March . . . 01-31
April . . . 01-30
May . . . 01-31
June . . . 01-30
July . . . 01-31
August . . . 01-31
September . . . 01-30
October . . . 01-31
November . . . 01-30
December . . . 01-31

YEAR ONE STATS & BUSINESS PLANS

Quarter 01 / Quarter 02 / Quarter 03 / Quarter 04 / Annual Report

YEAR TWO STATS & BUSINESS PLANS

Quarter 01 / Quarter 02 / Quarter 03 / Quarter 04 / Annual Report

YEAR THREE STATS & BUSINESS PLANS

Quarter 01 / Quarter 02 / Quarter 03 / Quarter 04 / Annual Report

ADDITIONAL REPORTS & TRACKERS

Tri-Annual Report
Referral Log
Education Log

FLOW CHARTS

Referral Flow Chart (RFC) . . . 341
Valuation Flow Chart (VFC) . . . 342
Buyer Flow Chart (BFC) . . . 344
Seller Flow Chart (SFC) . . . 345
Daily Flow Chart (DFC) . . . 346
Example Flow Chart (XFC) . . . 347

NOTE:

Roman numeral cross-references contained herein correspond to the INTRODUCTION pages of this book. *Flow Chart* page numbers and all three-digit cross-references correspond to pages in this book's parent publication: *The Politically Incorrect Real Estate Agent Handbook.*

You're Gonna Need:

Real Estate Activities
Daily Involvement
Pencil / Calculator
Introspection

How-to

Maximize this Book

This book is designed to help you (the real estate agent) make more money by combining three years of personal statistics with ongoing business contemplation. When you really know your numbers, think deeply about improvement, and then do something about it, more money is sure to come your way. Follow these steps to pad your pocket:

1 Study the System

Read-up on what's written down. Take the time to study every page of this introduction (all 14 pages). Then, make yourself familiar with the book's organization of pages; it's all about the tabs.

2 Be Deliberate & Truthful

Accurate reporting allows you to edit your business practices constructively, so be honest with daily figures. After all, accuracy and insight are achieved by dedicated record keeping of truthful data—not from lackadaisical estimations and self-pleasing fudgery.

3 Use It as a Tool for Growth

Agents who consistently improve their prospecting,[077] presentation,[167] valuation,[125] agency,[211] and negotiating skills[266] will eventually see an increased income stream. Each of these skills can be measured by a turnover rate.[XVI]

To foster your growth, use the turnover rates and other metrics measured in this book to choose which areas of your business to improve first.[XI] Start with your lowest turnover rate (which is your biggest bottleneck).[XVI] Use the *Flow Chart System*[341–347] to further identify and diagnose bottlenecks. Seek the education,[034] coaching,[043] and guidance you need to grow. Then, execute your real estate activities diligently. THINK→DO→TRACK→REPEAT.

Review your journal entries and keep thinking about ways to improve your scripts[048] and systems.[070] Think about the events that caused your numbers. How would a change of events have led to different metrics?

Use a BUSINESS PLAN to set realistic goals.[XVIII] Push yourself; get there.

4 Write in It Religiously

Write in this book every day; make it part of your routine. The sheer process of tracking your activities and calculating your stats will motivate you to prospect. Keep trying to out-perform last month; make it a game you play with yourself and you'll win every time. Plus, it's fun to see how your journal entries change from year to year. After three years of daily use, this book will be an historical record of your growth.

5 Get Your Rivals Involved

Urge your real estate buddies to buy a copy of this book. Then, compete with each other as motivation.[300] Comparing your numbers to other agents will instill in you a sense of pride or a reason to try harder.

tips

Don't be lazy. Track your daily activities and make your quarterly calculations; your wallet (and your clients) will thank you.

Raised, Roman numeral cross-references refer to pages within the introduction of this book.

Raised, three-digit cross-references refer to pages within this book's parent publication: *The Politically Incorrect Real Estate Agent Handbook.* These cross-references expound upon the topic they adorn. In other words, you can read all about it on that page (in the other book).

Don't wait until the new year to start tracking your activities; begin today, for an improved you.

So your paperback lays flat, cut the spine and spiral bind.

Be patient; it takes at least three months of data to create an accurate BUSINESS PLAN/GOALS and three consecutive quarters of math before a true trend of your stats is revealed.

Many more metrics may be calculated and studied from the datapoints in this book. If something is worth measuring to you, then track and measure it (NOTES pages in the back are great for such use).

Σ Growth comes to those who constructively foster themselves.

How-to Use this Book

PROLOGUE — STEP 1

Read the introduction and flip through this book; become familiar with its system.

PROLOGUE — STEP 2

Using your current metrics, establish your current goals with a BUSINESS PLAN (STARTER BUSINESS PLAN on page XVIII).

PROLOGUE — STEP 3

Transfer your current goals to this month's MONTHLY ACTIVITY TRACKER (found opposite DAY 01 of this month).

DAILY — STEP 4

Do your job; do that real estate voodoo that you do so well.

DAILY — STEP 5

Record today's real estate activities on the DAILY TRACKER (found on TODAY'S DATE).

DAILY — STEP 6

Answer today's journal prompt; think critically about your past so you can mindfully alter your future.

WEEKLY — STEP 7

Tally this week's activities & report them to the MONTHLY ACTIVITY TRACKER; this is an opportunity to adjust your goals mid-month (if need be).

MONTHLY — STEP 8

Transfer your activity tallies to this month's ACTIVITY LOG (found on QUARTERLY REPORT) & compare them to last month's activities.

MONTHLY — STEP 9

Repeat STEPS 3—9 until the end of the quarter.

QUARTERLY — STEP 10

Report your transaction data to the QUARTERLY REPORT & compare it to last quarter's figures.

QUARTERLY — STEP 11

Using your activity tallies and transaction data, calculate your metrics & compare them to last quarter.

QUARTERLY — STEP 12

Repeat STEPS 2—12 until the end of the year.

ANNUALLY — STEP 13

Transfer your quarterly activity tallies and transaction data to the ANNUAL REPORT. Calculate your metrics & compare to last year.

ANNUALLY — STEP 14

Repeat STEPS 4—14 until the end of three years. This is fun.

TRI-ANNUALLY — STEP 15

Transfer your annual stats to the TRI-ANNUAL REPORT & compare. Then, buy another copy of this book & repeat STEPS 4—15.

SYMBOL		EXPLAINED	EXAMPLE
Δ	delta	Delta represents change, and is used to compare datapoints & metrics from this period (month, quarter, or year) to the period proceeding.	Δ↑ 15 % :denotes a change of 15% *more* than last period.
|	naked arrow	The naked arrow immediately follows delta, allowing you to add its arrowhead, pointing in the direction of change—up or down.	Δ↓ 4 # :denotes a change of four tallies *less* than last period.

An Introduction to Your Stats & Their Formulas

The blanks in this book are meant for your figures. You supply the datapoints, which are then used to calculate turnover rates and other metrics. Don't worry; the formulas will be by your side during calculations.

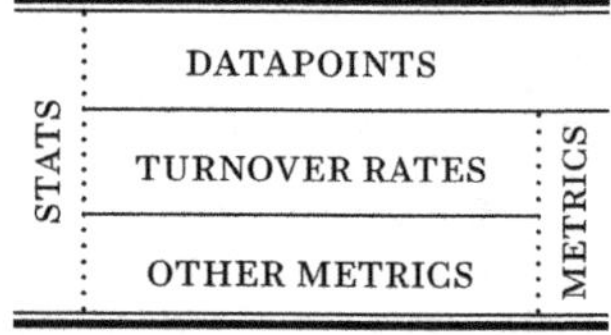

MODIFIERS

	FULL TITLE	EXPLAINED
L	LISTING	When a datapoint is written with L or B first, it measures listing or buyer-side only. *Example:* LP is listing presentation & BT is buyer transaction. Metrics may be calculated with modified datapoints. *Ex:* listing presentation turnover rate is LC/LP.
B	BUYER	

DATAPOINTS — Carefully log your datapoints and be mindful of their modifiers.

	FULL TITLE	WHAT IT MEASURES	WAYS TO IMPROVE
W	DAYS WORKED	the number of days you worked at real estate things	Ideally, you wanna work as few days as possible and make the most money possible. So, increase the effectiveness and efficiencies of your systems.[012]
D	DISCUSSIONS	the number of real estate conversations you have	Refine your scripts and prospect to a niche.[042]
P	PRESENTATIONS	the number of presentations you give	Have more discussions. Refine your scripts and follow the *Daily Flow Chart*.[346]
C	CLIENTS	the number of clients you sign	Give more presentations. Increase your presentation[167] and negotiation skills.[266]
K	CONTRACTS	the number of p&s contracts your clients sign	Increase your negotiation, agency,[229] and valuation skills.[125]
T	TRANSACTIONS	the number of transactions you close	Sign more clients.[213] Hire helpers,[286] improve agency,[224] refine your systems.[068]
GCI	GROSS COMMISSION INCOME	total dollars earned from sales, before your broker takes his cut	Close more transactions.[221] Increase your V, T, C, and/or commission rate.
DOM	DAYS ON MARKET	days between signing C and that client entering a K	Shorter is better. For listings: increase valuation, presentation, and negotiation skills.
V	SALES VOLUME	totalled sales prices of all transactions	Increase T and/or ATP.
OPV	ORIGINAL PRICE VOLUME	totalled (originally) listed prices of all transactions	OPV is measured to calculate SP/LP.
R	OUTBOUND REFERRALS	the number of referrals you sent to other agents to work	Send more referrals.[XXI] Prospect with your ears open.[107]
RT	REFERRAL TRANSACTIONS	the number of outbound referrals who actually closed	Pre-qualify agents to ensure they match the referrals you send.[112]
RGCI	REFERRAL GCI	total dollars earned from R	Send more R, negotiate higher commish rate.
Db	DATABASE MEMBERS	the number of people in your database	Measured to calculate MPR, MPC, RPM, & DbLR.
Db→C	CLIENTS FROM DATABASE	the number of clients you signed who are database members or were referred to you by database members. Measures the effectiveness of your database prospecting.	
Db→R	REFERRALS FROM DATABASE	the number of referrals you sent who are database members or were referred to you by database members. Measures the effectiveness of your database prospecting.	
L→C	CLIENTS FROM LISTINGS	the number of clients who you met as result of having listings: from open houses, sign calls, neighbors,.. Measures the effectiveness of your listing leverage.	

TURNOVER RATES — Measure your real estate activity successes as percentages.

	FULL TITLE	FORMULA	WHAT IT MEASURES	WAYS TO IMPROVE
DTR	DISCUSSION TURNOVER RATE	$\frac{P}{D}$	percentage of discussions that resulted in a presentation given	prospect more often[077] & practice scripts[050]
PTR	PRESENTATION TURNOVER RATE	$\frac{C}{P}$	percentage of presentations that resulted in a client signed	practice your scripts & presentations[167]
KTR	CONTRACT TURNOVER RATE	$\frac{T}{K}$	percentage of P&S contracts that resulted in a transaction	raise your valuation[125] & negotiation skills[266]
CTR	CLIENT TURNOVER RATE	$\frac{T}{C}$	percentage of clients signed who closed a transaction	improve your agency skills[211]
RTR	REFERRAL TURNOVER RATE	$\frac{RT}{R}$	percentage of outbound referrals that close	pre-qualify referral agents[110]

OTHER METRICS — Datapoints divided by datapoints provide business insight.

	FULL TITLE	FORMULA	WHAT IT MEASURES	WAYS TO IMPROVE
ACR	AVERAGE COMMISSION RATE	$\frac{GCI}{V}$	percentage of sales volume earned in commissions	Increase your commission rate, relative to your volume.
ATP	AVERAGE TRANSACTION PRICE	$\frac{V}{T}$	the average price of your closed transactions	Sell property of higher value.
ROP	RETURN ON PRESENTATIONS	$\frac{GCI}{P}$	dollars earned per presentation given	Increase GCI and/or DTR.
ROT	RETURN ON TRANSACTIONS	$\frac{GCI}{T}$	dollars earned per transaction	Increase GCI, KTR, and/or CTR. Improve agency skills.
ROC	RETURN ON CLIENTS	$\frac{GCI}{C}$	dollars earned per client signed	Increase GCI, ACR, ATP, and/or CTR. Improve your agency skills.
AVG. DOM	AVERAGE DAYS ON MARKET	$\frac{LDOM}{LT}$	the average number of days between you signing a listing client and that client entering a contract to buy/sell. Improve valuation skills.	
SP/LP	SALES PRICE TO LIST PRICE RATIO	$\frac{LV}{LOPV}$	the average difference between list price and sales price of your transactions, expressed as a percentage. Improve valuation skills.	
ROW	RETURN ON DAYS WORKED	$\frac{GCI}{W}$	dollars earned per day worked	Improve the effectiveness/ efficiency of systems. Hire helpers.
LOD	LOST OPPORTUNITY DIFFERENTIAL	$\frac{GCI}{T} - \frac{GCI}{C}$	ROT minus ROC. Measures the financial loss on your non-closing clients as the assumptive additional income you would have earned, per non-closing client, if those clients had closed	
ROR	RETURN ON REFERRALS	$\frac{RGCI}{R}$	dollars earned per outbound referral	Pre-qualify referral agents before sending them your referrals.
ARC	AVERAGE REFERRAL COMMISSION	$\frac{RGCI}{RT}$	dollars earned per closed referral	Negotiate higher rate or longer terms with referral agents.
MPR	MEMBERS PER REFERRAL	$\frac{Db}{R}$	the number of database members per outbound referral	Prospect to your database more often[094] and/or more effectively/efficiently.[089]
MPC	MEMBERS PER CLIENT	$\frac{Db}{C}$	the number of database members per client signed	Prospect to your database more often[092] and/or more effectively/efficiently.[090]
RPM	RETURN PER MEMBER	$\frac{GCI}{Db}$	dollars earned per database member	Keep your database clean and relationships ongoing.[089]
DbLR	DATABASE LEVERAGE RATE	$\frac{Db\rightarrow C}{C}$	measures the percentage of clients who came from your database To improve, systematically prospect to your database.[094]	
LLR	LISTING LEVERAGE RATE	$\frac{L\rightarrow C}{C}$	measures the percentage of clients who came by virtue of having listings. To improve, list with *The Right Price*.[154]	
T/RT	TRANSACTIONS PER REFERRAL TRANSACTION	$\frac{LT+BT}{RT}$	measures the number of laborious paydays for every referral payday	

Journal & Daily Tracker

found: THROUGHOUT

A brain-in-motion tends to start an arse-into-motion. Now you can keep track of both on the same page, for three years in a row. Fun!

Your personal real estate sales growth will lead to the ability of providing greater client service and increasing income. If THINK→DO→TRACK→REPEAT is the blueprint for growth, then this page is the cornerstone of success. When you supply ample DO on a daily basis, THINK & TRACK become a fun way to end each day. An enjoyable, evening ritual is an easy one to REPEAT. So, go DO real estate stuff all day, then report here to THINK & TRACK, building your success one brick at a time.

DISCUSSIONS (D) Count 1 each time that you and a human exchange words, thoughts, or grunts about real estate. Each person is counted only once per day, whether face-to-face, by telephone, or through the internet. Count every real estate DISCUSSION you have, whether it's with prospects, family members, friends, agents, your broker. It's simple: count every DISCUSSION whereby real estate is mentioned.

PRESENTATIONS (P) Count 1 each time you ask (or suggest) someone to enter into an agency relationship with you, whether by formal or informal means. Each PRESENTATION is counted once per prospect cycle (the time a prospect has a real estate need, but is unrepresented). Therefore, suppose you give a formal PRESENTATION to a prospect who is interviewing multiple agents. If, once the prospect meets each competing agent, she asks you to give another, follow-up presentation (just to make sure you're the right agent for the job), then this second meeting is not counted. Now, suppose this prospect becomes a client: if her listing expires, and you make a proposal/appeal to this client to list with you again, this re-listing PRESENTATION of the same property *is* counted as a new PRESENTATION.

CLIENTS (C) Count 1 each time you sign an agency agreement, entering into a client/agent relationship. If/when that agency relationship ends, and you enter into an extension of (or altogether new) agency agreement with the same person, then a new CLIENT is counted. This means if you re-list one of your expired listings, a CLIENT is counted again. Same goes for when a single person is a buyer CLIENT, then becomes a seller (listing) CLIENT: two CLIENTS are counted.

CONTRACTS (K) Count 1 for each purchase & sale agreement between each unique, buyer/seller combo. If a single CLIENT enters a purchase & sale (P&S) CONTRACT, but that CONTRACT later dissolves, and later the same CLIENT enters into another CONTRACT to buy/sell, then two CONTRACTS are counted. If both parties to a CONTRACT are your CLIENTS, then *two* CONTRACTS are counted: once per CLIENT who enters a CONTRACT to buy/sell real property.

TRANSACTION (T) Count 1 for each CLIENT who succeeds at transferring ownership of real property. If both parties to a TRANSACTION are CLIENTS, then count it twice: once per CLIENT who closes. If one side is a CLIENT and other side is unrepresented, then one TRANSACTION is counted. If both parties are unrepresented (*i.e.* you act as transaction broker), then just one TRANSACTION is counted.

Each activity follows a previous activity. In this way, you cannot count a PRESENTATION without first counting a DISCUSSION, and you cannot count a CLIENT without first counting a PRESENTATION. *Exception:* it is possible to close a TRANSACTION without first signing a CLIENT (whereby agent facilitates a TRANSACTION between a FSBO and an unrepresented buyer).

Who, recently, has been your favorite client and why? How might you find (or create) similar clients?

25

{20 17 } Helena was a great buyer client because she came to me prepared & informed. I can insist all buyers sit for my presentation! Perhaps make a quiz, or take-home digital info package w/ tips about mortgages, inspections, contracts, insurance, more...
Give mini presentation at each turn of process.

{20 18 } James was an awesome seller! His house was vacant & he was agreeable on price. Seek out sellers w/ lots equity, who have already bought a new residence. Look at expired, FSBO, withdrawn listings. Be picky with whom I sign listing agreements!
Concentrate on better ways to explain pricing to sellers. Ask for some help with scripts.

{20 }

{20 17 }

S M (T) W T F S

Today I mostly prospected: sphere of incluence

26 DISCUSSIONS

L	DAILY TRACKER	B
1	PRESENTATIONS	1
1	CLIENTS	1
	CONTRACTS	
	TRANSACTIONS	

☐ Did not work today; instead, I:

{20 18 }

S M T (W) T F S

Today I mostly prospected: nada

10 DISCUSSIONS

L	DAILY TRACKER	B
	PRESENTATIONS	
	CLIENTS	
	CONTRACTS	1
	TRANSACTIONS	

☒ Did not work today; instead, I: half day was fly fishing

{20 }

S M T W T F S

Today I mostly prospected:

DISCUSSIONS

L	DAILY TRACKER	B
	PRESENTATIONS	
	CLIENTS	
	CONTRACTS	
	TRANSACTIONS	

☐ Did not work today; instead, I:

ACTIVITY LOG

JANUARY				
DISCUSSIONS (D)	PRESENTATIONS (P)	CLIENTS (C)	CONTRACTS (K)	TRANSACTIONS (T)
total discussions had	L presentations given	listing clients signed	listing contracts	listing transactions
DAYS WORKED (W)	+ B presentations given	+ buyer clients signed	+ buyer contracts	+ buyer transactions
total days worked	= presentations given	= clients signed	= contracts written	= transactions closed

FEBRUARY				
DISCUSSIONS (D)	PRESENTATIONS (P)	CLIENTS (C)	CONTRACTS (K)	TRANSACTIONS (T)
137 #D; Δ| #	5 #LP; Δ| #	3 #LC; Δ| #	2 #LK; Δ| #	2 #LT; Δ| #
DAYS WORKED (W)	5 #BP; Δ| #	3 #BC; Δ| #	2 #BK; Δ| #	1 #BT; Δ| #
21 #W; Δ| #	10 #P; Δ| #	6 #C; Δ| #	4 #K; Δ| #	3 #T; Δ| #

MARCH				
DISCUSSIONS (D)	PRESENTATIONS (P)	CLIENTS (C)	CONTRACTS (K)	TRANSACTIONS (T)
158 #D; Δ↑21 #	12 #LP; Δ↑7 #	9 #LC; Δ↑6 #	5 #LK; Δ↑3 #	3 #LT; Δ↑1 #
DAYS WORKED (W)	4 #BP; Δ↓1 #	2 #BC; Δ↓1 #	2 #BK; Δ| ~ #	2 #BT; Δ↑1 #
25 #W; Δ↑4 #	16 #P; Δ↑6 #	11 #C; Δ↑5 #	7 #K; Δ↑3 #	5 #T; Δ↑2 #

QUARTER 01				
DISCUSSIONS (D)	PRESENTATIONS (P)	CLIENTS (C)	CONTRACTS (K)	TRANSACTIONS (T)
295 #D; Δ| #	17 #LP; Δ| #	12 #LC; Δ| #	7 #LK; Δ| #	5 #LT; Δ| #
DAYS WORKED (W)	9 #BP; Δ| #	5 #BC; Δ| #	4 #BK; Δ| #	3 #BT; Δ| #
46 #W; Δ| #	26 #P; Δ| #	17 #C; Δ| #	11 #K; Δ| #	8 #T; Δ| #

Activity Log

found on: QUARTERLY, ANNUAL & TRI-ANNUAL REPORTS

Add up and store your activities in their respective boxes. Simple!

STEP 1: At the end of each month, add up your daily activities (from the MONTHLY ACTIVITY TRACKER), then record them on this quarter's report (be sure to include actual DAYS WORKED). Notice that PRESENTATIONS given, new CLIENTS signed, new CONTRACTS written, and TRANSACTIONS closed are logged in three parts: listing-side (L), buyer-side (B), and total. *For example:* #LP is the number of listing PRESENTATIONS given during the period, #BP is the number of buyer PRESENTATIONS given, and #P is the total number of PRESENTATIONS given.

STEP 2: As each month passes, track activity changes from the previous month's log using the delta (Δ) and naked arrow (|) symbols.[XI] Delta measures the change from 'like period' to 'like period'; therefore, your first month's delta entry will be left blank due to lack of data from a previous month to compare; the same goes for your first quarterly and annual activity logs. *The example above shows an agent who began tracking real estate activities in February.*

STEP 3: At the end of each quarter, add your monthly tallies to get quarterly tallies.

STEP 4: At the end of each year, add up the quarterly tallies, and report them to the ANNUAL REPORT. Likewise, the TRI-ANNUAL REPORT requires three ANNUAL ACTIVITY LOGS to be added together.

To keep things simple, the shaded headings on a page denote the figures to be used within that period's stat calculations.

TRANSACTION DATA

GROSS COMMISSION INCOME (GCI)				DAYS ON MARKET (DOM)			
LGCI $	31,754	;Δ↑$	2687	LDOM	198	DAYS; Δ↓	20 DAYS
BGCI $	19,162	;Δ↑$	1657	BDOM	73	DAYS; Δ↑	27 DAYS
GCI $	50,916	;Δ↑$	4344	DOM	271	DAYS; Δ↑	7 DAYS
SALES VOLUME (V)				**ORIGINAL PRICE VOLUME (OPV)**			
LV $	1,122,300	;Δ↑$	6750	LOPV $	1,159,000	;Δ↓$	10,500
BV $	657,800	;Δ↓$	4400	BOPV $	650,000	;Δ↑$	25,890
V $	1,780,100	;Δ↑$	2350	OPV $	1,809,000	;Δ↑$	15,390

MARKET COMPARISON

	#TRANSACTIONS	Δ	AVERAGE TRANS. PRICE (ATP)	AVG. LDOM	SP/LP
METRO	10,454	↑ 261	$ 178,664 ;Δ↑$ 1658	85	94.5 %
MACRO #1	589	↑ 75	$ 201,003 ;Δ↑$ 2460	72	95 %
MACRO #2 / MACRO #3	all TRANSACTIONS for this period	the change in TRANSACTIONS from last time	VOLUME (V) / TRANSACTIONS (T)	LDOM / LT	SP/LP is equal to LV/LOPV
PERSONAL	8	↑ 1	$ 222,512 ;Δ↓$ 16,480	40	97 %

Transaction Data & Market Comparison

found on: QUARTERLY, ANNUAL & TRI-ANNUAL REPORTS

Track transaction details and compare them to the market. Cool!

TRANSACTION DATA entries are sectioned into listing-side, buyer-side, and total. These figures will be used to calculate metrics, and ultimately, your quarterly BUSINESS PLAN. So, keep track of the details for each of your TRANSACTIONS in the NOTES section of this book or another convenient place. For each buyer and listing transaction, record GROSS COMMISSION INCOME (GCI), DAYS ON MARKET (DOM), SALES VOLUME (V), and the ORIGINAL PRICE OF VOLUME (OPV), which is the price initially offered for each listing sold.

MARKET COMPARISON entries are meant to compare your performance to markets of your choice; designate each of your niche markets[042] to a MACRO market. By comparing your performance to the markets within which you work, you may glean stats to brag about (especially if your AVG. LDOM and/or SP/LP are beating the market).

TRANSACTION DATA QUICK REFERENCE

GROSS COMMISSION INCOME (GCI)	DAYS ON MARKET (DOM)
total commissions from listings this period	total days between LC and LK, for all listing transactions
+ total commissions from buyers this period	+ total days between BC and BK, for all buyer transactions
= total commissions earned this period	= total days between C and K, for all transactions this period
SALES VOLUME (V)	**ORIGINAL PRICE VOLUME (OPV)**
totalled sales prices from listing transactions this period	totalled (original) listed prices from listing transactions
+ totalled sales prices from buyer transactions this period	+ totalled (original) listed prices from buyer transactions
= total sales prices from all transactions this period	= total listed prices from all transactions this period

During Quarter 01, I mostly prospected:	1 FSBO	2 expired listings	3 sphere of influence

CONVERSION RATIOS & TURNOVER RATES

	CONVERSION RATIOS		TURNOVER	Δ	L TURNOVER	Δ	B TURNOVER	Δ
DISCUSSIONS TO PRESENTATIONS	295 #D / 26 #P = 11 D:P	DTR	#P / #D = 9 %	↑3 %	#LP / #D = 6 %	↑2%	#BP / #D = 3 %	↑1 %
PRESENTATIONS TO CLIENTS	26 #P / 17 #C = 1.5 P:C	PTR	#C / #P = 65 %	↓5 %	#LC / #LP = 71 %	↓6%	#BC / #BP = 56%	↑3 %
CLIENTS TO TRANSACTIONS	17 #C / 8 #T = 2.1 T:C	CTR	#T / #C = 47 %	↑7 %	#LT / #LC = 42%	↓4%	#BT / #BC = 60 %	↑10%
CONTRACTS TO TRANSACTIONS	11 #K / 8 #T = 1.4 K:T	KTR	#T / #K = 73 %	↑11 %	#LT / #LK = 71 %	↑5%	#BT / #BK = 75%	↑7 %

METRICS

AVERAGE COMMISSION RATE (ACR)	AVERAGE TRANSACTION PRICE (ATP)	CLIENT TURNOVER RATE (CTR)
GCI / V = 2.86 %; Δ↑ 0.14 %	V / T = $222,512; Δ↓$ 16,458	T / C = 47 %; Δ↑ 7 %
RETURN ON PRESENTATIONS (ROP)	**RETURN ON TRANSACTIONS (ROT)**	**RETURN ON CLIENTS (ROC)**
GCI / P = $ 1958 ; Δ↓$ 189	GCI / T = $ 6365 ; Δ↑$ 425	GCI / C = $ 2995 ; Δ↑$ 386
AVG. LIST DAYS ON MKT (AVG. LDOM)	**SALES PRICE TO LIST PRICE (SP/LP)**	**RETURN ON DAYS WORKED (ROW)**
LDOM / LT = 40 DAYS; Δ↓ 5 DAYS	LV / LOPV = 97 %; Δ↑ 2.5 %	GCI / W = $ 1107 ; Δ↓$ 144

Conversion Ratios, Turnover Rates & Other Metrics

found on: QUARTERLY, ANNUAL & TRI-ANNUAL REPORTS

Analysis of conversion ratios & turnover rates will highlight bottlenecks (slowdowns in the process). Analysis of metrics will highlight the value of your efforts. Each affect your paycheck. Right on!

This is when you do some real math. All datapoints used in your calculations are found on the same page spread. In other words, quarterly turnover rates and metrics are calculated from quarterly datapoints, found on the page it faces. Turn now to see for yourself. Likewise, annual turnover rates and metrics are calculated from the annual data, found on its facing page.

IMPORTANT: pay attention to the L & B modifiers when making your calculations. Any datapoint that begins with an L or B are for listing or buyer data, and the formula will output a metric related to either listing or buyer-side work. Datapoints that do not start with an L or B measure listing and buyer-side work, combined.

Notice that some entry titles are shaded. These shaded metrics are factors of either the quarterly BUSINESS PLAN[XVIII] or the LEVERAGE LOG.[XVII]

Conversion ratios are the inverse of turnover rates. In the example above, the DISCUSSION-TO-PRESENTATION conversion ratio is 11 D to 1 P. This means that (statistically) it takes eleven discussions before one presentation is given. Inversely, the discussion turnover rate is 9%. This means that (statistically) nine percent of discussions had resulted in a presentation given.

NOTE: calculate ACR to two decimal points. Agents who charge a flat fee must make this calculation so that the BUSINESS PLAN[XVIII] will output the proper goals.

ALSO NOTE: AVG. DOM and SP/LP used on the MARKET COMPARISON table.[XV]

LEVERAGE LOG

		$\frac{GCI}{V}$ ×	$\frac{V}{T}$ ×	$\frac{T}{C}$ =	$\frac{GCI}{C}$	$\frac{GCI}{T} - \frac{GCI}{C}$
		AVERAGE COMMISSION RATE	AVERAGE TRANSACTION PRICE	CLIENT TURNOVER RATE	RETURN ON CLIENTS	LOST OPPORTUNITY DIFFERENTIAL
QUARTER 01	LISTINGS	2.83 %	$ 224,460	42 %	$ 2646	$ 3705
	BUYERS	2.91 %	$ 219,267	60 %	$ 3832	$ 2555
	OVERALL	2.86 %	$ 222,512	47 %	$ 2995	$ 3370

Leverage Log

found on: QUARTERLY, ANNUAL & TRI-ANNUAL REPORTS

When you track the factors of your income, a pay raise is *always your choice*. Gnarly.

So long as you have TRANSACTIONS, you may track the value of each CLIENT signed—in dollars *i.e.* RETURN ON CLIENTS (ROC). This is an important metric because you expend time, money, and effort on each CLIENT signed. Non-closing CLIENTS are a loss (financial and otherwise).

ROC measures that loss as *earnings*, spreading the loss amongst all CLIENTS signed. The LEVERAGE LOG breaks ROC into its three factors:

AVERAGE COMMISSION RATE (ACR),
AVERAGE TRANSACTION PRICE (ATP), &
CLIENT TURNOVER RATE (CTR).

Multiplying these factors together gives ROC. *Therefore, an increase in any of these factors will result in increased* ROC.

The LOST OPPORTUNITY DIFFERENTIAL (LOD) measures your non-closing client loss as the assumptive additional income you would have earned this period, per non-closing CLIENT (if those CLIENTS had closed). LOD measures the difference between the money earned per TRANSACTION and the money earned per CLIENT. In other words, ROC is the value of each CLIENT signed, and LOD is the additional money you earn if/when each CLIENT closes a TRANSACTION. When ROC increases, LOD decreases.

Not all CONTRACTS will close, but (theoretically) all CLIENTS should. This is because, ideally, you should only sign CLIENTS you believe are qualified/motivated to close. Your knowledge of current market conditions & trends,[125] combined with the aid of competent tools (MLS) & resources (loan officers), and a thorough CLIENT interview process,[167] should enable you to determine which prospects are likely to close (or not). You know when you've met a slam dunk CLIENT, just as when you've met a dud. You'll make more money by leaving the duds for other agents, and searching for more slam dunk CLIENTS to sign.[077]

	FACTORS	LIST	BUY	WAYS TO INCREASE
$\frac{GCI}{V}$	AVERAGE COMMISSION RATE	$\frac{LGCI}{LV}$	$\frac{BGCI}{BV}$	• charge higher commission rates and/or sell property of higher value • do not negotiate away commission as part of your clients' transactions
$\frac{V}{T}$	AVERAGE TRANSACTION PRICE	$\frac{LV}{LT}$	$\frac{BV}{BT}$	• sell property of higher value
$\frac{T}{C}$	CLIENT TURNOVER RATE	$\frac{LT}{LC}$	$\frac{BT}{BC}$	• increase your skills: valuation,[150] negotiation,[153] agency[211] • hire help for support activities[286] • sign pre-qualified clients[170]
$\frac{GCI}{C}$	RETURN ON CLIENTS	$\frac{LGCI}{LC}$	$\frac{BGCI}{BC}$	• an increase in one or more of ACR, ATP, or CTR will increase ROC (so long as any non-increasing factors do not decrease)

BUSINESS PLAN (FOR EACH MONTH OF QUARTER 02)

STEP	CALCULATION	QUARTER 01 STATS	QUARTER 02 GOALS	
1	ANNUAL GCI GOAL	$ 250,000	ANNUAL GCI GOAL	$ 250,000
2	− GCI EARNED TO DATE	− $ 50,916	REMAINING GCI GOAL	$ 199,084
3	÷ MONTHS REMAINING	÷ 9 MONTHS	MONTHLY GCI GOAL	$ 22,120
4	÷ ACR	÷ 2.86 %	MONTHLY SALES VOLUME GOAL	$ 773,442
5	÷ ATP	÷ $ 222,512	MONTHLY TRANSACTIONS GOAL	4 #T
6	÷ CTR	÷ 47 %	MONTHLY NEW CLIENTS GOAL	9 #C
7	÷ PTR	÷ 65 %	MONTHLY PRESENTATIONS GOAL	14 #P
8	÷ DTR	÷ 9 %	MONTHLY DISCUSSIONS GOAL	156 #D
9	÷ WORKING DAYS/MTH	÷ 20 DAYS	DAILY DISCUSSIONS GOAL	8 #D/W

Business Plan

found on: QUARTERLY REPORTS

Pick any GCI you desire, enter your quarterly metrics, do some math, and *wha-la!*: the result is your workload for the next three months. Easy!

By tracking your activities and resulting metrics, you are able to choose accurate goals. Use this handy calculator to find your monthly goals for each activity. Then, simply work to achieve your DAILY DISCUSSIONS GOAL, and (statistically) you should achieve your MONTHLY GCI GOAL. Recalculate each quarter, and before you know it, your ANNUAL GCI GOAL is achieved.

Make each calculation from left to right, then take that result down to the next step. To ensure you hit your goals, always round up (as shown above). QUARTER 01 metrics are used to calculate monthly goals for QUARTER 02, and QUARTER 02 metrics are used for QUARTER 03 calculations, and so on. Because this BUSINESS PLAN is calculated quarterly (and good for the following three months), MONTHS REMAINING has been entered for you (to keep it simple).

VARIATION: if desired, you may create *two* BUSINESS PLANS, one calculated with buyer metrics and the other with listing metrics; however, most agents will fare well with what's provided.

NOTE: *This business plan calculator is most accurate with three, full months of data.*

STARTER BUSINESS PLAN

STEP	CALCULATION	GUESS YOUR STATS	YOUR GOALS UNTIL END OF NEXT QUARTER	
1	ANNUAL GCI GOAL	$	(REMAINING) ANNUAL GCI GOAL	$
3	÷ MONTHS REMAINING IN THIS YEAR	÷	MONTHLY GCI GOAL	$
4	÷ ACR (2.50 %)	÷ %	MONTHLY SALES VOLUME GOAL	$
5	÷ ATP (your choice)	÷ $	MONTHLY TRANSACTIONS GOAL	#T
6	÷ CTR (50 %)	÷ %	MONTHLY NEW CLIENTS GOAL	#C
7	÷ PTR (30 %)	÷ %	MONTHLY PRESENTATIONS GOAL	#P
8	÷ DTR (3 %)	÷ %	MONTHLY DISCUSSIONS GOAL	#D
9	÷ WORKING DAYS/MTH	÷ DAYS	DAILY DISCUSSIONS GOAL	#D/W

To use the STARTER BUSINESS PLAN:
Enter a GCI GOAL to last through year's end, and your best guess at your statistics. New agents are encouraged to use the suggested stats (shown in parenthesis). STEP 2 has been eliminated from the STARTER BUSINESS PLAN because it's not needed.

{20 18 } MONTHLY ACTIVITY TRACKER (GOALS→RESULTS)

GOALS	ACTIVITY	WK 1	WK 2	WK 3	WK 4	WK 5	TOTAL RESULTS
4	TRANSACTIONS (T)	L 0 : 0 B	L 0 : 0 B	L 1 : 0 B	L 1 : 1 B	L 0 : 0 B	L 2 : 1 B : 3
9	NEW CLIENTS (C)	L 1 : 0 B	L 1 : 1 B	L 1 : 0 B	L 0 : 0 B	L 0 : 1 B	L 3 : 2 B : 5
14	PRESENTATIONS (P)	L 2 : 0 B	L 3 : 2 B	L 2 : 1 B	L 2 : 0 B	L 0 : 0 B	L 9 : 3 B : 12
156	DISCUSSIONS (D)	14	53	46	68	29	210
21	DAYS WORKED (W)	4	5	6	6	2	23
10	DAILY DISCUSSIONS (D/W)	ACTUAL DAILY DISCUSSION AVERAGE				D/W	9
$ 22,120	GCI	$ 5100 + 6258 + 5598 = $16,956					

Monthly Activity Tracker

found: OPPOSITE DAY 01 OF EACH MONTH

Whilst mired in the trenches of daily activities, it's easy to lose sight of your goals. Use this tracker to pop your head up and keep an eye on progress (or lack thereof). Jeepers!

At the beginning of each month, transfer the monthly goals from your quarterly BUSINESS PLAN to the MONTHLY ACTIVITY TRACKER, and fill-in the left column (labeled above as: GOALS). Then, count your activities each week and record them here. Doing so serves two purposes: 1) it's easier to count-up activity tallies at month's end, and 2) if you're slipping behind on your goals, you may adjust your actions mid-month.

For example: if, by the end of WK 2, you notice that your PRESENTATION and/or new CLIENTS goals are lacking, you can purposely increase your prospecting efforts. Insert yourself into more DISCUSSIONS about real estate and (according to your statistics) you're likely to hit your monthly goals.

Remember: activities are built upon each other. DISCUSSIONS lead to PRESENTATIONS, which lead to CLIENTS, which lead to TRANSACTIONS. Because no agent's conversion ratios are perfect, to increase TRANSACTIONS, you must increase the activities that TRANSACTIONS are built upon. For this reason, your daily activities control your results. The concept is simple: have more DISCUSSIONS and (statistically) you will have more TRANSACTIONS.

So, report to this page at least once per week. If you're slacking on goal achievement, look at it every day to remind you to increase your activities (*i.e.* prospect more often and/or more efficiently).

NOTE: You want to record activities from this month only. In doing so, remember that weeks begin on Sundays and end on Saturdays. Therefore, (depending on the month) WK 1 and/or WK 5 may be shorter on days than WKS 2—4.

ANOTHER NOTE: Any goals missed in months one and two of each quarter should be added to next month's goals. Do not subtract goals when you have an overage (unless you want your business to stagnate, that is). If goal achievement is too easy, increase your goals next month. If GCI is out-pacing your goals, then raise your ANNUAL GCI GOAL on next quarter's BUSINESS PLAN.[XVIII]

CLIENTS FROM LISTINGS (L→C)

JAN	FEB	MAR	APR	MAY	JUN	JUL	AUG	SEP	OCT	NOV	DEC
0	0	1	0	1	2	2	1	0	1	2	0
TOTAL (L→C) = 10 ; Δ↑ 3				AVG. (L→C) PER MONTH = 0.8 ; Δ↑ 0.2							

DATABASE (Db)			OUTBOUND REFERRALS (R)		
#MEMBERS EXISTING	215		REFERRALS SENT (R)	10 #R	Δ↑ 2 #
#NEW MEMBERS	+ 62	Δ↑ 11	REFERRAL TRANS. (RT)	7 #RT	Δ↑ 5 #
#MEMBERS PURGED	- 33	Δ↑ 33	REFERRAL GCI (RGCI)	$ 7850	Δ↑$ 5230
#Db	= 244	Δ↑ 29	REFERRALS FROM DATABASE (Db→R): 12 Δ↑ 3		
CLIENTS FROM DATABASE (Db→C): 7 Δ 1					

DATABASE & REFERRAL METRICS

RETURN ON REFERRALS (ROR)	AVG. REFERRAL COMMISSION (ARC)	REFERRAL TURNOVER RATE (RTR)
$\frac{RGCI}{R}$ = \$ 785 ; Δ↑\$ 458	$\frac{RGCI}{RT}$ = \$ 1121 ; Δ↓\$ 189	$\frac{RT}{R}$ = 70 %; Δ↑ 45 %
MEMBERS PER REFERRAL (MPR)	**MEMBERS PER CLIENT (MPC)**	**RETURN PER MEMBER (RPM)**
$\frac{Db}{R}$ = 24 Db:R; Δ↓ 3 Db:R	$\frac{Db}{C}$ = 5 Db:C; Δ↓ 4 Db:C	$\frac{GCI}{Db}$ = \$ 774 ; Δ↑\$ 258
DATABASE LEVERAGE RATE (DbLR)	**LISTING LEVERAGE RATE (LLR)**	**TRANS. PER REFERRAL TRANS. (T/RT)**
$\frac{Db \to C}{C}$ = 10 %; Δ↑ 3.7 %	$\frac{L \to C}{C}$ = 14 %; Δ↑ 7.5 %	$\frac{LT+BT}{RT}$ = 6 T:RT; Δ↓ 4 T:RT

Database & Referral Metrics

found on: ANNUAL REPORTS

Log your database and referral datapoints, so you can measure how efficiently you leverage these resources. Insightful!

CLIENTS FROM LISTINGS (L→C)

The following passage does not advocate becoming a listing slut,[190] rather it acknowledges how listings with *The Right Price* will generate so much interest that additional client opportunities inevitably surface.[154] Marked by the notation (L→C), you can now keep track of how many CLIENTS you meet through your listings' sign calls, open houses, neighbors, and marketing. Your results are sure to show why 'tis far better to prospect for listings, and let the buyers come to you.[096]

DATABASE (Db)

It is said that an agent's business is his database. A clean, organized database of a manageable size may be used to mine lots of real estate money.[089] To keep your mine primed, systematically add to it, prospect to it, and trim its fat (toss out the duds). Then come here to document how many CLIENTS and REFERRALS your extracted from it and then calculate how efficiently your operation runs.

OUTBOUND REFERRALS (R)

There is a huge advantage to agents who consistently send lots of OUTBOUND REFERRALS: very high dollars per working hour. Keep track of your REFERRALS on the REFERRAL LOG.[XXI] At the end of the year, tally how many REFERRALS you sent, how many of them closed, and how much money you made from them. Then, come here to enter those datapoints and calculate how efficient your referral venture was. NOTE: *All* REFERRALS *mentioned/measured in this book are those you are sending out for other agents to work.*

OUTBOUND REFERRALS (R)

NO.	REFERRED PARTY	NOTIFIED?	AGENT REFERRED	DATE SENT
10	Bobby Sue Radcliff	YES	Agent Andy (800)555-1234	13 Feb. 2018

L, B, OR BOTH	COMMISH. RATE	ANTICIPATED CLOSE DATE	CLOSED?	RGCI
listing	30%	01 APRIL 2018	YES!	$ 4280

Referral Log

found: IN THE BACK (notice the page tab)

Sometimes agents forget about outbound referrals; this tracker will prevent yours from slipping through the cracks. Brilliant!

Individually, OUTBOUND REFERRALS usually have a very high dollars-earned per hour-worked ratio. That being the case, an agent who consistently earns commissions from just one REFERRAL per month may reasonably earn ten to thirty percent more money annually than an agent who does not.

However, simply dealing names to any agent with her hand out is an effort least likely to see returns. When the agent you refer is good at her job and her niche is appropriately matched to the prospect's need, the odds you see a return go way up.[112]

While each negotiated referral agreement is different, a single OUTBOUND REFERRAL could pay you twice within two weeks (if you refer a seller who also buys). Another could pay you once a month for two years (if you've referred an investor), or it could pay you four times a month for twelve months straight (if you've referred a builder). A commercial REFERRAL may pay you one time, a year from now, and may be large enough to double your income that year. Any way you manage it, REFERRALS are a worthwhile expense of your diligent effort.

The more quality time you spend speaking with people about real estate, the more REFERRAL opportunities you should notice, as there are scores more people out there with the need for real estate help than your time and niche allow. Matching these people with good agents doesn't only pay good money, it's also great service on your part.

When you track your REFERRALS, you may easily remain engaged in each REFERRAL's progress, allowing you to learn from the failed ones. In turn, you may more artfully arrange your REFERRAL prospects with your referral agents into a more harmonious fashion, returning you more money per future-hour worked.

REFERRED PARTY (R) Place the prospect's name here.

NOTIFIED? Whether or not your State law requires a signed acknowledgement by referred prospects, it is the right thing to do. When referred prospects know you will receive money for your referral, and that your referral is not solely for the enrichment of your pure and joyous heart, the prospect is able to make an honest assessment of your referral, with all relevant information in hand—totally fair.

AGENT REFERRED Place the agent's info here.

DATE SENT That would be today.

L, B, OR BOTH Place the type of agency the referred party needs here. Also denote if referred party is special type: investor, builder, HR manager, property manager...

COMMISH. RATE Note the agreement for commission paid to you here.

ANTICIPATED CLOSE DATE Once the referred party goes under contract to buy/sell, you should be notified of the transaction close date; this is the day you get paid.

CLOSED? Call to ensure the transaction closed. Now look for your check in the mail.

RGCI (REFERRAL GROSS COMMISSION INCOME) This is the total amount of money you earned on this REFERRAL.

Reconcile your REFERRALS *annually, and report them to the* ANNUAL REPORT. *Use this* REFERRAL TRACKER *in conjunction with The Referral Flow Chart.*[341]

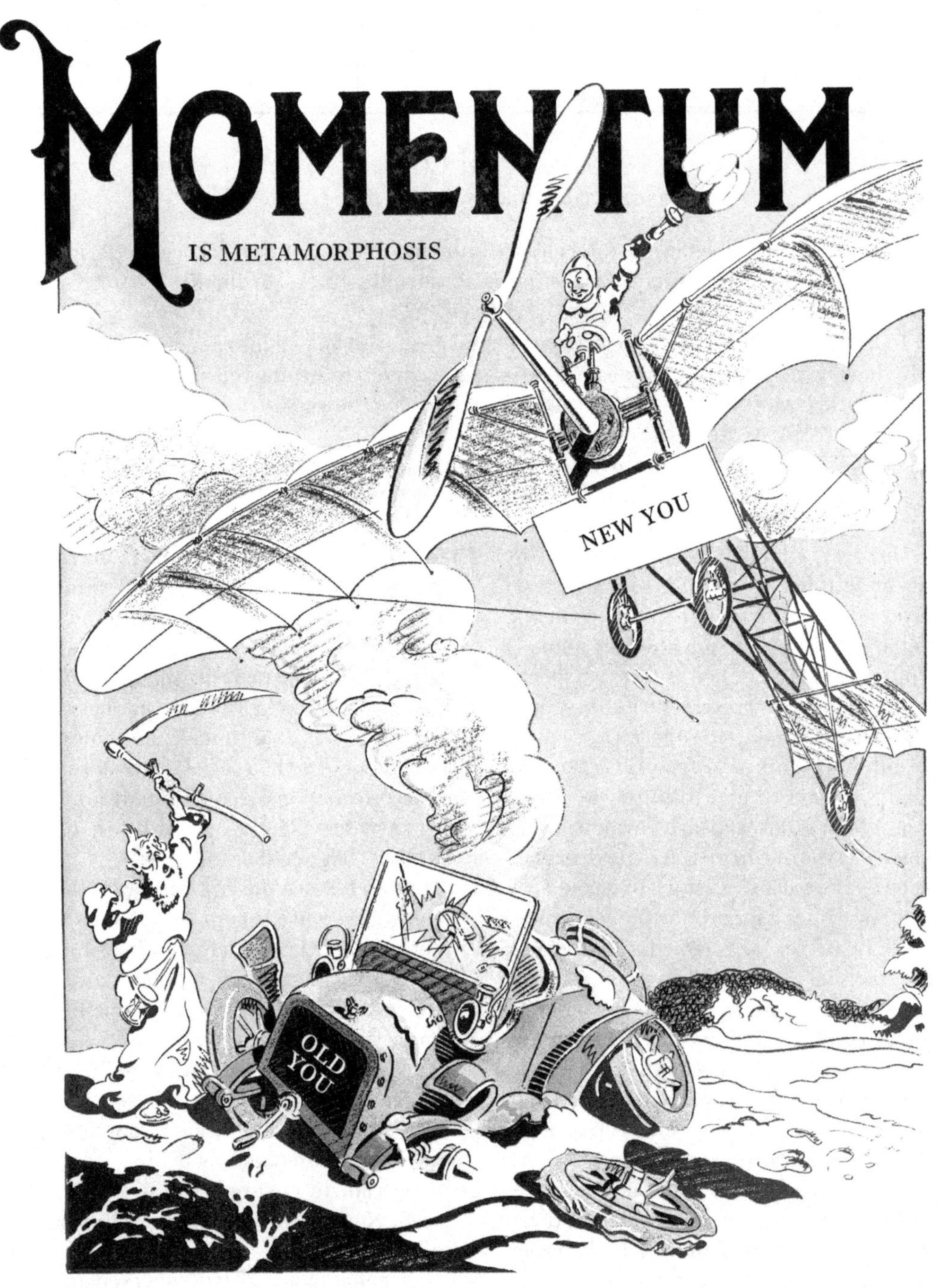
MOMENTUM
IS METAMORPHOSIS
NEW YOU
OLD YOU

Real Estate Freedom is an intoxicating slurry of desire.

Though scores of agents have sipped from its cup,
it's taste is evasive, so soon, most give up.
If only they knew what eludes all but the few
who practice with gusto what's now shared with you:

Motion, action, and movement of mind
followed by feet, mouth, and arse in kind
spring forth numbers, from which it is easy to find
the inclined path forward, however it winds.

Through the thickets and wickets and all of that jive
spew forth thoughts and figures of the daily grind
from which notes may be taken and later outlined,
with hopes that tomorrow will soon be refined.

Steady progression begets knowledge and drive
when improvement to systems is prescribed by archive.
With eyes open, keep going; it gets easier with time.
Perseverance is what keeps this business alive!

Think, do, track, and repeat.
Alas, it's happened: my transformation's complete.
On the horizon, I see a new me is dawned
The trick is momentum; stick with it, from here to beyond.

Real Estate, you're like putty—Let's get it on!

THE POLITICALLY INCORRECT REAL ESTATE AGENT LOG-BOOK

{20 } MONTHLY ACTIVITY TRACKER (GOALS→RESULTS)

GOALS	ACTIVITY	WK 1	WK 2	WK 3	WK 4	WK 5	TOTAL RESULTS
	TRANSACTIONS (T)	L B	L B	L B	L B	L B	L B
	NEW CLIENTS (C)	L B	L B	L B	L B	L B	L B
	PRESENTATIONS (P)	L B	L B	L B	L B	L B	L B
	DISCUSSIONS (D)						
	DAYS WORKED (W)						
	DAILY DISCUSSIONS (D/W)	**ACTUAL DAILY DISCUSSION AVERAGE**				**D/W**	
$	**GCI**	$					

{20 } MONTHLY ACTIVITY TRACKER (GOALS→RESULTS)

GOALS	ACTIVITY	WK 1	WK 2	WK 3	WK 4	WK 5	TOTAL RESULTS
	TRANSACTIONS (T)	L B	L B	L B	L B	L B	L B
	NEW CLIENTS (C)	L B	L B	L B	L B	L B	L B
	PRESENTATIONS (P)	L B	L B	L B	L B	L B	L B
	DISCUSSIONS (D)						
	DAYS WORKED (W)						
	DAILY DISCUSSIONS (D/W)	**ACTUAL DAILY DISCUSSION AVERAGE**				**D/W**	
$	**GCI**	$					

{20 } MONTHLY ACTIVITY TRACKER (GOALS→RESULTS)

GOALS	ACTIVITY	WK 1	WK 2	WK 3	WK 4	WK 5	TOTAL RESULTS
	TRANSACTIONS (T)	L B	L B	L B	L B	L B	L B
	NEW CLIENTS (C)	L B	L B	L B	L B	L B	L B
	PRESENTATIONS (P)	L B	L B	L B	L B	L B	L B
	DISCUSSIONS (D)						
	DAYS WORKED (W)						
	DAILY DISCUSSIONS (D/W)	**ACTUAL DAILY DISCUSSION AVERAGE**				**D/W**	
$	**GCI**	$					

January

01

Today is Business Plan Day.[XVIII]
Review/revise yours, and contemplate the past/future.
What is your plan to improve upon last month's performance?

{20 }

{20 }

{20 }

{20 }

S M T W T F S

Today I mostly prospected:

	DISCUSSIONS	
L	DAILY TRACKER	B
	PRESENTATIONS	
	CLIENTS	
	CONTRACTS	
	TRANSACTIONS	

☐ Did not work today; instead, I:

{20 }

S M T W T F S

Today I mostly prospected:

	DISCUSSIONS	
L	DAILY TRACKER	B
	PRESENTATIONS	
	CLIENTS	
	CONTRACTS	
	TRANSACTIONS	

☐ Did not work today; instead, I:

{20 }

S M T W T F S

Today I mostly prospected:

	DISCUSSIONS	
L	DAILY TRACKER	B
	PRESENTATIONS	
	CLIENTS	
	CONTRACTS	
	TRANSACTIONS	

☐ Did not work today; instead, I:

02

January

*List a good habit you wanna adopt this month.
How will you implement this habit
and make it a permanent part of your routine?*

{20 }

{20 }

{20 }

{20 }
S M T W T F S
Today I mostly prospected:

L	DISCUSSIONS	B
	DAILY TRACKER	
	PRESENTATIONS	
	CLIENTS	
	CONTRACTS	
	TRANSACTIONS	

☐ Did not work today; instead, I:

{20 }
S M T W T F S
Today I mostly prospected:

L	DISCUSSIONS	B
	DAILY TRACKER	
	PRESENTATIONS	
	CLIENTS	
	CONTRACTS	
	TRANSACTIONS	

☐ Did not work today; instead, I:

{20 }
S M T W T F S
Today I mostly prospected:

L	DISCUSSIONS	B
	DAILY TRACKER	
	PRESENTATIONS	
	CLIENTS	
	CONTRACTS	
	TRANSACTIONS	

☐ Did not work today; instead, I:

January

03

What would make your prospecting efforts more efficient?[012]
How could your message reach more prospects in less time?
How could you increase your discussion turnover rate (DTR)*?*[XVI]

{20 }

{20 }

{20 }

{20 }

S M T W T F S

Today I mostly prospected:

	DISCUSSIONS	
L	DAILY TRACKER	B
	PRESENTATIONS	
	CLIENTS	
	CONTRACTS	
	TRANSACTIONS	

☐ Did not work today; instead, I:

{20 }

S M T W T F S

Today I mostly prospected:

	DISCUSSIONS	
L	DAILY TRACKER	B
	PRESENTATIONS	
	CLIENTS	
	CONTRACTS	
	TRANSACTIONS	

☐ Did not work today; instead, I:

{20 }

S M T W T F S

Today I mostly prospected:

	DISCUSSIONS	
L	DAILY TRACKER	B
	PRESENTATIONS	
	CLIENTS	
	CONTRACTS	
	TRANSACTIONS	

☐ Did not work today; instead, I:

January

Write three professional goals and three personal goals for this year. Then write a quick plan to achieve each.

{20 }

{20 }

{20 }

{20 }		
S M T W T F S		
Today I mostly prospected:		
	DISCUSSIONS	
L	DAILY TRACKER	B
	PRESENTATIONS	
	CLIENTS	
	CONTRACTS	
	TRANSACTIONS	
☐ Did not work today; instead, I:		

{20 }		
S M T W T F S		
Today I mostly prospected:		
	DISCUSSIONS	
L	DAILY TRACKER	B
	PRESENTATIONS	
	CLIENTS	
	CONTRACTS	
	TRANSACTIONS	
☐ Did not work today; instead, I:		

{20 }		
S M T W T F S		
Today I mostly prospected:		
	DISCUSSIONS	
L	DAILY TRACKER	B
	PRESENTATIONS	
	CLIENTS	
	CONTRACTS	
	TRANSACTIONS	
☐ Did not work today; instead, I:		

January

Where else could you be looking for buyers and sellers?
Name three new ways to meet prospects[084]
and a plan to implement.

{20 } ______________________________

{20 } ______________________________

{20 } ______________________________

{20 }

S M T W T F S

Today I mostly prospected:

	DISCUSSIONS	
L	DAILY TRACKER	B
	PRESENTATIONS	
	CLIENTS	
	CONTRACTS	
	TRANSACTIONS	

☐ Did not work today; instead, I:

{20 }

S M T W T F S

Today I mostly prospected:

	DISCUSSIONS	
L	DAILY TRACKER	B
	PRESENTATIONS	
	CLIENTS	
	CONTRACTS	
	TRANSACTIONS	

☐ Did not work today; instead, I:

{20 }

S M T W T F S

Today I mostly prospected:

	DISCUSSIONS	
L	DAILY TRACKER	B
	PRESENTATIONS	
	CLIENTS	
	CONTRACTS	
	TRANSACTIONS	

☐ Did not work today; instead, I:

06 January

List ten words to describe your current real estate skill level.
Which words would you like to add, but are not yet true?
Which ones would you like to toss out the window?

{20 }

{20 }

{20 }

{20 }

S M T W T F S

Today I mostly prospected:

	DISCUSSIONS	
L	DAILY TRACKER	B
	PRESENTATIONS	
	CLIENTS	
	CONTRACTS	
	TRANSACTIONS	

☐ Did not work today; instead, I:

{20 }

S M T W T F S

Today I mostly prospected:

	DISCUSSIONS	
L	DAILY TRACKER	B
	PRESENTATIONS	
	CLIENTS	
	CONTRACTS	
	TRANSACTIONS	

☐ Did not work today; instead, I:

{20 }

S M T W T F S

Today I mostly prospected:

	DISCUSSIONS	
L	DAILY TRACKER	B
	PRESENTATIONS	
	CLIENTS	
	CONTRACTS	
	TRANSACTIONS	

☐ Did not work today; instead, I:

January

Write a script for this seller objection:
"We're gonna wait until the spring to list, when more buyers are looking."

{20 }

{20 }

{20 }

{20 }		
S M T W T F S		
Today I mostly prospected:		
	DISCUSSIONS	
L	DAILY TRACKER	B
	PRESENTATIONS	
	CLIENTS	
	CONTRACTS	
	TRANSACTIONS	
☐ Did not work today; instead, I:		

{20 }		
S M T W T F S		
Today I mostly prospected:		
	DISCUSSIONS	
L	DAILY TRACKER	B
	PRESENTATIONS	
	CLIENTS	
	CONTRACTS	
	TRANSACTIONS	
☐ Did not work today; instead, I:		

{20 }		
S M T W T F S		
Today I mostly prospected:		
	DISCUSSIONS	
L	DAILY TRACKER	B
	PRESENTATIONS	
	CLIENTS	
	CONTRACTS	
	TRANSACTIONS	
☐ Did not work today; instead, I:		

08 January

Why did you choose (or choose to stay with) your broker? [028]
Are you getting your money's worth? [282]

{20 }

{20 }

{20 }

{20 }
S M T W T F S
Today I mostly prospected:

	DISCUSSIONS	
L	DAILY TRACKER	B
	PRESENTATIONS	
	CLIENTS	
	CONTRACTS	
	TRANSACTIONS	

☐ Did not work today; instead, I:

{20 }
S M T W T F S
Today I mostly prospected:

	DISCUSSIONS	
L	DAILY TRACKER	B
	PRESENTATIONS	
	CLIENTS	
	CONTRACTS	
	TRANSACTIONS	

☐ Did not work today; instead, I:

{20 }
S M T W T F S
Today I mostly prospected:

	DISCUSSIONS	
L	DAILY TRACKER	B
	PRESENTATIONS	
	CLIENTS	
	CONTRACTS	
	TRANSACTIONS	

☐ Did not work today; instead, I:

January

09

Are you keeping your database clean and organized?[089]
What value are you giving to its members?[090]
Who can you call for a referral?

{20 }

{20 }

{20 }

{20 }	{20 }	{20 }
S M T W T F S	S M T W T F S	S M T W T F S
Today I mostly prospected:	Today I mostly prospected:	Today I mostly prospected:
DISCUSSIONS	DISCUSSIONS	DISCUSSIONS
L · DAILY TRACKER · B	L · DAILY TRACKER · B	L · DAILY TRACKER · B
PRESENTATIONS	PRESENTATIONS	PRESENTATIONS
CLIENTS	CLIENTS	CLIENTS
CONTRACTS	CONTRACTS	CONTRACTS
TRANSACTIONS	TRANSACTIONS	TRANSACTIONS
☐ Did not work today; instead, I:	☐ Did not work today; instead, I:	☐ Did not work today; instead, I:

10

January

*If you could possess a real estate superpower,
what would it be and why?
How might you make such power a reality?*

{20 }

{20 }

{20 }

{20 }		{20 }		{20 }	
S M T W T F S		S M T W T F S		S M T W T F S	
Today I mostly prospected:		Today I mostly prospected:		Today I mostly prospected:	

	DISCUSSIONS			DISCUSSIONS			DISCUSSIONS	
L	DAILY TRACKER	B	L	DAILY TRACKER	B	L	DAILY TRACKER	B
	PRESENTATIONS			PRESENTATIONS			PRESENTATIONS	
	CLIENTS			CLIENTS			CLIENTS	
	CONTRACTS			CONTRACTS			CONTRACTS	
	TRANSACTIONS			TRANSACTIONS			TRANSACTIONS	

☐ Did not work today; instead, I:

☐ Did not work today; instead, I:

☐ Did not work today; instead, I:

January

11

How could today have gone better?
Even if it was great, what would have made it the best day ever?

{20 }

{20 }

{20 }

{20 }
S M T W T F S
Today I mostly prospected:

	DISCUSSIONS	
L	DAILY TRACKER	B
	PRESENTATIONS	
	CLIENTS	
	CONTRACTS	
	TRANSACTIONS	

☐ Did not work today; instead, I:

{20 }
S M T W T F S
Today I mostly prospected:

	DISCUSSIONS	
L	DAILY TRACKER	B
	PRESENTATIONS	
	CLIENTS	
	CONTRACTS	
	TRANSACTIONS	

☐ Did not work today; instead, I:

{20 }
S M T W T F S
Today I mostly prospected:

	DISCUSSIONS	
L	DAILY TRACKER	B
	PRESENTATIONS	
	CLIENTS	
	CONTRACTS	
	TRANSACTIONS	

☐ Did not work today; instead, I:

12

January

What could you do tomorrow to get a well-priced listing?[098]
How would doing so impact your business?
...impact your life?

{20 }

{20 }

{20 }

{20 }		
S M T W T F S		
Today I mostly prospected:		
	DISCUSSIONS	
L	DAILY TRACKER	B
	PRESENTATIONS	
	CLIENTS	
	CONTRACTS	
	TRANSACTIONS	
☐ Did not work today; instead, I:		

{20 }		
S M T W T F S		
Today I mostly prospected:		
	DISCUSSIONS	
L	DAILY TRACKER	B
	PRESENTATIONS	
	CLIENTS	
	CONTRACTS	
	TRANSACTIONS	
☐ Did not work today; instead, I:		

{20 }		
S M T W T F S		
Today I mostly prospected:		
	DISCUSSIONS	
L	DAILY TRACKER	B
	PRESENTATIONS	
	CLIENTS	
	CONTRACTS	
	TRANSACTIONS	
☐ Did not work today; instead, I:		

13

What is your number one best tip for buyers?
How well are you communicating that to prospects?[090]

{20 }

{20 }

{20 }

{20 }

S M T W T F S

Today I mostly prospected:

	DISCUSSIONS	
L	DAILY TRACKER	B
	PRESENTATIONS	
	CLIENTS	
	CONTRACTS	
	TRANSACTIONS	

☐ Did not work today; instead, I:

{20 }

S M T W T F S

Today I mostly prospected:

	DISCUSSIONS	
L	DAILY TRACKER	B
	PRESENTATIONS	
	CLIENTS	
	CONTRACTS	
	TRANSACTIONS	

☐ Did not work today; instead, I:

{20 }

S M T W T F S

Today I mostly prospected:

	DISCUSSIONS	
L	DAILY TRACKER	B
	PRESENTATIONS	
	CLIENTS	
	CONTRACTS	
	TRANSACTIONS	

☐ Did not work today; instead, I:

14 January

What is currently your biggest bottleneck (slowdown in the transaction process)? [VII]
What are you doing to improve that turnover rate? [XVI]

{20 }

{20 }

{20 }

{20 }

S M T W T F S

Today I mostly prospected:

L	DISCUSSIONS	B
	DAILY TRACKER	
	PRESENTATIONS	
	CLIENTS	
	CONTRACTS	
	TRANSACTIONS	

☐ Did not work today; instead, I:

{20 }

S M T W T F S

Today I mostly prospected:

L	DISCUSSIONS	B
	DAILY TRACKER	
	PRESENTATIONS	
	CLIENTS	
	CONTRACTS	
	TRANSACTIONS	

☐ Did not work today; instead, I:

{20 }

S M T W T F S

Today I mostly prospected:

L	DISCUSSIONS	B
	DAILY TRACKER	
	PRESENTATIONS	
	CLIENTS	
	CONTRACTS	
	TRANSACTIONS	

☐ Did not work today; instead, I:

January

15

Are you falling behind (or surging ahead) on any monthly goals?
What's your plan to achieve them all?[XIX]
Adjust your activities now, so you will meet or exceed all.

{20 }

{20 }

{20 }

{20 }		
S M T W T F S		
Today I mostly prospected:		
	DISCUSSIONS	
L	DAILY TRACKER	B
	PRESENTATIONS	
	CLIENTS	
	CONTRACTS	
	TRANSACTIONS	
☐ Did not work today; instead, I:		

{20 }		
S M T W T F S		
Today I mostly prospected:		
	DISCUSSIONS	
L	DAILY TRACKER	B
	PRESENTATIONS	
	CLIENTS	
	CONTRACTS	
	TRANSACTIONS	
☐ Did not work today; instead, I:		

{20 }		
S M T W T F S		
Today I mostly prospected:		
	DISCUSSIONS	
L	DAILY TRACKER	B
	PRESENTATIONS	
	CLIENTS	
	CONTRACTS	
	TRANSACTIONS	
☐ Did not work today; instead, I:		

16

January

Rank your mental health on a scale of one to ten.
List one thing you could do to improve
and a plan to achieve.

{20 }

{20 }

{20 }

{20 }

S M T W T F S

Today I mostly prospected:

	DISCUSSIONS	
L	DAILY TRACKER	B
	PRESENTATIONS	
	CLIENTS	
	CONTRACTS	
	TRANSACTIONS	

☐ Did not work today; instead, I:

{20 }

S M T W T F S

Today I mostly prospected:

	DISCUSSIONS	
L	DAILY TRACKER	B
	PRESENTATIONS	
	CLIENTS	
	CONTRACTS	
	TRANSACTIONS	

☐ Did not work today; instead, I:

{20 }

S M T W T F S

Today I mostly prospected:

	DISCUSSIONS	
L	DAILY TRACKER	B
	PRESENTATIONS	
	CLIENTS	
	CONTRACTS	
	TRANSACTIONS	

☐ Did not work today; instead, I:

January

17

Recall a recent class or educational session.
What was the number one thing you learned?
How will you implement it into your business?

{20 }

{20 }

{20 }

{20 }

S M T W T F S

Today I mostly prospected:

	DISCUSSIONS	
L	DAILY TRACKER	B
	PRESENTATIONS	
	CLIENTS	
	CONTRACTS	
	TRANSACTIONS	

☐ Did not work today; instead, I:

{20 }

S M T W T F S

Today I mostly prospected:

	DISCUSSIONS	
L	DAILY TRACKER	B
	PRESENTATIONS	
	CLIENTS	
	CONTRACTS	
	TRANSACTIONS	

☐ Did not work today; instead, I:

{20 }

S M T W T F S

Today I mostly prospected:

	DISCUSSIONS	
L	DAILY TRACKER	B
	PRESENTATIONS	
	CLIENTS	
	CONTRACTS	
	TRANSACTIONS	

☐ Did not work today; instead, I:

18

January

List three systems that need improvement.[070]
Reward yourself with deadlines.

{20 }

{20 }

{20 }

{20 }
S M T W T F S
Today I mostly prospected:

	DISCUSSIONS	
L	DAILY TRACKER	B
	PRESENTATIONS	
	CLIENTS	
	CONTRACTS	
	TRANSACTIONS	

☐ Did not work today; instead, I:

{20 }
S M T W T F S
Today I mostly prospected:

	DISCUSSIONS	
L	DAILY TRACKER	B
	PRESENTATIONS	
	CLIENTS	
	CONTRACTS	
	TRANSACTIONS	

☐ Did not work today; instead, I:

{20 }
S M T W T F S
Today I mostly prospected:

	DISCUSSIONS	
L	DAILY TRACKER	B
	PRESENTATIONS	
	CLIENTS	
	CONTRACTS	
	TRANSACTIONS	

☐ Did not work today; instead, I:

January

19

Today is Pat Yourself on the Back Day.
Recall a recent thing you did well.
How can you implement this thing into your systems?

{20 } ______

{20 } ______

{20 } ______

{20 }	{20 }	{20 }
S M T W T F S	S M T W T F S	S M T W T F S
Today I mostly prospected:	Today I mostly prospected:	Today I mostly prospected:

	DISCUSSIONS	
L	DAILY TRACKER	B
	PRESENTATIONS	
	CLIENTS	
	CONTRACTS	
	TRANSACTIONS	

☐ Did not work today; instead, I:

	DISCUSSIONS	
L	DAILY TRACKER	B
	PRESENTATIONS	
	CLIENTS	
	CONTRACTS	
	TRANSACTIONS	

☐ Did not work today; instead, I:

	DISCUSSIONS	
L	DAILY TRACKER	B
	PRESENTATIONS	
	CLIENTS	
	CONTRACTS	
	TRANSACTIONS	

☐ Did not work today; instead, I:

20

January

How many referrals did you send out last year, and how much additional income did you make? What is your plan to improve on those numbers?

{20 }

{20 }

{20 }

{20 }

S M T W T F S

Today I mostly prospected:

L	DISCUSSIONS	B
	DAILY TRACKER	
	PRESENTATIONS	
	CLIENTS	
	CONTRACTS	
	TRANSACTIONS	

☐ Did not work today; instead, I:

{20 }

S M T W T F S

Today I mostly prospected:

L	DISCUSSIONS	B
	DAILY TRACKER	
	PRESENTATIONS	
	CLIENTS	
	CONTRACTS	
	TRANSACTIONS	

☐ Did not work today; instead, I:

{20 }

S M T W T F S

Today I mostly prospected:

L	DISCUSSIONS	B
	DAILY TRACKER	
	PRESENTATIONS	
	CLIENTS	
	CONTRACTS	
	TRANSACTIONS	

☐ Did not work today; instead, I:

January

21

Describe your excitement and commitment to keeping up with this book. What is your plan to write in it everyday? What are your expectations?

{20 }

{20 }

{20 }

{20 }

S M T W T F S

Today I mostly prospected:

	DISCUSSIONS	
L	DAILY TRACKER	B
	PRESENTATIONS	
	CLIENTS	
	CONTRACTS	
	TRANSACTIONS	

☐ Did not work today; instead, I:

{20 }

S M T W T F S

Today I mostly prospected:

	DISCUSSIONS	
L	DAILY TRACKER	B
	PRESENTATIONS	
	CLIENTS	
	CONTRACTS	
	TRANSACTIONS	

☐ Did not work today; instead, I:

{20 }

S M T W T F S

Today I mostly prospected:

	DISCUSSIONS	
L	DAILY TRACKER	B
	PRESENTATIONS	
	CLIENTS	
	CONTRACTS	
	TRANSACTIONS	

☐ Did not work today; instead, I:

22 January

Recall a recent, unexpected surprise.
Was it good or bad? How did you handle it?

{20 }

{20 }

{20 }

{20 }

S M T W T F S

Today I mostly prospected:

	DISCUSSIONS	
L	DAILY TRACKER	B
	PRESENTATIONS	
	CLIENTS	
	CONTRACTS	
	TRANSACTIONS	

☐ Did not work today; instead, I:

{20 }

S M T W T F S

Today I mostly prospected:

	DISCUSSIONS	
L	DAILY TRACKER	B
	PRESENTATIONS	
	CLIENTS	
	CONTRACTS	
	TRANSACTIONS	

☐ Did not work today; instead, I:

{20 }

S M T W T F S

Today I mostly prospected:

	DISCUSSIONS	
L	DAILY TRACKER	B
	PRESENTATIONS	
	CLIENTS	
	CONTRACTS	
	TRANSACTIONS	

☐ Did not work today; instead, I:

January

23

List twenty words that describe your prospecting efforts/habits/results.[077]
Which ones would you like to change?

{20 }

{20 }

{20 }

{20 }	{20 }	{20 }
S M T W T F S	S M T W T F S	S M T W T F S
Today I mostly prospected:	Today I mostly prospected:	Today I mostly prospected:
DISCUSSIONS	DISCUSSIONS	DISCUSSIONS
L · DAILY TRACKER · B	L · DAILY TRACKER · B	L · DAILY TRACKER · B
PRESENTATIONS	PRESENTATIONS	PRESENTATIONS
CLIENTS	CLIENTS	CLIENTS
CONTRACTS	CONTRACTS	CONTRACTS
TRANSACTIONS	TRANSACTIONS	TRANSACTIONS
☐ Did not work today; instead, I:	☐ Did not work today; instead, I:	☐ Did not work today; instead, I:

24 January

If your business was a car, what kind of car would it be?
How would you describe its performance?
Why do you say that?

{20 }

{20 }

{20 }

{20 }	{20 }	{20 }
S M T W T F S	S M T W T F S	S M T W T F S
Today I mostly prospected:	Today I mostly prospected:	Today I mostly prospected:
DISCUSSIONS	DISCUSSIONS	DISCUSSIONS
L · DAILY TRACKER · B	L · DAILY TRACKER · B	L · DAILY TRACKER · B
PRESENTATIONS	PRESENTATIONS	PRESENTATIONS
CLIENTS	CLIENTS	CLIENTS
CONTRACTS	CONTRACTS	CONTRACTS
TRANSACTIONS	TRANSACTIONS	TRANSACTIONS
☐ Did not work today; instead, I:	☐ Did not work today; instead, I:	☐ Did not work today; instead, I:

January

25

Who, recently, has been your favorite client and why?
How might you find (or create) similar clients?

{20 }

{20 }

{20 }

{20 }

S M T W T F S

Today I mostly prospected:

	DISCUSSIONS	
L	DAILY TRACKER	B
	PRESENTATIONS	
	CLIENTS	
	CONTRACTS	
	TRANSACTIONS	

☐ Did not work today; instead, I:

{20 }

S M T W T F S

Today I mostly prospected:

	DISCUSSIONS	
L	DAILY TRACKER	B
	PRESENTATIONS	
	CLIENTS	
	CONTRACTS	
	TRANSACTIONS	

☐ Did not work today; instead, I:

{20 }

S M T W T F S

Today I mostly prospected:

	DISCUSSIONS	
L	DAILY TRACKER	B
	PRESENTATIONS	
	CLIENTS	
	CONTRACTS	
	TRANSACTIONS	

☐ Did not work today; instead, I:

26 January

List three bad habits you'd like to lose. Reward yourself with deadlines and a plan to ditch each offending habit.

{20 }

{20 }

{20 }

{20 }	{20 }	{20 }
S M T W T F S	S M T W T F S	S M T W T F S
Today I mostly prospected:	Today I mostly prospected:	Today I mostly prospected:
DISCUSSIONS	DISCUSSIONS	DISCUSSIONS
L | DAILY TRACKER | B	L | DAILY TRACKER | B	L | DAILY TRACKER | B
PRESENTATIONS	PRESENTATIONS	PRESENTATIONS
CLIENTS	CLIENTS	CLIENTS
CONTRACTS	CONTRACTS	CONTRACTS
TRANSACTIONS	TRANSACTIONS	TRANSACTIONS
☐ Did not work today; instead, I:	☐ Did not work today; instead, I:	☐ Did not work today; instead, I:

January

27

Do you host/attend broker open houses?[284]
What have you learned from these events?

{20 }

{20 }

{20 }

{20 }		
S M T W T F S		
Today I mostly prospected:		
	DISCUSSIONS	
L	DAILY TRACKER	B
	PRESENTATIONS	
	CLIENTS	
	CONTRACTS	
	TRANSACTIONS	
☐ Did not work today; instead, I:		

{20 }		
S M T W T F S		
Today I mostly prospected:		
	DISCUSSIONS	
L	DAILY TRACKER	B
	PRESENTATIONS	
	CLIENTS	
	CONTRACTS	
	TRANSACTIONS	
☐ Did not work today; instead, I:		

{20 }		
S M T W T F S		
Today I mostly prospected:		
	DISCUSSIONS	
L	DAILY TRACKER	B
	PRESENTATIONS	
	CLIENTS	
	CONTRACTS	
	TRANSACTIONS	
☐ Did not work today; instead, I:		

28 January

Name one thing that would improve your average transaction price (ATP).[XVI]

{20 }

{20 }

{20 }

{20 }		
S M T W T F S		
Today I mostly prospected:		
	DISCUSSIONS	
L	DAILY TRACKER	B
	PRESENTATIONS	
	CLIENTS	
	CONTRACTS	
	TRANSACTIONS	
☐ Did not work today; instead, I:		

{20 }		
S M T W T F S		
Today I mostly prospected:		
	DISCUSSIONS	
L	DAILY TRACKER	B
	PRESENTATIONS	
	CLIENTS	
	CONTRACTS	
	TRANSACTIONS	
☐ Did not work today; instead, I:		

{20 }		
S M T W T F S		
Today I mostly prospected:		
	DISCUSSIONS	
L	DAILY TRACKER	B
	PRESENTATIONS	
	CLIENTS	
	CONTRACTS	
	TRANSACTIONS	
☐ Did not work today; instead, I:		

January

29

Write a script for this double-dipping objection:
"If I both list and buy with you,
you'll have to cut your commission."

{20 }

{20 }

{20 }

{20 }
S M T W T F S
Today I mostly prospected:

	DISCUSSIONS	
L	DAILY TRACKER	B
	PRESENTATIONS	
	CLIENTS	
	CONTRACTS	
	TRANSACTIONS	

☐ Did not work today; instead, I:

{20 }
S M T W T F S
Today I mostly prospected:

	DISCUSSIONS	
L	DAILY TRACKER	B
	PRESENTATIONS	
	CLIENTS	
	CONTRACTS	
	TRANSACTIONS	

☐ Did not work today; instead, I:

{20 }
S M T W T F S
Today I mostly prospected:

	DISCUSSIONS	
L	DAILY TRACKER	B
	PRESENTATIONS	
	CLIENTS	
	CONTRACTS	
	TRANSACTIONS	

☐ Did not work today; instead, I:

30

January

My grandest achievement this month was...
My plan to repeat this victory is...

{20 } ______________________________

{20 } ______________________________

{20 } ______________________________

{20 }

S M T W T F S

Today I mostly prospected:

	DISCUSSIONS	
L	DAILY TRACKER	B
	PRESENTATIONS	
	CLIENTS	
	CONTRACTS	
	TRANSACTIONS	

☐ Did not work today; instead, I:

{20 }

S M T W T F S

Today I mostly prospected:

	DISCUSSIONS	
L	DAILY TRACKER	B
	PRESENTATIONS	
	CLIENTS	
	CONTRACTS	
	TRANSACTIONS	

☐ Did not work today; instead, I:

{20 }

S M T W T F S

Today I mostly prospected:

	DISCUSSIONS	
L	DAILY TRACKER	B
	PRESENTATIONS	
	CLIENTS	
	CONTRACTS	
	TRANSACTIONS	

☐ Did not work today; instead, I:

January

31

The biggest mistake/misstep I made this month was...
My plan to prevent the same mishap from recurring is...

{20 }

{20 }

{20 }

{20 }

S M T W T F S

Today I mostly prospected:

	DISCUSSIONS	
L	DAILY TRACKER	B
	PRESENTATIONS	
	CLIENTS	
	CONTRACTS	
	TRANSACTIONS	

☐ Did not work today; instead, I:

{20 }

S M T W T F S

Today I mostly prospected:

	DISCUSSIONS	
L	DAILY TRACKER	B
	PRESENTATIONS	
	CLIENTS	
	CONTRACTS	
	TRANSACTIONS	

☐ Did not work today; instead, I:

{20 }

S M T W T F S

Today I mostly prospected:

	DISCUSSIONS	
L	DAILY TRACKER	B
	PRESENTATIONS	
	CLIENTS	
	CONTRACTS	
	TRANSACTIONS	

☐ Did not work today; instead, I:

{20 } MONTHLY ACTIVITY TRACKER (GOALS→RESULTS)

GOALS	ACTIVITY	WK 1	WK 2	WK 3	WK 4	WK 5	TOTAL RESULTS
	TRANSACTIONS (T)	L B	L B	L B	L B	L B	L B
	NEW CLIENTS (C)	L B	L B	L B	L B	L B	L B
	PRESENTATIONS (P)	L B	L B	L B	L B	L B	L B
	DISCUSSIONS (D)						
	DAYS WORKED (W)						
	DAILY DISCUSSIONS (D/W)	ACTUAL DAILY DISCUSSION AVERAGE				D/W	
$	GCI	$					

{20 } MONTHLY ACTIVITY TRACKER (GOALS→RESULTS)

GOALS	ACTIVITY	WK 1	WK 2	WK 3	WK 4	WK 5	TOTAL RESULTS
	TRANSACTIONS (T)	L B	L B	L B	L B	L B	L B
	NEW CLIENTS (C)	L B	L B	L B	L B	L B	L B
	PRESENTATIONS (P)	L B	L B	L B	L B	L B	L B
	DISCUSSIONS (D)						
	DAYS WORKED (W)						
	DAILY DISCUSSIONS (D/W)	ACTUAL DAILY DISCUSSION AVERAGE				D/W	
$	GCI	$					

{20 } MONTHLY ACTIVITY TRACKER (GOALS→RESULTS)

GOALS	ACTIVITY	WK 1	WK 2	WK 3	WK 4	WK 5	TOTAL RESULTS
	TRANSACTIONS (T)	L B	L B	L B	L B	L B	L B
	NEW CLIENTS (C)	L B	L B	L B	L B	L B	L B
	PRESENTATIONS (P)	L B	L B	L B	L B	L B	L B
	DISCUSSIONS (D)						
	DAYS WORKED (W)						
	DAILY DISCUSSIONS (D/W)	ACTUAL DAILY DISCUSSION AVERAGE				D/W	
$	GCI	$					

February

01

Today is Business Plan Day.[XVIII]
Review/revise yours, and contemplate the past/future.
What is your plan to improve upon last month's performance?

{20 }

{20 }

{20 }

{20 }
S M T W T F S
Today I mostly prospected:

L	DISCUSSIONS	B
	DAILY TRACKER	
	PRESENTATIONS	
	CLIENTS	
	CONTRACTS	
	TRANSACTIONS	

☐ Did not work today; instead, I:

{20 }
S M T W T F S
Today I mostly prospected:

L	DISCUSSIONS	B
	DAILY TRACKER	
	PRESENTATIONS	
	CLIENTS	
	CONTRACTS	
	TRANSACTIONS	

☐ Did not work today; instead, I:

{20 }
S M T W T F S
Today I mostly prospected:

L	DISCUSSIONS	B
	DAILY TRACKER	
	PRESENTATIONS	
	CLIENTS	
	CONTRACTS	
	TRANSACTIONS	

☐ Did not work today; instead, I:

02 February

Today is Groundhog Day.
Did you see your shadow? What are you doing now to prepare for the spring buying/selling season?

{20 }

{20 }

{20 }

{20 }

S M T W T F S

Today I mostly prospected:

L	DISCUSSIONS	B
	DAILY TRACKER	
	PRESENTATIONS	
	CLIENTS	
	CONTRACTS	
	TRANSACTIONS	

☐ Did not work today; instead, I:

{20 }

S M T W T F S

Today I mostly prospected:

L	DISCUSSIONS	B
	DAILY TRACKER	
	PRESENTATIONS	
	CLIENTS	
	CONTRACTS	
	TRANSACTIONS	

☐ Did not work today; instead, I:

{20 }

S M T W T F S

Today I mostly prospected:

L	DISCUSSIONS	B
	DAILY TRACKER	
	PRESENTATIONS	
	CLIENTS	
	CONTRACTS	
	TRANSACTIONS	

☐ Did not work today; instead, I:

February

List a good habit you wanna adopt this month. How will you implement and make it a permanent part of your routine? Has last month's habit stuck yet?

{20 }

{20 }

{20 }

{20 }
S M T W T F S
Today I mostly prospected:

	DISCUSSIONS	
L	DAILY TRACKER	B
	PRESENTATIONS	
	CLIENTS	
	CONTRACTS	
	TRANSACTIONS	

☐ Did not work today; instead, I:

{20 }
S M T W T F S
Today I mostly prospected:

	DISCUSSIONS	
L	DAILY TRACKER	B
	PRESENTATIONS	
	CLIENTS	
	CONTRACTS	
	TRANSACTIONS	

☐ Did not work today; instead, I:

{20 }
S M T W T F S
Today I mostly prospected:

	DISCUSSIONS	
L	DAILY TRACKER	B
	PRESENTATIONS	
	CLIENTS	
	CONTRACTS	
	TRANSACTIONS	

☐ Did not work today; instead, I:

04

February

Write a script for this objection:
"My friend has a real estate license, so I should work with him."

{20 }

{20 }

{20 }

{20 }
S M T W T F S
Today I mostly prospected:

	DISCUSSIONS	
L	DAILY TRACKER	B
	PRESENTATIONS	
	CLIENTS	
	CONTRACTS	
	TRANSACTIONS	

☐ Did not work today; instead, I:

{20 }
S M T W T F S
Today I mostly prospected:

	DISCUSSIONS	
L	DAILY TRACKER	B
	PRESENTATIONS	
	CLIENTS	
	CONTRACTS	
	TRANSACTIONS	

☐ Did not work today; instead, I:

{20 }
S M T W T F S
Today I mostly prospected:

	DISCUSSIONS	
L	DAILY TRACKER	B
	PRESENTATIONS	
	CLIENTS	
	CONTRACTS	
	TRANSACTIONS	

☐ Did not work today; instead, I:

February

Write an affirmation to soothe your prospecting pains.
Otherwise, write one to encourage your enthusiasm.

{20 }

{20 }

{20 }

{20 }

S M T W T F S

Today I mostly prospected:

	DISCUSSIONS	
L	DAILY TRACKER	B
	PRESENTATIONS	
	CLIENTS	
	CONTRACTS	
	TRANSACTIONS	

☐ Did not work today; instead, I:

{20 }

S M T W T F S

Today I mostly prospected:

	DISCUSSIONS	
L	DAILY TRACKER	B
	PRESENTATIONS	
	CLIENTS	
	CONTRACTS	
	TRANSACTIONS	

☐ Did not work today; instead, I:

{20 }

S M T W T F S

Today I mostly prospected:

	DISCUSSIONS	
L	DAILY TRACKER	B
	PRESENTATIONS	
	CLIENTS	
	CONTRACTS	
	TRANSACTIONS	

☐ Did not work today; instead, I:

06

February

List ten words that describe your listing copy[232]
and other marketing efforts.[234]
Which of these words should you be sharing with prospects?

{20 }

{20 }

{20 }

{20 }

S M T W T F S

Today I mostly prospected:

DISCUSSIONS

L	DAILY TRACKER	B
	PRESENTATIONS	
	CLIENTS	
	CONTRACTS	
	TRANSACTIONS	

☐ Did not work today; instead, I:

{20 }

S M T W T F S

Today I mostly prospected:

DISCUSSIONS

L	DAILY TRACKER	B
	PRESENTATIONS	
	CLIENTS	
	CONTRACTS	
	TRANSACTIONS	

☐ Did not work today; instead, I:

{20 }

S M T W T F S

Today I mostly prospected:

DISCUSSIONS

L	DAILY TRACKER	B
	PRESENTATIONS	
	CLIENTS	
	CONTRACTS	
	TRANSACTIONS	

☐ Did not work today; instead, I:

February

A funny (real estate related) thing happened recently...

07

{20 }

{20 }

{20 }

{20 }	{20 }	{20 }
S M T W T F S	S M T W T F S	S M T W T F S
Today I mostly prospected:	Today I mostly prospected:	Today I mostly prospected:
DISCUSSIONS	DISCUSSIONS	DISCUSSIONS
L · DAILY TRACKER · B	L · DAILY TRACKER · B	L · DAILY TRACKER · B
PRESENTATIONS	PRESENTATIONS	PRESENTATIONS
CLIENTS	CLIENTS	CLIENTS
CONTRACTS	CONTRACTS	CONTRACTS
TRANSACTIONS	TRANSACTIONS	TRANSACTIONS
☐ Did not work today; instead, I:	☐ Did not work today; instead, I:	☐ Did not work today; instead, I:

08

February

Name one thing that would improve your return on presentations (ROP).[XVI]

{20 }

{20 }

{20 }

{20 }		
S M T W T F S		
Today I mostly prospected:		
	DISCUSSIONS	
L	DAILY TRACKER	B
	PRESENTATIONS	
	CLIENTS	
	CONTRACTS	
	TRANSACTIONS	
☐ Did not work today; instead, I:		

{20 }		
S M T W T F S		
Today I mostly prospected:		
	DISCUSSIONS	
L	DAILY TRACKER	B
	PRESENTATIONS	
	CLIENTS	
	CONTRACTS	
	TRANSACTIONS	
☐ Did not work today; instead, I:		

{20 }		
S M T W T F S		
Today I mostly prospected:		
	DISCUSSIONS	
L	DAILY TRACKER	B
	PRESENTATIONS	
	CLIENTS	
	CONTRACTS	
	TRANSACTIONS	
☐ Did not work today; instead, I:		

February

09

Write about the last time you implemented newfound knowledge and it resulted in money/success (whether it induced/saved a transaction or client signing). Have you adopted this practice into your systems?

{20 }

{20 }

{20 }

{20 }

S M T W T F S

Today I mostly prospected:

	DISCUSSIONS	
L	DAILY TRACKER	B
	PRESENTATIONS	
	CLIENTS	
	CONTRACTS	
	TRANSACTIONS	

☐ Did not work today; instead, I:

{20 }

S M T W T F S

Today I mostly prospected:

	DISCUSSIONS	
L	DAILY TRACKER	B
	PRESENTATIONS	
	CLIENTS	
	CONTRACTS	
	TRANSACTIONS	

☐ Did not work today; instead, I:

{20 }

S M T W T F S

Today I mostly prospected:

	DISCUSSIONS	
L	DAILY TRACKER	B
	PRESENTATIONS	
	CLIENTS	
	CONTRACTS	
	TRANSACTIONS	

☐ Did not work today; instead, I:

10

February

What first attracted you to real estate sales?
Why do you stay?
How often do you think about the reasons you remain?

{20 }

{20 }

{20 }

{20 }

S M T W T F S

Today I mostly prospected:

	DISCUSSIONS	
L	DAILY TRACKER	B
	PRESENTATIONS	
	CLIENTS	
	CONTRACTS	
	TRANSACTIONS	

☐ Did not work today; instead, I:

{20 }

S M T W T F S

Today I mostly prospected:

	DISCUSSIONS	
L	DAILY TRACKER	B
	PRESENTATIONS	
	CLIENTS	
	CONTRACTS	
	TRANSACTIONS	

☐ Did not work today; instead, I:

{20 }

S M T W T F S

Today I mostly prospected:

	DISCUSSIONS	
L	DAILY TRACKER	B
	PRESENTATIONS	
	CLIENTS	
	CONTRACTS	
	TRANSACTIONS	

☐ Did not work today; instead, I:

February

11

Where else could you be looking for buyers and sellers? Name three new ways to meet prospects[084] *and a plan to implement.*

{20 }

{20 }

{20 }

{20 }

S M T W T F S

Today I mostly prospected:

	DISCUSSIONS	
L	DAILY TRACKER	B
	PRESENTATIONS	
	CLIENTS	
	CONTRACTS	
	TRANSACTIONS	

☐ Did not work today; instead, I:

{20 }

S M T W T F S

Today I mostly prospected:

	DISCUSSIONS	
L	DAILY TRACKER	B
	PRESENTATIONS	
	CLIENTS	
	CONTRACTS	
	TRANSACTIONS	

☐ Did not work today; instead, I:

{20 }

S M T W T F S

Today I mostly prospected:

	DISCUSSIONS	
L	DAILY TRACKER	B
	PRESENTATIONS	
	CLIENTS	
	CONTRACTS	
	TRANSACTIONS	

☐ Did not work today; instead, I:

12 February

*If your business was a heartbeat,
would it be smooth and steady, or erratic and jumpy?
Explain yourself.*

{20 }

{20 }

{20 }

{20 }

S M T W T F S

Today I mostly prospected:

L	DISCUSSIONS	B
	DAILY TRACKER	
	PRESENTATIONS	
	CLIENTS	
	CONTRACTS	
	TRANSACTIONS	

☐ Did not work today; instead, I:

{20 }

S M T W T F S

Today I mostly prospected:

L	DISCUSSIONS	B
	DAILY TRACKER	
	PRESENTATIONS	
	CLIENTS	
	CONTRACTS	
	TRANSACTIONS	

☐ Did not work today; instead, I:

{20 }

S M T W T F S

Today I mostly prospected:

L	DISCUSSIONS	B
	DAILY TRACKER	
	PRESENTATIONS	
	CLIENTS	
	CONTRACTS	
	TRANSACTIONS	

☐ Did not work today; instead, I:

February

13

Rank your personal relationship health on a scale of one to ten. List one thing you could do to improve and a plan to achieve.

{20 }

{20 }

{20 }

{20 }

S M T W T F S

Today I mostly prospected:

	DISCUSSIONS	
L	DAILY TRACKER	B
	PRESENTATIONS	
	CLIENTS	
	CONTRACTS	
	TRANSACTIONS	

☐ Did not work today; instead, I:

{20 }

S M T W T F S

Today I mostly prospected:

	DISCUSSIONS	
L	DAILY TRACKER	B
	PRESENTATIONS	
	CLIENTS	
	CONTRACTS	
	TRANSACTIONS	

☐ Did not work today; instead, I:

{20 }

S M T W T F S

Today I mostly prospected:

	DISCUSSIONS	
L	DAILY TRACKER	B
	PRESENTATIONS	
	CLIENTS	
	CONTRACTS	
	TRANSACTIONS	

☐ Did not work today; instead, I:

14 February

Today is Valentine's Day.
Which part(s) of your business are you in love with?
What would it take to spread that love to another part of your business?

{20 } ____________________

{20 } ____________________

{20 } ____________________

{20 }

S M T W T F S

Today I mostly prospected:

L	DISCUSSIONS DAILY TRACKER	B
	PRESENTATIONS	
	CLIENTS	
	CONTRACTS	
	TRANSACTIONS	

☐ Did not work today; instead, I:

{20 }

S M T W T F S

Today I mostly prospected:

L	DISCUSSIONS DAILY TRACKER	B
	PRESENTATIONS	
	CLIENTS	
	CONTRACTS	
	TRANSACTIONS	

☐ Did not work today; instead, I:

{20 }

S M T W T F S

Today I mostly prospected:

L	DISCUSSIONS DAILY TRACKER	B
	PRESENTATIONS	
	CLIENTS	
	CONTRACTS	
	TRANSACTIONS	

☐ Did not work today; instead, I:

February

15

Are you falling behind (or surging ahead) on any monthly goals?
What's your plan to achieve them all?[XIX]
Adjust your activities now, so you will meet or exceed all.

{20 }

{20 }

{20 }

{20 }

S M T W T F S

Today I mostly prospected:

	DISCUSSIONS	
L	DAILY TRACKER	B
	PRESENTATIONS	
	CLIENTS	
	CONTRACTS	
	TRANSACTIONS	

☐ Did not work today; instead, I:

{20 }

S M T W T F S

Today I mostly prospected:

	DISCUSSIONS	
L	DAILY TRACKER	B
	PRESENTATIONS	
	CLIENTS	
	CONTRACTS	
	TRANSACTIONS	

☐ Did not work today; instead, I:

{20 }

S M T W T F S

Today I mostly prospected:

	DISCUSSIONS	
L	DAILY TRACKER	B
	PRESENTATIONS	
	CLIENTS	
	CONTRACTS	
	TRANSACTIONS	

☐ Did not work today; instead, I:

February

Describe a recent situation (with a prospect, client, or another agent) that could have gone differently. If you could have a do-over, how would you handle it?

{20 }

{20 }

{20 }

{20 }		
S M T W T F S		
Today I mostly prospected:		
	DISCUSSIONS	
L	DAILY TRACKER	B
	PRESENTATIONS	
	CLIENTS	
	CONTRACTS	
	TRANSACTIONS	
☐ Did not work today; instead, I:		

{20 }		
S M T W T F S		
Today I mostly prospected:		
	DISCUSSIONS	
L	DAILY TRACKER	B
	PRESENTATIONS	
	CLIENTS	
	CONTRACTS	
	TRANSACTIONS	
☐ Did not work today; instead, I:		

{20 }		
S M T W T F S		
Today I mostly prospected:		
	DISCUSSIONS	
L	DAILY TRACKER	B
	PRESENTATIONS	
	CLIENTS	
	CONTRACTS	
	TRANSACTIONS	
☐ Did not work today; instead, I:		

February

17

Which aspect of your business needs the most improvement?
What did you do today to help your situation?

{20 } ____________________

{20 } ____________________

{20 } ____________________

{20 }

S M T W T F S

Today I mostly prospected:

	DISCUSSIONS	
L	DAILY TRACKER	B
	PRESENTATIONS	
	CLIENTS	
	CONTRACTS	
	TRANSACTIONS	

☐ Did not work today; instead, I:

{20 }

S M T W T F S

Today I mostly prospected:

	DISCUSSIONS	
L	DAILY TRACKER	B
	PRESENTATIONS	
	CLIENTS	
	CONTRACTS	
	TRANSACTIONS	

☐ Did not work today; instead, I:

{20 }

S M T W T F S

Today I mostly prospected:

	DISCUSSIONS	
L	DAILY TRACKER	B
	PRESENTATIONS	
	CLIENTS	
	CONTRACTS	
	TRANSACTIONS	

☐ Did not work today; instead, I:

18

February

Today is Let There Be Light Day.
Recall a recent thing you learned that has helped your business.
How will you implement it into your systems?

{20 }

{20 }

{20 }

{20 }

S M T W T F S

Today I mostly prospected:

	DISCUSSIONS	
L	DAILY TRACKER	B
	PRESENTATIONS	
	CLIENTS	
	CONTRACTS	
	TRANSACTIONS	

☐ Did not work today; instead, I:

{20 }

S M T W T F S

Today I mostly prospected:

	DISCUSSIONS	
L	DAILY TRACKER	B
	PRESENTATIONS	
	CLIENTS	
	CONTRACTS	
	TRANSACTIONS	

☐ Did not work today; instead, I:

{20 }

S M T W T F S

Today I mostly prospected:

	DISCUSSIONS	
L	DAILY TRACKER	B
	PRESENTATIONS	
	CLIENTS	
	CONTRACTS	
	TRANSACTIONS	

☐ Did not work today; instead, I:

February

19

Write a script for this seller objection:
"Other agents have told me they will
list my house for more money."

{20 }

{20 }

{20 }

{20 }	{20 }	{20 }
S M T W T F S	S M T W T F S	S M T W T F S
Today I mostly prospected:	Today I mostly prospected:	Today I mostly prospected:
DISCUSSIONS	DISCUSSIONS	DISCUSSIONS
L · DAILY TRACKER · B	L · DAILY TRACKER · B	L · DAILY TRACKER · B
PRESENTATIONS	PRESENTATIONS	PRESENTATIONS
CLIENTS	CLIENTS	CLIENTS
CONTRACTS	CONTRACTS	CONTRACTS
TRANSACTIONS	TRANSACTIONS	TRANSACTIONS
☐ Did not work today; instead, I:	☐ Did not work today; instead, I:	☐ Did not work today; instead, I:

20

February

List twenty words that describe your agency/services/support to clients.[211]
Which of these words should you be sharing with prospects?

{20 }

{20 }

{20 }

{20 }

S M T W T F S

Today I mostly prospected:

	DISCUSSIONS	
L	DAILY TRACKER	B
	PRESENTATIONS	
	CLIENTS	
	CONTRACTS	
	TRANSACTIONS	

☐ Did not work today; instead, I:

{20 }

S M T W T F S

Today I mostly prospected:

	DISCUSSIONS	
L	DAILY TRACKER	B
	PRESENTATIONS	
	CLIENTS	
	CONTRACTS	
	TRANSACTIONS	

☐ Did not work today; instead, I:

{20 }

S M T W T F S

Today I mostly prospected:

	DISCUSSIONS	
L	DAILY TRACKER	B
	PRESENTATIONS	
	CLIENTS	
	CONTRACTS	
	TRANSACTIONS	

☐ Did not work today; instead, I:

February

21

What is the best advice you've recently received?
Have you implemented it into your life?

{20 }

{20 }

{20 }

{20 }

S M T W T F S

Today I mostly prospected:

L	DAILY TRACKER	B
	DISCUSSIONS	
	PRESENTATIONS	
	CLIENTS	
	CONTRACTS	
	TRANSACTIONS	

☐ Did not work today; instead, I:

{20 }

S M T W T F S

Today I mostly prospected:

L	DAILY TRACKER	B
	DISCUSSIONS	
	PRESENTATIONS	
	CLIENTS	
	CONTRACTS	
	TRANSACTIONS	

☐ Did not work today; instead, I:

{20 }

S M T W T F S

Today I mostly prospected:

L	DAILY TRACKER	B
	DISCUSSIONS	
	PRESENTATIONS	
	CLIENTS	
	CONTRACTS	
	TRANSACTIONS	

☐ Did not work today; instead, I:

22 February

If you died today, what would fellow agents/ brokers say about your business?

{20 }

{20 }

{20 }

{20 }
S M T W T F S
Today I mostly prospected:

L	DAILY TRACKER	B
	DISCUSSIONS	
	PRESENTATIONS	
	CLIENTS	
	CONTRACTS	
	TRANSACTIONS	

☐ Did not work today; instead, I:

{20 }
S M T W T F S
Today I mostly prospected:

L	DAILY TRACKER	B
	DISCUSSIONS	
	PRESENTATIONS	
	CLIENTS	
	CONTRACTS	
	TRANSACTIONS	

☐ Did not work today; instead, I:

{20 }
S M T W T F S
Today I mostly prospected:

L	DAILY TRACKER	B
	DISCUSSIONS	
	PRESENTATIONS	
	CLIENTS	
	CONTRACTS	
	TRANSACTIONS	

☐ Did not work today; instead, I:

February

23

Is real estate sales a fun profession?
Justify your response.

{20 }

{20 }

{20 }

{20 }
S M T W T F S
Today I mostly prospected:

	DISCUSSIONS	
L	DAILY TRACKER	B
	PRESENTATIONS	
	CLIENTS	
	CONTRACTS	
	TRANSACTIONS	

☐ Did not work today; instead, I:

{20 }
S M T W T F S
Today I mostly prospected:

	DISCUSSIONS	
L	DAILY TRACKER	B
	PRESENTATIONS	
	CLIENTS	
	CONTRACTS	
	TRANSACTIONS	

☐ Did not work today; instead, I:

{20 }
S M T W T F S
Today I mostly prospected:

	DISCUSSIONS	
L	DAILY TRACKER	B
	PRESENTATIONS	
	CLIENTS	
	CONTRACTS	
	TRANSACTIONS	

☐ Did not work today; instead, I:

24

February

How could you lower expenses without harming client services? Otherwise, how could you increase GCI *without raising expenses?*

{20 }

{20 }

{20 }

{20 }

S M T W T F S

Today I mostly prospected:

	DISCUSSIONS	
L	DAILY TRACKER	B
	PRESENTATIONS	
	CLIENTS	
	CONTRACTS	
	TRANSACTIONS	

☐ Did not work today; instead, I:

{20 }

S M T W T F S

Today I mostly prospected:

	DISCUSSIONS	
L	DAILY TRACKER	B
	PRESENTATIONS	
	CLIENTS	
	CONTRACTS	
	TRANSACTIONS	

☐ Did not work today; instead, I:

{20 }

S M T W T F S

Today I mostly prospected:

	DISCUSSIONS	
L	DAILY TRACKER	B
	PRESENTATIONS	
	CLIENTS	
	CONTRACTS	
	TRANSACTIONS	

☐ Did not work today; instead, I:

February

25

How do your marketing efforts for listings compare to other agents?[236]
How could you reach more buyers?

{20 }

{20 }

{20 }

{20 }
S M T W T F S
Today I mostly prospected:

	DISCUSSIONS	
L	DAILY TRACKER	B
	PRESENTATIONS	
	CLIENTS	
	CONTRACTS	
	TRANSACTIONS	

☐ Did not work today; instead, I:

{20 }
S M T W T F S
Today I mostly prospected:

	DISCUSSIONS	
L	DAILY TRACKER	B
	PRESENTATIONS	
	CLIENTS	
	CONTRACTS	
	TRANSACTIONS	

☐ Did not work today; instead, I:

{20 }
S M T W T F S
Today I mostly prospected:

	DISCUSSIONS	
L	DAILY TRACKER	B
	PRESENTATIONS	
	CLIENTS	
	CONTRACTS	
	TRANSACTIONS	

☐ Did not work today; instead, I:

February

Describe your system(s) for keeping clients updated.[243]
How could you improve this communication?

{20 }

{20 }

{20 }

{20 }

S M T W T F S

Today I mostly prospected:

	DISCUSSIONS	
L	DAILY TRACKER	B
	PRESENTATIONS	
	CLIENTS	
	CONTRACTS	
	TRANSACTIONS	

☐ Did not work today; instead, I:

{20 }

S M T W T F S

Today I mostly prospected:

	DISCUSSIONS	
L	DAILY TRACKER	B
	PRESENTATIONS	
	CLIENTS	
	CONTRACTS	
	TRANSACTIONS	

☐ Did not work today; instead, I:

{20 }

S M T W T F S

Today I mostly prospected:

	DISCUSSIONS	
L	DAILY TRACKER	B
	PRESENTATIONS	
	CLIENTS	
	CONTRACTS	
	TRANSACTIONS	

☐ Did not work today; instead, I:

February

27

My grandest achievement this month was...
My plan to repeat this victory is...

{20 }

{20 }

{20 }

{20 }		
S M T W T F S		
Today I mostly prospected:		
	DISCUSSIONS	
L	DAILY TRACKER	B
	PRESENTATIONS	
	CLIENTS	
	CONTRACTS	
	TRANSACTIONS	
☐ Did not work today; instead, I:		

{20 }		
S M T W T F S		
Today I mostly prospected:		
	DISCUSSIONS	
L	DAILY TRACKER	B
	PRESENTATIONS	
	CLIENTS	
	CONTRACTS	
	TRANSACTIONS	
☐ Did not work today; instead, I:		

{20 }		
S M T W T F S		
Today I mostly prospected:		
	DISCUSSIONS	
L	DAILY TRACKER	B
	PRESENTATIONS	
	CLIENTS	
	CONTRACTS	
	TRANSACTIONS	
☐ Did not work today; instead, I:		

28 February

The biggest mistake/misstep I made this month was...
My plan to prevent the same mishap from recurring is...

{20 }

{20 }

{20 }

{20 }
S M T W T F S
Today I mostly prospected:

	DISCUSSIONS	
L	DAILY TRACKER	B
	PRESENTATIONS	
	CLIENTS	
	CONTRACTS	
	TRANSACTIONS	

☐ Did not work today; instead, I:

{20 }
S M T W T F S
Today I mostly prospected:

	DISCUSSIONS	
L	DAILY TRACKER	B
	PRESENTATIONS	
	CLIENTS	
	CONTRACTS	
	TRANSACTIONS	

☐ Did not work today; instead, I:

{20 }
S M T W T F S
Today I mostly prospected:

	DISCUSSIONS	
L	DAILY TRACKER	B
	PRESENTATIONS	
	CLIENTS	
	CONTRACTS	
	TRANSACTIONS	

☐ Did not work today; instead, I:

February

29

Today is Leap Day.
If you could have an extra day every year,
how would you spend it?

{20 }

{20 }

S M T W T F S

Today I mostly prospected:

L	DAILY TRACKER	B
	DISCUSSIONS	
	PRESENTATIONS	
	CLIENTS	
	CONTRACTS	
	TRANSACTIONS	

☐ Did not work today; instead, I:

{20 } MONTHLY ACTIVITY TRACKER (GOALS→RESULTS)

GOALS	ACTIVITY	WK 1	WK 2	WK 3	WK 4	WK 5	TOTAL RESULTS
	TRANSACTIONS (T)	L : B	L : B	L : B	L : B	L : B	L : B
	NEW CLIENTS (C)	L : B	L : B	L : B	L : B	L : B	L : B
	PRESENTATIONS (P)	L : B	L : B	L : B	L : B	L : B	L : B
	DISCUSSIONS (D)						
	DAYS WORKED (W)						
	DAILY DISCUSSIONS (D/W)	ACTUAL DAILY DISCUSSION AVERAGE				D/W	
$	GCI	$					

{20 } MONTHLY ACTIVITY TRACKER (GOALS→RESULTS)

GOALS	ACTIVITY	WK 1	WK 2	WK 3	WK 4	WK 5	TOTAL RESULTS
	TRANSACTIONS (T)	L : B	L : B	L : B	L : B	L : B	L : B
	NEW CLIENTS (C)	L : B	L : B	L : B	L : B	L : B	L : B
	PRESENTATIONS (P)	L : B	L : B	L : B	L : B	L : B	L : B
	DISCUSSIONS (D)						
	DAYS WORKED (W)						
	DAILY DISCUSSIONS (D/W)	ACTUAL DAILY DISCUSSION AVERAGE				D/W	
$	GCI	$					

{20 } MONTHLY ACTIVITY TRACKER (GOALS→RESULTS)

GOALS	ACTIVITY	WK 1	WK 2	WK 3	WK 4	WK 5	TOTAL RESULTS
	TRANSACTIONS (T)	L : B	L : B	L : B	L : B	L : B	L : B
	NEW CLIENTS (C)	L : B	L : B	L : B	L : B	L : B	L : B
	PRESENTATIONS (P)	L : B	L : B	L : B	L : B	L : B	L : B
	DISCUSSIONS (D)						
	DAYS WORKED (W)						
	DAILY DISCUSSIONS (D/W)	ACTUAL DAILY DISCUSSION AVERAGE				D/W	
$	GCI	$					

March

01

Today is Business Plan Day.[XVIII]
Review/revise yours, and contemplate the past/future.
What is your plan to improve upon last month's performance?

{20 }

{20 }

{20 }

{20 }

S	M	T	W	T	F	S

Today I mostly prospected:

L	DAILY TRACKER	B
	DISCUSSIONS	
	PRESENTATIONS	
	CLIENTS	
	CONTRACTS	
	TRANSACTIONS	

☐ Did not work today; instead, I:

{20 }

S	M	T	W	T	F	S

Today I mostly prospected:

L	DAILY TRACKER	B
	DISCUSSIONS	
	PRESENTATIONS	
	CLIENTS	
	CONTRACTS	
	TRANSACTIONS	

☐ Did not work today; instead, I:

{20 }

S	M	T	W	T	F	S

Today I mostly prospected:

L	DAILY TRACKER	B
	DISCUSSIONS	
	PRESENTATIONS	
	CLIENTS	
	CONTRACTS	
	TRANSACTIONS	

☐ Did not work today; instead, I:

02

March

List a good habit you wanna adopt this month.
How will you implement and make it a permanent part
of your routine? Has last month's habit stuck yet?

{20 } ____________________

{20 } ____________________

{20 } ____________________

{20 }
S M T W T F S
Today I mostly prospected:

	DISCUSSIONS	
L	DAILY TRACKER	B
	PRESENTATIONS	
	CLIENTS	
	CONTRACTS	
	TRANSACTIONS	

☐ Did not work today; instead, I:

{20 }
S M T W T F S
Today I mostly prospected:

	DISCUSSIONS	
L	DAILY TRACKER	B
	PRESENTATIONS	
	CLIENTS	
	CONTRACTS	
	TRANSACTIONS	

☐ Did not work today; instead, I:

{20 }
S M T W T F S
Today I mostly prospected:

	DISCUSSIONS	
L	DAILY TRACKER	B
	PRESENTATIONS	
	CLIENTS	
	CONTRACTS	
	TRANSACTIONS	

☐ Did not work today; instead, I:

March

03

How many different ways do you prospect for clients?[084]
Which ones provide the most presentations? ...the least?
Should you alter your strategy?[004]

{20 }

{20 }

{20 }

{20 }

S M T W T F S

Today I mostly prospected:

	DISCUSSIONS	
L	DAILY TRACKER	B
	PRESENTATIONS	
	CLIENTS	
	CONTRACTS	
	TRANSACTIONS	

☐ Did not work today; instead, I:

{20 }

S M T W T F S

Today I mostly prospected:

	DISCUSSIONS	
L	DAILY TRACKER	B
	PRESENTATIONS	
	CLIENTS	
	CONTRACTS	
	TRANSACTIONS	

☐ Did not work today; instead, I:

{20 }

S M T W T F S

Today I mostly prospected:

	DISCUSSIONS	
L	DAILY TRACKER	B
	PRESENTATIONS	
	CLIENTS	
	CONTRACTS	
	TRANSACTIONS	

☐ Did not work today; instead, I:

04 March

List ten words that describe your commitment to business growth and improvement. Which of these words are worthy of sharing with others?

{20 }

{20 }

{20 }

{20 }	{20 }	{20 }
S M T W T F S	S M T W T F S	S M T W T F S
Today I mostly prospected:	Today I mostly prospected:	Today I mostly prospected:

	DISCUSSIONS	
L	DAILY TRACKER	B
	PRESENTATIONS	
	CLIENTS	
	CONTRACTS	
	TRANSACTIONS	

☐ Did not work today; instead, I:

	DISCUSSIONS	
L	DAILY TRACKER	B
	PRESENTATIONS	
	CLIENTS	
	CONTRACTS	
	TRANSACTIONS	

☐ Did not work today; instead, I:

	DISCUSSIONS	
L	DAILY TRACKER	B
	PRESENTATIONS	
	CLIENTS	
	CONTRACTS	
	TRANSACTIONS	

☐ Did not work today; instead, I:

March

Describe your morning routine, up to the point of prospecting. Does your routine prepare you properly for prospecting proficiently?

{20 }

{20 }

{20 }

{20 }

S M T W T F S

Today I mostly prospected:

	DISCUSSIONS	
L	DAILY TRACKER	B
	PRESENTATIONS	
	CLIENTS	
	CONTRACTS	
	TRANSACTIONS	

☐ Did not work today; instead, I:

{20 }

S M T W T F S

Today I mostly prospected:

	DISCUSSIONS	
L	DAILY TRACKER	B
	PRESENTATIONS	
	CLIENTS	
	CONTRACTS	
	TRANSACTIONS	

☐ Did not work today; instead, I:

{20 }

S M T W T F S

Today I mostly prospected:

	DISCUSSIONS	
L	DAILY TRACKER	B
	PRESENTATIONS	
	CLIENTS	
	CONTRACTS	
	TRANSACTIONS	

☐ Did not work today; instead, I:

March

If you could change the "rules" of real estate,[036]
what would you change and why?

{20 }

{20 }

{20 }

{20 }

S M T W T F S

Today I mostly prospected:

	DISCUSSIONS	
L	DAILY TRACKER	B
	PRESENTATIONS	
	CLIENTS	
	CONTRACTS	
	TRANSACTIONS	

☐ Did not work today; instead, I:

{20 }

S M T W T F S

Today I mostly prospected:

	DISCUSSIONS	
L	DAILY TRACKER	B
	PRESENTATIONS	
	CLIENTS	
	CONTRACTS	
	TRANSACTIONS	

☐ Did not work today; instead, I:

{20 }

S M T W T F S

Today I mostly prospected:

	DISCUSSIONS	
L	DAILY TRACKER	B
	PRESENTATIONS	
	CLIENTS	
	CONTRACTS	
	TRANSACTIONS	

☐ Did not work today; instead, I:

March

When a seller is interviewing multiple agents,
how do you respond?[201]
How well do you compete?

{20 }

{20 }

{20 }

{20 }		
S M T W T F S		
Today I mostly prospected:		
	DISCUSSIONS	
L	DAILY TRACKER	B
	PRESENTATIONS	
	CLIENTS	
	CONTRACTS	
	TRANSACTIONS	

☐ Did not work today; instead, I:

{20 }		
S M T W T F S		
Today I mostly prospected:		
	DISCUSSIONS	
L	DAILY TRACKER	B
	PRESENTATIONS	
	CLIENTS	
	CONTRACTS	
	TRANSACTIONS	

☐ Did not work today; instead, I:

{20 }		
S M T W T F S		
Today I mostly prospected:		
	DISCUSSIONS	
L	DAILY TRACKER	B
	PRESENTATIONS	
	CLIENTS	
	CONTRACTS	
	TRANSACTIONS	

☐ Did not work today; instead, I:

08

March

How long have you been a real estate agent?
Are you up-to-speed?[303]
What is your biggest real estate challenge?

{20 }

{20 }

{20 }

{20 }

S M T W T F S

Today I mostly prospected:

	DISCUSSIONS	
L	DAILY TRACKER	B
	PRESENTATIONS	
	CLIENTS	
	CONTRACTS	
	TRANSACTIONS	

☐ Did not work today; instead, I:

{20 }

S M T W T F S

Today I mostly prospected:

	DISCUSSIONS	
L	DAILY TRACKER	B
	PRESENTATIONS	
	CLIENTS	
	CONTRACTS	
	TRANSACTIONS	

☐ Did not work today; instead, I:

{20 }

S M T W T F S

Today I mostly prospected:

	DISCUSSIONS	
L	DAILY TRACKER	B
	PRESENTATIONS	
	CLIENTS	
	CONTRACTS	
	TRANSACTIONS	

☐ Did not work today; instead, I:

March

09

Describe a recent win, ah-ha moment, loss, disappointment, or surprise.

{20 }

{20 }

{20 }

{20 }

S M T W T F S

Today I mostly prospected:

	DISCUSSIONS	
L	DAILY TRACKER	B
	PRESENTATIONS	
	CLIENTS	
	CONTRACTS	
	TRANSACTIONS	

☐ Did not work today; instead, I:

{20 }

S M T W T F S

Today I mostly prospected:

	DISCUSSIONS	
L	DAILY TRACKER	B
	PRESENTATIONS	
	CLIENTS	
	CONTRACTS	
	TRANSACTIONS	

☐ Did not work today; instead, I:

{20 }

S M T W T F S

Today I mostly prospected:

	DISCUSSIONS	
L	DAILY TRACKER	B
	PRESENTATIONS	
	CLIENTS	
	CONTRACTS	
	TRANSACTIONS	

☐ Did not work today; instead, I:

10

March

Name one thing that would improve your discussion turnover rate (DTR).[XVI]

{20 }

{20 }

{20 }

{20 }		
S M T W T F S		
Today I mostly prospected:		
	DISCUSSIONS	
L	DAILY TRACKER	B
	PRESENTATIONS	
	CLIENTS	
	CONTRACTS	
	TRANSACTIONS	
☐ Did not work today; instead, I:		

{20 }		
S M T W T F S		
Today I mostly prospected:		
	DISCUSSIONS	
L	DAILY TRACKER	B
	PRESENTATIONS	
	CLIENTS	
	CONTRACTS	
	TRANSACTIONS	
☐ Did not work today; instead, I:		

{20 }		
S M T W T F S		
Today I mostly prospected:		
	DISCUSSIONS	
L	DAILY TRACKER	B
	PRESENTATIONS	
	CLIENTS	
	CONTRACTS	
	TRANSACTIONS	
☐ Did not work today; instead, I:		

March

11

How could you increase GCI *without adding time to your day?*
List three ways and a plan to implement.

{20 }

{20 }

{20 }

{20 }
S M T W T F S
Today I mostly prospected:

	DISCUSSIONS	
L	DAILY TRACKER	B
	PRESENTATIONS	
	CLIENTS	
	CONTRACTS	
	TRANSACTIONS	

☐ Did not work today; instead, I:

{20 }
S M T W T F S
Today I mostly prospected:

	DISCUSSIONS	
L	DAILY TRACKER	B
	PRESENTATIONS	
	CLIENTS	
	CONTRACTS	
	TRANSACTIONS	

☐ Did not work today; instead, I:

{20 }
S M T W T F S
Today I mostly prospected:

	DISCUSSIONS	
L	DAILY TRACKER	B
	PRESENTATIONS	
	CLIENTS	
	CONTRACTS	
	TRANSACTIONS	

☐ Did not work today; instead, I:

12

March

Name something about the real estate sales industry that is changing.[304] *What is your plan to adapt?*

{20 }

{20 }

{20 }

{20 }	{20 }	{20 }
S M T W T F S	S M T W T F S	S M T W T F S
Today I mostly prospected:	Today I mostly prospected:	Today I mostly prospected:
DISCUSSIONS	DISCUSSIONS	DISCUSSIONS
L DAILY TRACKER B	L DAILY TRACKER B	L DAILY TRACKER B
PRESENTATIONS	PRESENTATIONS	PRESENTATIONS
CLIENTS	CLIENTS	CLIENTS
CONTRACTS	CONTRACTS	CONTRACTS
TRANSACTIONS	TRANSACTIONS	TRANSACTIONS
☐ Did not work today; instead, I:	☐ Did not work today; instead, I:	☐ Did not work today; instead, I:

March

13

Write a script for this seller objection:
"I wanna price my house high,
so we can have some negotiating room."

{20 }

{20 }

{20 }

{20 }
S M T W T F S
Today I mostly prospected:

	DISCUSSIONS	
L	DAILY TRACKER	B
	PRESENTATIONS	
	CLIENTS	
	CONTRACTS	
	TRANSACTIONS	

☐ Did not work today; instead, I:

{20 }
S M T W T F S
Today I mostly prospected:

	DISCUSSIONS	
L	DAILY TRACKER	B
	PRESENTATIONS	
	CLIENTS	
	CONTRACTS	
	TRANSACTIONS	

☐ Did not work today; instead, I:

{20 }
S M T W T F S
Today I mostly prospected:

	DISCUSSIONS	
L	DAILY TRACKER	B
	PRESENTATIONS	
	CLIENTS	
	CONTRACTS	
	TRANSACTIONS	

☐ Did not work today; instead, I:

14

March

When was the last time you tried something new?
What was the result?
Would you do it again?

{20 }

{20 }

{20 }

{20 }

S M T W T F S

Today I mostly prospected:

	DISCUSSIONS	
L	DAILY TRACKER	B
	PRESENTATIONS	
	CLIENTS	
	CONTRACTS	
	TRANSACTIONS	

☐ Did not work today; instead, I:

{20 }

S M T W T F S

Today I mostly prospected:

	DISCUSSIONS	
L	DAILY TRACKER	B
	PRESENTATIONS	
	CLIENTS	
	CONTRACTS	
	TRANSACTIONS	

☐ Did not work today; instead, I:

{20 }

S M T W T F S

Today I mostly prospected:

	DISCUSSIONS	
L	DAILY TRACKER	B
	PRESENTATIONS	
	CLIENTS	
	CONTRACTS	
	TRANSACTIONS	

☐ Did not work today; instead, I:

March

15

Today is the Ides of March.
Which part of your business should be killed off
(because it's a waste of time/effort/return)?

{20 }

{20 }

{20 }

{20 }
S M T W T F S
Today I mostly prospected:

	DISCUSSIONS	
L	DAILY TRACKER	B
	PRESENTATIONS	
	CLIENTS	
	CONTRACTS	
	TRANSACTIONS	

☐ Did not work today; instead, I:

{20 }
S M T W T F S
Today I mostly prospected:

	DISCUSSIONS	
L	DAILY TRACKER	B
	PRESENTATIONS	
	CLIENTS	
	CONTRACTS	
	TRANSACTIONS	

☐ Did not work today; instead, I:

{20 }
S M T W T F S
Today I mostly prospected:

	DISCUSSIONS	
L	DAILY TRACKER	B
	PRESENTATIONS	
	CLIENTS	
	CONTRACTS	
	TRANSACTIONS	

☐ Did not work today; instead, I:

16

March

Are you falling behind (or surging ahead) on any monthly goals?
What's your plan to achieve them all?[XIX]
Adjust your activities now, so you will meet or exceed all.

{20 }

{20 }

{20 }

{20 }
S M T W T F S
Today I mostly prospected:

L	DAILY TRACKER	B
	DISCUSSIONS	
	PRESENTATIONS	
	CLIENTS	
	CONTRACTS	
	TRANSACTIONS	

☐ Did not work today; instead, I:

{20 }
S M T W T F S
Today I mostly prospected:

L	DAILY TRACKER	B
	DISCUSSIONS	
	PRESENTATIONS	
	CLIENTS	
	CONTRACTS	
	TRANSACTIONS	

☐ Did not work today; instead, I:

{20 }
S M T W T F S
Today I mostly prospected:

L	DAILY TRACKER	B
	DISCUSSIONS	
	PRESENTATIONS	
	CLIENTS	
	CONTRACTS	
	TRANSACTIONS	

☐ Did not work today; instead, I:

March

17

Today is St. Patrick's Day.
Recall and record a time when you got lucky.
How might have things gone differently?

{20 }

{20 }

{20 }

{20 }

S M T W T F S

Today I mostly prospected:

	DISCUSSIONS	
L	DAILY TRACKER	B
	PRESENTATIONS	
	CLIENTS	
	CONTRACTS	
	TRANSACTIONS	

☐ Did not work today; instead, I:

{20 }

S M T W T F S

Today I mostly prospected:

	DISCUSSIONS	
L	DAILY TRACKER	B
	PRESENTATIONS	
	CLIENTS	
	CONTRACTS	
	TRANSACTIONS	

☐ Did not work today; instead, I:

{20 }

S M T W T F S

Today I mostly prospected:

	DISCUSSIONS	
L	DAILY TRACKER	B
	PRESENTATIONS	
	CLIENTS	
	CONTRACTS	
	TRANSACTIONS	

☐ Did not work today; instead, I:

18

March

*If your business was a movie,
would it be an action adventure, sad tale, or comedy?
Explain yourself.*

{20 }

{20 }

{20 }

{20 }
S M T W T F S
Today I mostly prospected:

	DISCUSSIONS	
L	DAILY TRACKER	B
	PRESENTATIONS	
	CLIENTS	
	CONTRACTS	
	TRANSACTIONS	

☐ Did not work today; instead, I:

{20 }
S M T W T F S
Today I mostly prospected:

	DISCUSSIONS	
L	DAILY TRACKER	B
	PRESENTATIONS	
	CLIENTS	
	CONTRACTS	
	TRANSACTIONS	

☐ Did not work today; instead, I:

{20 }
S M T W T F S
Today I mostly prospected:

	DISCUSSIONS	
L	DAILY TRACKER	B
	PRESENTATIONS	
	CLIENTS	
	CONTRACTS	
	TRANSACTIONS	

☐ Did not work today; instead, I:

March

19

Have you ever been fired by a client?[311]
If YES: *Why were you fired? How will you prevent it from happening again? If* NO: *Tell about a close call.*

{20 }

{20 }

{20 }

{20 }	{20 }	{20 }
S M T W T F S	S M T W T F S	S M T W T F S
Today I mostly prospected:	Today I mostly prospected:	Today I mostly prospected:

	DISCUSSIONS	
L	DAILY TRACKER	B
	PRESENTATIONS	
	CLIENTS	
	CONTRACTS	
	TRANSACTIONS	

☐ Did not work today; instead, I:

	DISCUSSIONS	
L	DAILY TRACKER	B
	PRESENTATIONS	
	CLIENTS	
	CONTRACTS	
	TRANSACTIONS	

☐ Did not work today; instead, I:

	DISCUSSIONS	
L	DAILY TRACKER	B
	PRESENTATIONS	
	CLIENTS	
	CONTRACTS	
	TRANSACTIONS	

☐ Did not work today; instead, I:

20 March

List twenty words that describe your valuation methods.[125]
Which of these words should you be sharing with prospects?

{20 }

{20 }

{20 }

{20 }

S M T W T F S

Today I mostly prospected:

	DISCUSSIONS	
L	DAILY TRACKER	B
	PRESENTATIONS	
	CLIENTS	
	CONTRACTS	
	TRANSACTIONS	

☐ Did not work today; instead, I:

{20 }

S M T W T F S

Today I mostly prospected:

	DISCUSSIONS	
L	DAILY TRACKER	B
	PRESENTATIONS	
	CLIENTS	
	CONTRACTS	
	TRANSACTIONS	

☐ Did not work today; instead, I:

{20 }

S M T W T F S

Today I mostly prospected:

	DISCUSSIONS	
L	DAILY TRACKER	B
	PRESENTATIONS	
	CLIENTS	
	CONTRACTS	
	TRANSACTIONS	

☐ Did not work today; instead, I:

March

21

Spring has sprung.
What are your plans to clean up this season?[213]
Who can you call for a referral?

{20 }

{20 }

{20 }

{20 }

S	M	T	W	T	F	S

Today I mostly prospected:

	DISCUSSIONS	
L	DAILY TRACKER	B
	PRESENTATIONS	
	CLIENTS	
	CONTRACTS	
	TRANSACTIONS	

☐ Did not work today; instead, I:

{20 }

S	M	T	W	T	F	S

Today I mostly prospected:

	DISCUSSIONS	
L	DAILY TRACKER	B
	PRESENTATIONS	
	CLIENTS	
	CONTRACTS	
	TRANSACTIONS	

☐ Did not work today; instead, I:

{20 }

S	M	T	W	T	F	S

Today I mostly prospected:

	DISCUSSIONS	
L	DAILY TRACKER	B
	PRESENTATIONS	
	CLIENTS	
	CONTRACTS	
	TRANSACTIONS	

☐ Did not work today; instead, I:

22

March

Recall a recent class or educational session.
What was the number one thing you learned?
How will you implement it into your business?

{20 }

{20 }

{20 }

{20 }
S M T W T F S
Today I mostly prospected:

	DISCUSSIONS	
L	DAILY TRACKER	B
	PRESENTATIONS	
	CLIENTS	
	CONTRACTS	
	TRANSACTIONS	

☐ Did not work today; instead, I:

{20 }
S M T W T F S
Today I mostly prospected:

	DISCUSSIONS	
L	DAILY TRACKER	B
	PRESENTATIONS	
	CLIENTS	
	CONTRACTS	
	TRANSACTIONS	

☐ Did not work today; instead, I:

{20 }
S M T W T F S
Today I mostly prospected:

	DISCUSSIONS	
L	DAILY TRACKER	B
	PRESENTATIONS	
	CLIENTS	
	CONTRACTS	
	TRANSACTIONS	

☐ Did not work today; instead, I:

March

23

Which part of your job do you enjoy the least?
How could you outsource this bit,
or otherwise learn to embrace it?

{20 }

{20 }

{20 }

{20 }
S M T W T F S
Today I mostly prospected:

	DISCUSSIONS	
L	DAILY TRACKER	B
	PRESENTATIONS	
	CLIENTS	
	CONTRACTS	
	TRANSACTIONS	

☐ Did not work today; instead, I:

{20 }
S M T W T F S
Today I mostly prospected:

	DISCUSSIONS	
L	DAILY TRACKER	B
	PRESENTATIONS	
	CLIENTS	
	CONTRACTS	
	TRANSACTIONS	

☐ Did not work today; instead, I:

{20 }
S M T W T F S
Today I mostly prospected:

	DISCUSSIONS	
L	DAILY TRACKER	B
	PRESENTATIONS	
	CLIENTS	
	CONTRACTS	
	TRANSACTIONS	

☐ Did not work today; instead, I:

24 March

What bit of technology could you do without?
What bit of tech do you rely upon too much?
What bit of tech should you perhaps adopt?

{20 }

{20 }

{20 }

{20 }
S M T W T F S
Today I mostly prospected:

L	DISCUSSIONS	B
	DAILY TRACKER	
	PRESENTATIONS	
	CLIENTS	
	CONTRACTS	
	TRANSACTIONS	

☐ Did not work today; instead, I:

{20 }
S M T W T F S
Today I mostly prospected:

L	DISCUSSIONS	B
	DAILY TRACKER	
	PRESENTATIONS	
	CLIENTS	
	CONTRACTS	
	TRANSACTIONS	

☐ Did not work today; instead, I:

{20 }
S M T W T F S
Today I mostly prospected:

L	DISCUSSIONS	B
	DAILY TRACKER	
	PRESENTATIONS	
	CLIENTS	
	CONTRACTS	
	TRANSACTIONS	

☐ Did not work today; instead, I:

March

25

Describe a recent day off.[306]
Did you sharpen your blade,
or simply swing your axe at another tree?[308]

{20 }

{20 }

{20 }

{20 }

S M T W T F S

Today I mostly prospected:

	DISCUSSIONS	
L	DAILY TRACKER	B
	PRESENTATIONS	
	CLIENTS	
	CONTRACTS	
	TRANSACTIONS	

☐ Did not work today; instead, I:

{20 }

S M T W T F S

Today I mostly prospected:

	DISCUSSIONS	
L	DAILY TRACKER	B
	PRESENTATIONS	
	CLIENTS	
	CONTRACTS	
	TRANSACTIONS	

☐ Did not work today; instead, I:

{20 }

S M T W T F S

Today I mostly prospected:

	DISCUSSIONS	
L	DAILY TRACKER	B
	PRESENTATIONS	
	CLIENTS	
	CONTRACTS	
	TRANSACTIONS	

☐ Did not work today; instead, I:

26 March

Are you getting enough exercise?
Are you eating right and loving those that deserve your love?
How are you taking care of you?

{20 }

{20 }

{20 }

{20 }

S M T W T F S

Today I mostly prospected:

	DISCUSSIONS	
L	DAILY TRACKER	B
	PRESENTATIONS	
	CLIENTS	
	CONTRACTS	
	TRANSACTIONS	

☐ Did not work today; instead, I:

{20 }

S M T W T F S

Today I mostly prospected:

	DISCUSSIONS	
L	DAILY TRACKER	B
	PRESENTATIONS	
	CLIENTS	
	CONTRACTS	
	TRANSACTIONS	

☐ Did not work today; instead, I:

{20 }

S M T W T F S

Today I mostly prospected:

	DISCUSSIONS	
L	DAILY TRACKER	B
	PRESENTATIONS	
	CLIENTS	
	CONTRACTS	
	TRANSACTIONS	

☐ Did not work today; instead, I:

March

27

Write a script for this seller objection:
"I wanna find a house to buy
before I think about listing the one I live in."

{20 }

{20 }

{20 }

{20 }

S M T W T F S

Today I mostly prospected:

	DISCUSSIONS	
L	DAILY TRACKER	B
	PRESENTATIONS	
	CLIENTS	
	CONTRACTS	
	TRANSACTIONS	

☐ Did not work today; instead, I:

{20 }

S M T W T F S

Today I mostly prospected:

	DISCUSSIONS	
L	DAILY TRACKER	B
	PRESENTATIONS	
	CLIENTS	
	CONTRACTS	
	TRANSACTIONS	

☐ Did not work today; instead, I:

{20 }

S M T W T F S

Today I mostly prospected:

	DISCUSSIONS	
L	DAILY TRACKER	B
	PRESENTATIONS	
	CLIENTS	
	CONTRACTS	
	TRANSACTIONS	

☐ Did not work today; instead, I:

28 March

What keeps you motivated to prospect?[300]
How would your extra effort today payoff tomorrow?

{20 }

{20 }

{20 }

{20 }
S M T W T F S
Today I mostly prospected:

	DISCUSSIONS	
L	DAILY TRACKER	B
	PRESENTATIONS	
	CLIENTS	
	CONTRACTS	
	TRANSACTIONS	

☐ Did not work today; instead, I:

{20 }
S M T W T F S
Today I mostly prospected:

	DISCUSSIONS	
L	DAILY TRACKER	B
	PRESENTATIONS	
	CLIENTS	
	CONTRACTS	
	TRANSACTIONS	

☐ Did not work today; instead, I:

{20 }
S M T W T F S
Today I mostly prospected:

	DISCUSSIONS	
L	DAILY TRACKER	B
	PRESENTATIONS	
	CLIENTS	
	CONTRACTS	
	TRANSACTIONS	

☐ Did not work today; instead, I:

March

29

My grandest achievement this month was...
My plan to repeat this victory is...

{20 }

{20 }

{20 }

{20 }

S M T W T F S

Today I mostly prospected:

	DISCUSSIONS	
L	DAILY TRACKER	B
	PRESENTATIONS	
	CLIENTS	
	CONTRACTS	
	TRANSACTIONS	

☐ Did not work today; instead, I:

{20 }

S M T W T F S

Today I mostly prospected:

	DISCUSSIONS	
L	DAILY TRACKER	B
	PRESENTATIONS	
	CLIENTS	
	CONTRACTS	
	TRANSACTIONS	

☐ Did not work today; instead, I:

{20 }

S M T W T F S

Today I mostly prospected:

	DISCUSSIONS	
L	DAILY TRACKER	B
	PRESENTATIONS	
	CLIENTS	
	CONTRACTS	
	TRANSACTIONS	

☐ Did not work today; instead, I:

30 March

Summarize the last three months with one word.
Given the opportunity, would you take a do-over?
Which parts would you like to forget?.. never forget?

{20 }

{20 }

{20 }

{20 }
S M T W T F S
Today I mostly prospected:

	DISCUSSIONS	
L	DAILY TRACKER	B
	PRESENTATIONS	
	CLIENTS	
	CONTRACTS	
	TRANSACTIONS	

☐ Did not work today; instead, I:

{20 }
S M T W T F S
Today I mostly prospected:

	DISCUSSIONS	
L	DAILY TRACKER	B
	PRESENTATIONS	
	CLIENTS	
	CONTRACTS	
	TRANSACTIONS	

☐ Did not work today; instead, I:

{20 }
S M T W T F S
Today I mostly prospected:

	DISCUSSIONS	
L	DAILY TRACKER	B
	PRESENTATIONS	
	CLIENTS	
	CONTRACTS	
	TRANSACTIONS	

☐ Did not work today; instead, I:

March

31

The biggest mistake/misstep I made this month was...
My plan to prevent the same mishap from recurring is...

{20 }

{20 }

{20 }

{20 }

S M T W T F S

Today I mostly prospected:

	DISCUSSIONS	
L	DAILY TRACKER	B
	PRESENTATIONS	
	CLIENTS	
	CONTRACTS	
	TRANSACTIONS	

☐ Did not work today; instead, I:

{20 }

S M T W T F S

Today I mostly prospected:

	DISCUSSIONS	
L	DAILY TRACKER	B
	PRESENTATIONS	
	CLIENTS	
	CONTRACTS	
	TRANSACTIONS	

☐ Did not work today; instead, I:

{20 }

S M T W T F S

Today I mostly prospected:

	DISCUSSIONS	
L	DAILY TRACKER	B
	PRESENTATIONS	
	CLIENTS	
	CONTRACTS	
	TRANSACTIONS	

☐ Did not work today; instead, I:

{20 }

MONTHLY ACTIVITY TRACKER (GOALS→RESULTS)

GOALS	ACTIVITY	WK 1	WK 2	WK 3	WK 4	WK 5	TOTAL RESULTS
	TRANSACTIONS (T)	L B	L B	L B	L B	L B	L B
	NEW CLIENTS (C)	L B	L B	L B	L B	L B	L B
	PRESENTATIONS (P)	L B	L B	L B	L B	L B	L B
	DISCUSSIONS (D)						
	DAYS WORKED (W)						
	DAILY DISCUSSIONS (D/W)	**ACTUAL DAILY DISCUSSION AVERAGE**				**D/W**	
$	**GCI**	$					

{20 }

MONTHLY ACTIVITY TRACKER (GOALS→RESULTS)

GOALS	ACTIVITY	WK 1	WK 2	WK 3	WK 4	WK 5	TOTAL RESULTS
	TRANSACTIONS (T)	L B	L B	L B	L B	L B	L B
	NEW CLIENTS (C)	L B	L B	L B	L B	L B	L B
	PRESENTATIONS (P)	L B	L B	L B	L B	L B	L B
	DISCUSSIONS (D)						
	DAYS WORKED (W)						
	DAILY DISCUSSIONS (D/W)	**ACTUAL DAILY DISCUSSION AVERAGE**				**D/W**	
$	**GCI**	$					

{20 }

MONTHLY ACTIVITY TRACKER (GOALS→RESULTS)

GOALS	ACTIVITY	WK 1	WK 2	WK 3	WK 4	WK 5	TOTAL RESULTS
	TRANSACTIONS (T)	L B	L B	L B	L B	L B	L B
	NEW CLIENTS (C)	L B	L B	L B	L B	L B	L B
	PRESENTATIONS (P)	L B	L B	L B	L B	L B	L B
	DISCUSSIONS (D)						
	DAYS WORKED (W)						
	DAILY DISCUSSIONS (D/W)	**ACTUAL DAILY DISCUSSION AVERAGE**				**D/W**	
$	**GCI**	$					

April

01

Today is April Fool's Day.
Recall the last time someone took advantage of you.
How will you prevent the same recurrence?

{20 }

{20 }

{20 }

{20 }

S M T W T F S

Today I mostly prospected:

		DISCUSSIONS
L	DAILY TRACKER	B
	PRESENTATIONS	
	CLIENTS	
	CONTRACTS	
	TRANSACTIONS	

☐ Did not work today; instead, I:

{20 }

S M T W T F S

Today I mostly prospected:

		DISCUSSIONS
L	DAILY TRACKER	B
	PRESENTATIONS	
	CLIENTS	
	CONTRACTS	
	TRANSACTIONS	

☐ Did not work today; instead, I:

{20 }

S M T W T F S

Today I mostly prospected:

		DISCUSSIONS
L	DAILY TRACKER	B
	PRESENTATIONS	
	CLIENTS	
	CONTRACTS	
	TRANSACTIONS	

☐ Did not work today; instead, I:

02

April

Today is Business Plan Day.[XVIII]
Review/revise yours, and contemplate the past/future.
What is your plan to improve upon last month's performance?

{20 }

{20 }

{20 }

{20 }

S M T W T F S

Today I mostly prospected:

	DISCUSSIONS	
L	DAILY TRACKER	B
	PRESENTATIONS	
	CLIENTS	
	CONTRACTS	
	TRANSACTIONS	

☐ Did not work today; instead, I:

{20 }

S M T W T F S

Today I mostly prospected:

	DISCUSSIONS	
L	DAILY TRACKER	B
	PRESENTATIONS	
	CLIENTS	
	CONTRACTS	
	TRANSACTIONS	

☐ Did not work today; instead, I:

{20 }

S M T W T F S

Today I mostly prospected:

	DISCUSSIONS	
L	DAILY TRACKER	B
	PRESENTATIONS	
	CLIENTS	
	CONTRACTS	
	TRANSACTIONS	

☐ Did not work today; instead, I:

April

03

*List a good habit you wanna adopt this month.
How will you implement and make it a permanent part
of your routine? Has last month's habit stuck yet?*

{20 }

{20 }

{20 }

{20 }

S M T W T F S

Today I mostly prospected:

	DISCUSSIONS	
L	DAILY TRACKER	B
	PRESENTATIONS	
	CLIENTS	
	CONTRACTS	
	TRANSACTIONS	

☐ Did not work today; instead, I:

{20 }

S M T W T F S

Today I mostly prospected:

	DISCUSSIONS	
L	DAILY TRACKER	B
	PRESENTATIONS	
	CLIENTS	
	CONTRACTS	
	TRANSACTIONS	

☐ Did not work today; instead, I:

{20 }

S M T W T F S

Today I mostly prospected:

	DISCUSSIONS	
L	DAILY TRACKER	B
	PRESENTATIONS	
	CLIENTS	
	CONTRACTS	
	TRANSACTIONS	

☐ Did not work today; instead, I:

04

April

How do you help wary buyers decide?[219]
Which buying signals do you receive most often?[218]

{20 }

{20 }

{20 }

{20 }

S M T W T F S

Today I mostly prospected:

	DISCUSSIONS	
L	DAILY TRACKER	B
	PRESENTATIONS	
	CLIENTS	
	CONTRACTS	
	TRANSACTIONS	

☐ Did not work today; instead, I:

{20 }

S M T W T F S

Today I mostly prospected:

	DISCUSSIONS	
L	DAILY TRACKER	B
	PRESENTATIONS	
	CLIENTS	
	CONTRACTS	
	TRANSACTIONS	

☐ Did not work today; instead, I:

{20 }

S M T W T F S

Today I mostly prospected:

	DISCUSSIONS	
L	DAILY TRACKER	B
	PRESENTATIONS	
	CLIENTS	
	CONTRACTS	
	TRANSACTIONS	

☐ Did not work today; instead, I:

April

05

List ten words that describe your niche.[042]
How loyal to your niche are you?
How often do you sign clients that should be referred?[112]

{20 }

{20 }

{20 }

{20 }		
S M T W T F S		
Today I mostly prospected:		
	DISCUSSIONS	
L	DAILY TRACKER	B
	PRESENTATIONS	
	CLIENTS	
	CONTRACTS	
	TRANSACTIONS	
☐ Did not work today; instead, I:		

{20 }		
S M T W T F S		
Today I mostly prospected:		
	DISCUSSIONS	
L	DAILY TRACKER	B
	PRESENTATIONS	
	CLIENTS	
	CONTRACTS	
	TRANSACTIONS	
☐ Did not work today; instead, I:		

{20 }		
S M T W T F S		
Today I mostly prospected:		
	DISCUSSIONS	
L	DAILY TRACKER	B
	PRESENTATIONS	
	CLIENTS	
	CONTRACTS	
	TRANSACTIONS	
☐ Did not work today; instead, I:		

06 April

Describe your last 'perfect' day?
When was it? What happened?

{20 }

{20 }

{20 }

{20 }

S M T W T F S

Today I mostly prospected:

L	DISCUSSIONS	B
	DAILY TRACKER	
	PRESENTATIONS	
	CLIENTS	
	CONTRACTS	
	TRANSACTIONS	

☐ Did not work today; instead, I:

{20 }

S M T W T F S

Today I mostly prospected:

L	DISCUSSIONS	B
	DAILY TRACKER	
	PRESENTATIONS	
	CLIENTS	
	CONTRACTS	
	TRANSACTIONS	

☐ Did not work today; instead, I:

{20 }

S M T W T F S

Today I mostly prospected:

L	DISCUSSIONS	B
	DAILY TRACKER	
	PRESENTATIONS	
	CLIENTS	
	CONTRACTS	
	TRANSACTIONS	

☐ Did not work today; instead, I:

April

07

The three biggest troubles with my business are...
My plan to correct each one is...

{20 }

{20 }

{20 }

{20 }		
S M T W T F S		
Today I mostly prospected:		
	DISCUSSIONS	
L	DAILY TRACKER	B
	PRESENTATIONS	
	CLIENTS	
	CONTRACTS	
	TRANSACTIONS	
☐ Did not work today; instead, I:		

{20 }		
S M T W T F S		
Today I mostly prospected:		
	DISCUSSIONS	
L	DAILY TRACKER	B
	PRESENTATIONS	
	CLIENTS	
	CONTRACTS	
	TRANSACTIONS	
☐ Did not work today; instead, I:		

{20 }		
S M T W T F S		
Today I mostly prospected:		
	DISCUSSIONS	
L	DAILY TRACKER	B
	PRESENTATIONS	
	CLIENTS	
	CONTRACTS	
	TRANSACTIONS	
☐ Did not work today; instead, I:		

08

April

Do your presentations include a closing script?[198]
If NO: *write one now.*
If YES: *revise it now, or write a better one.*

{20 }

{20 }

{20 }

{20 }

S M T W T F S

Today I mostly prospected:

	DISCUSSIONS	
L	DAILY TRACKER	B
	PRESENTATIONS	
	CLIENTS	
	CONTRACTS	
	TRANSACTIONS	

☐ Did not work today; instead, I:

{20 }

S M T W T F S

Today I mostly prospected:

	DISCUSSIONS	
L	DAILY TRACKER	B
	PRESENTATIONS	
	CLIENTS	
	CONTRACTS	
	TRANSACTIONS	

☐ Did not work today; instead, I:

{20 }

S M T W T F S

Today I mostly prospected:

	DISCUSSIONS	
L	DAILY TRACKER	B
	PRESENTATIONS	
	CLIENTS	
	CONTRACTS	
	TRANSACTIONS	

☐ Did not work today; instead, I:

April

09

List three systems that need improvement.[070]
Reward yourself with deadlines.

{20 }

{20 }

{20 }

{20 }
S M T W T F S
Today I mostly prospected:

L	DISCUSSIONS	B
	DAILY TRACKER	
	PRESENTATIONS	
	CLIENTS	
	CONTRACTS	
	TRANSACTIONS	

☐ Did not work today; instead, I:

{20 }
S M T W T F S
Today I mostly prospected:

L	DISCUSSIONS	B
	DAILY TRACKER	
	PRESENTATIONS	
	CLIENTS	
	CONTRACTS	
	TRANSACTIONS	

☐ Did not work today; instead, I:

{20 }
S M T W T F S
Today I mostly prospected:

L	DISCUSSIONS	B
	DAILY TRACKER	
	PRESENTATIONS	
	CLIENTS	
	CONTRACTS	
	TRANSACTIONS	

☐ Did not work today; instead, I:

10

April

Are you keeping your database clean and organized?[089]
What value are you giving to its members?[090]
Who can you call for a referral?

{20 }

{20 }

{20 }

{20 }

S M T W T F S

Today I mostly prospected:

	DISCUSSIONS	
L	DAILY TRACKER	B
	PRESENTATIONS	
	CLIENTS	
	CONTRACTS	
	TRANSACTIONS	

☐ Did not work today; instead, I:

{20 }

S M T W T F S

Today I mostly prospected:

	DISCUSSIONS	
L	DAILY TRACKER	B
	PRESENTATIONS	
	CLIENTS	
	CONTRACTS	
	TRANSACTIONS	

☐ Did not work today; instead, I:

{20 }

S M T W T F S

Today I mostly prospected:

	DISCUSSIONS	
L	DAILY TRACKER	B
	PRESENTATIONS	
	CLIENTS	
	CONTRACTS	
	TRANSACTIONS	

☐ Did not work today; instead, I:

April

11

Name one thing that would improve your average commission rate (ACR).[XVI]

{20 }

{20 }

{20 }

{20 }

S M T W T F S

Today I mostly prospected:

	DISCUSSIONS	
L	DAILY TRACKER	B
	PRESENTATIONS	
	CLIENTS	
	CONTRACTS	
	TRANSACTIONS	

☐ Did not work today; instead, I:

{20 }

S M T W T F S

Today I mostly prospected:

	DISCUSSIONS	
L	DAILY TRACKER	B
	PRESENTATIONS	
	CLIENTS	
	CONTRACTS	
	TRANSACTIONS	

☐ Did not work today; instead, I:

{20 }

S M T W T F S

Today I mostly prospected:

	DISCUSSIONS	
L	DAILY TRACKER	B
	PRESENTATIONS	
	CLIENTS	
	CONTRACTS	
	TRANSACTIONS	

☐ Did not work today; instead, I:

12

April

What could you do tomorrow to get a well-priced listing?[098]
How would doing so impact your business?
...impact your life?

{20 }

{20 }

{20 }

{20 }
S M T W T F S
Today I mostly prospected:

	DISCUSSIONS	
L	DAILY TRACKER	B
	PRESENTATIONS	
	CLIENTS	
	CONTRACTS	
	TRANSACTIONS	

☐ Did not work today; instead, I:

{20 }
S M T W T F S
Today I mostly prospected:

	DISCUSSIONS	
L	DAILY TRACKER	B
	PRESENTATIONS	
	CLIENTS	
	CONTRACTS	
	TRANSACTIONS	

☐ Did not work today; instead, I:

{20 }
S M T W T F S
Today I mostly prospected:

	DISCUSSIONS	
L	DAILY TRACKER	B
	PRESENTATIONS	
	CLIENTS	
	CONTRACTS	
	TRANSACTIONS	

☐ Did not work today; instead, I:

April

13

What is currently your biggest bottleneck (slowdown in the transaction process)?[VII]
What are you doing to improve that turnover rate?[XVI]

{20 }

{20 }

{20 }

{20 }

S M T W T F S

Today I mostly prospected:

	DISCUSSIONS	
L	DAILY TRACKER	B
	PRESENTATIONS	
	CLIENTS	
	CONTRACTS	
	TRANSACTIONS	

☐ Did not work today; instead, I:

{20 }

S M T W T F S

Today I mostly prospected:

	DISCUSSIONS	
L	DAILY TRACKER	B
	PRESENTATIONS	
	CLIENTS	
	CONTRACTS	
	TRANSACTIONS	

☐ Did not work today; instead, I:

{20 }

S M T W T F S

Today I mostly prospected:

	DISCUSSIONS	
L	DAILY TRACKER	B
	PRESENTATIONS	
	CLIENTS	
	CONTRACTS	
	TRANSACTIONS	

☐ Did not work today; instead, I:

14

April

Are you falling behind (or surging ahead) on any monthly goals? What's your plan to achieve them all?[XIX] *Adjust your activities now, so you will meet or exceed all.*

{20 }

{20 }

{20 }

{20 }

S M T W T F S

Today I mostly prospected:

	DISCUSSIONS	
L	DAILY TRACKER	B
	PRESENTATIONS	
	CLIENTS	
	CONTRACTS	
	TRANSACTIONS	

☐ Did not work today; instead, I:

{20 }

S M T W T F S

Today I mostly prospected:

	DISCUSSIONS	
L	DAILY TRACKER	B
	PRESENTATIONS	
	CLIENTS	
	CONTRACTS	
	TRANSACTIONS	

☐ Did not work today; instead, I:

{20 }

S M T W T F S

Today I mostly prospected:

	DISCUSSIONS	
L	DAILY TRACKER	B
	PRESENTATIONS	
	CLIENTS	
	CONTRACTS	
	TRANSACTIONS	

☐ Did not work today; instead, I:

April

15

Write a script for this seller objection:
"I need an agent who has listed property in my neighborhood, previously."

{20 }

{20 }

{20 }

{20 }
S M T W T F S
Today I mostly prospected:

	DISCUSSIONS	
L	DAILY TRACKER	B
	PRESENTATIONS	
	CLIENTS	
	CONTRACTS	
	TRANSACTIONS	

☐ Did not work today; instead, I:

{20 }
S M T W T F S
Today I mostly prospected:

	DISCUSSIONS	
L	DAILY TRACKER	B
	PRESENTATIONS	
	CLIENTS	
	CONTRACTS	
	TRANSACTIONS	

☐ Did not work today; instead, I:

{20 }
S M T W T F S
Today I mostly prospected:

	DISCUSSIONS	
L	DAILY TRACKER	B
	PRESENTATIONS	
	CLIENTS	
	CONTRACTS	
	TRANSACTIONS	

☐ Did not work today; instead, I:

16

April

Recall a recent time when you received excellent customer service.
How did it make you feel?
How could you pass the same feeling to your clients?

{20 }

{20 }

{20 }

{20 }

S M T W T F S

Today I mostly prospected:

	DISCUSSIONS	
L	DAILY TRACKER	B
	PRESENTATIONS	
	CLIENTS	
	CONTRACTS	
	TRANSACTIONS	

☐ Did not work today; instead, I:

{20 }

S M T W T F S

Today I mostly prospected:

	DISCUSSIONS	
L	DAILY TRACKER	B
	PRESENTATIONS	
	CLIENTS	
	CONTRACTS	
	TRANSACTIONS	

☐ Did not work today; instead, I:

{20 }

S M T W T F S

Today I mostly prospected:

	DISCUSSIONS	
L	DAILY TRACKER	B
	PRESENTATIONS	
	CLIENTS	
	CONTRACTS	
	TRANSACTIONS	

☐ Did not work today; instead, I:

April

17

Describe your ideal work day.
How could every day be as you describe?

{20 }

{20 }

{20 }

{20 }

S M T W T F S

Today I mostly prospected:

	DISCUSSIONS	
L	DAILY TRACKER	B
	PRESENTATIONS	
	CLIENTS	
	CONTRACTS	
	TRANSACTIONS	

☐ Did not work today; instead, I:

{20 }

S M T W T F S

Today I mostly prospected:

	DISCUSSIONS	
L	DAILY TRACKER	B
	PRESENTATIONS	
	CLIENTS	
	CONTRACTS	
	TRANSACTIONS	

☐ Did not work today; instead, I:

{20 }

S M T W T F S

Today I mostly prospected:

	DISCUSSIONS	
L	DAILY TRACKER	B
	PRESENTATIONS	
	CLIENTS	
	CONTRACTS	
	TRANSACTIONS	

☐ Did not work today; instead, I:

18 April

Today is Market Value Awareness Day.
Rank your valuation skills on a scale of one to ten.[125]
How could you improve your awareness? How will you implement?

{20 }

{20 }

{20 }

{20 }	{20 }	{20 }
S M T W T F S	S M T W T F S	S M T W T F S
Today I mostly prospected:	Today I mostly prospected:	Today I mostly prospected:
DISCUSSIONS	DISCUSSIONS	DISCUSSIONS
L · DAILY TRACKER · B	L · DAILY TRACKER · B	L · DAILY TRACKER · B
PRESENTATIONS	PRESENTATIONS	PRESENTATIONS
CLIENTS	CLIENTS	CLIENTS
CONTRACTS	CONTRACTS	CONTRACTS
TRANSACTIONS	TRANSACTIONS	TRANSACTIONS
☐ Did not work today; instead, I:	☐ Did not work today; instead, I:	☐ Did not work today; instead, I:

April

19

How does your attitude effect your outcomes?[005]
What do you do when there's work to be done,
but you'd rather be on vacation?

{20 }

{20 }

{20 }

{20 }

S M T W T F S

Today I mostly prospected:

	DISCUSSIONS	
L	DAILY TRACKER	B
	PRESENTATIONS	
	CLIENTS	
	CONTRACTS	
	TRANSACTIONS	

☐ Did not work today; instead, I:

{20 }

S M T W T F S

Today I mostly prospected:

	DISCUSSIONS	
L	DAILY TRACKER	B
	PRESENTATIONS	
	CLIENTS	
	CONTRACTS	
	TRANSACTIONS	

☐ Did not work today; instead, I:

{20 }

S M T W T F S

Today I mostly prospected:

	DISCUSSIONS	
L	DAILY TRACKER	B
	PRESENTATIONS	
	CLIENTS	
	CONTRACTS	
	TRANSACTIONS	

☐ Did not work today; instead, I:

20 April

List twenty words that describe your presentation skills.[167]
Which of these would you like to change?

{20 }

{20 }

{20 }

{20 }
S M T W T F S
Today I mostly prospected:

	DISCUSSIONS	
L	DAILY TRACKER	B
	PRESENTATIONS	
	CLIENTS	
	CONTRACTS	
	TRANSACTIONS	

☐ Did not work today; instead, I:

{20 }
S M T W T F S
Today I mostly prospected:

	DISCUSSIONS	
L	DAILY TRACKER	B
	PRESENTATIONS	
	CLIENTS	
	CONTRACTS	
	TRANSACTIONS	

☐ Did not work today; instead, I:

{20 }
S M T W T F S
Today I mostly prospected:

	DISCUSSIONS	
L	DAILY TRACKER	B
	PRESENTATIONS	
	CLIENTS	
	CONTRACTS	
	TRANSACTIONS	

☐ Did not work today; instead, I:

April

21

Rank your business health on a scale of one to ten. List one thing you could do to improve and a plan to achieve.

{20 }

{20 }

{20 }

{20 }

S M T W T F S

Today I mostly prospected:

	DISCUSSIONS	
L	DAILY TRACKER	B
	PRESENTATIONS	
	CLIENTS	
	CONTRACTS	
	TRANSACTIONS	

☐ Did not work today; instead, I:

{20 }

S M T W T F S

Today I mostly prospected:

	DISCUSSIONS	
L	DAILY TRACKER	B
	PRESENTATIONS	
	CLIENTS	
	CONTRACTS	
	TRANSACTIONS	

☐ Did not work today; instead, I:

{20 }

S M T W T F S

Today I mostly prospected:

	DISCUSSIONS	
L	DAILY TRACKER	B
	PRESENTATIONS	
	CLIENTS	
	CONTRACTS	
	TRANSACTIONS	

☐ Did not work today; instead, I:

22 April

List three admirable qualities of other agents' businesses. How can you be more like them?[068]

{20 }

{20 }

{20 }

{20 }
S M T W T F S
Today I mostly prospected:

	DISCUSSIONS	
L	DAILY TRACKER	B
	PRESENTATIONS	
	CLIENTS	
	CONTRACTS	
	TRANSACTIONS	

☐ Did not work today; instead, I:

{20 }
S M T W T F S
Today I mostly prospected:

	DISCUSSIONS	
L	DAILY TRACKER	B
	PRESENTATIONS	
	CLIENTS	
	CONTRACTS	
	TRANSACTIONS	

☐ Did not work today; instead, I:

{20 }
S M T W T F S
Today I mostly prospected:

	DISCUSSIONS	
L	DAILY TRACKER	B
	PRESENTATIONS	
	CLIENTS	
	CONTRACTS	
	TRANSACTIONS	

☐ Did not work today; instead, I:

April

23

Name the number one objection you hear from seller prospects.
What is your best script to overcome this objection?

{20 }

{20 }

{20 }

{20 }

S M T W T F S

Today I mostly prospected:

	DISCUSSIONS	
L	DAILY TRACKER	B
	PRESENTATIONS	
	CLIENTS	
	CONTRACTS	
	TRANSACTIONS	

☐ Did not work today; instead, I:

{20 }

S M T W T F S

Today I mostly prospected:

	DISCUSSIONS	
L	DAILY TRACKER	B
	PRESENTATIONS	
	CLIENTS	
	CONTRACTS	
	TRANSACTIONS	

☐ Did not work today; instead, I:

{20 }

S M T W T F S

Today I mostly prospected:

	DISCUSSIONS	
L	DAILY TRACKER	B
	PRESENTATIONS	
	CLIENTS	
	CONTRACTS	
	TRANSACTIONS	

☐ Did not work today; instead, I:

24 April

Where else could you be looking for buyers and sellers? Name three new ways to meet prospects[084] *and a plan to implement.*

{20 }

{20 }

{20 }

{20 }
S M T W T F S
Today I mostly prospected:

L	DISCUSSIONS	B
	DAILY TRACKER	
	PRESENTATIONS	
	CLIENTS	
	CONTRACTS	
	TRANSACTIONS	

☐ Did not work today; instead, I:

{20 }
S M T W T F S
Today I mostly prospected:

L	DISCUSSIONS	B
	DAILY TRACKER	
	PRESENTATIONS	
	CLIENTS	
	CONTRACTS	
	TRANSACTIONS	

☐ Did not work today; instead, I:

{20 }
S M T W T F S
Today I mostly prospected:

L	DISCUSSIONS	B
	DAILY TRACKER	
	PRESENTATIONS	
	CLIENTS	
	CONTRACTS	
	TRANSACTIONS	

☐ Did not work today; instead, I:

April

25

Name an agent whose business you admire.
How could your business be more like theirs?

{20 }

{20 }

{20 }

{20 }

S M T W T F S

Today I mostly prospected:

	DISCUSSIONS	
L	DAILY TRACKER	B
	PRESENTATIONS	
	CLIENTS	
	CONTRACTS	
	TRANSACTIONS	

☐ Did not work today; instead, I:

{20 }

S M T W T F S

Today I mostly prospected:

	DISCUSSIONS	
L	DAILY TRACKER	B
	PRESENTATIONS	
	CLIENTS	
	CONTRACTS	
	TRANSACTIONS	

☐ Did not work today; instead, I:

{20 }

S M T W T F S

Today I mostly prospected:

	DISCUSSIONS	
L	DAILY TRACKER	B
	PRESENTATIONS	
	CLIENTS	
	CONTRACTS	
	TRANSACTIONS	

☐ Did not work today; instead, I:

26 April

What would make your prospecting efforts more efficient? [012]
How could your message reach more prospects in less time?
How could you increase your discussion turnover rate (DTR)*?* [XVI]

{20 } ______________________

{20 } ______________________

{20 } ______________________

{20 }	{20 }	{20 }
S M T W T F S	S M T W T F S	S M T W T F S
Today I mostly prospected:	Today I mostly prospected:	Today I mostly prospected:

	DISCUSSIONS	
L	DAILY TRACKER	B
	PRESENTATIONS	
	CLIENTS	
	CONTRACTS	
	TRANSACTIONS	

	DISCUSSIONS	
L	DAILY TRACKER	B
	PRESENTATIONS	
	CLIENTS	
	CONTRACTS	
	TRANSACTIONS	

	DISCUSSIONS	
L	DAILY TRACKER	B
	PRESENTATIONS	
	CLIENTS	
	CONTRACTS	
	TRANSACTIONS	

☐ Did not work today; instead, I:

☐ Did not work today; instead, I:

☐ Did not work today; instead, I:

April

27

Write a script for this objection:
"I don't wanna list that high.
We can always lower the price later."

{20 }

{20 }

{20 }

{20 }

S M T W T F S

Today I mostly prospected:

	DISCUSSIONS	
L	DAILY TRACKER	B
	PRESENTATIONS	
	CLIENTS	
	CONTRACTS	
	TRANSACTIONS	

☐ Did not work today; instead, I:

{20 }

S M T W T F S

Today I mostly prospected:

	DISCUSSIONS	
L	DAILY TRACKER	B
	PRESENTATIONS	
	CLIENTS	
	CONTRACTS	
	TRANSACTIONS	

☐ Did not work today; instead, I:

{20 }

S M T W T F S

Today I mostly prospected:

	DISCUSSIONS	
L	DAILY TRACKER	B
	PRESENTATIONS	
	CLIENTS	
	CONTRACTS	
	TRANSACTIONS	

☐ Did not work today; instead, I:

28 April

*If your business was a song, which song would it be?
Would you sing it from the rafters, or mumble it under your breath?
Justify your response.*

{20 }

{20 }

{20 }

{20 }
S M T W T F S
Today I mostly prospected:

	DISCUSSIONS	
L	DAILY TRACKER	B
	PRESENTATIONS	
	CLIENTS	
	CONTRACTS	
	TRANSACTIONS	

☐ Did not work today; instead, I:

{20 }
S M T W T F S
Today I mostly prospected:

	DISCUSSIONS	
L	DAILY TRACKER	B
	PRESENTATIONS	
	CLIENTS	
	CONTRACTS	
	TRANSACTIONS	

☐ Did not work today; instead, I:

{20 }
S M T W T F S
Today I mostly prospected:

	DISCUSSIONS	
L	DAILY TRACKER	B
	PRESENTATIONS	
	CLIENTS	
	CONTRACTS	
	TRANSACTIONS	

☐ Did not work today; instead, I:

April

29

My grandest achievement this month was...
My plan to repeat this victory is...

{20 }

{20 }

{20 }

{20 }

S M T W T F S

Today I mostly prospected:

	DISCUSSIONS	
L	DAILY TRACKER	B
	PRESENTATIONS	
	CLIENTS	
	CONTRACTS	
	TRANSACTIONS	

☐ Did not work today; instead, I:

{20 }

S M T W T F S

Today I mostly prospected:

	DISCUSSIONS	
L	DAILY TRACKER	B
	PRESENTATIONS	
	CLIENTS	
	CONTRACTS	
	TRANSACTIONS	

☐ Did not work today; instead, I:

{20 }

S M T W T F S

Today I mostly prospected:

	DISCUSSIONS	
L	DAILY TRACKER	B
	PRESENTATIONS	
	CLIENTS	
	CONTRACTS	
	TRANSACTIONS	

☐ Did not work today; instead, I:

30 April

The biggest mistake/misstep I made this month was...
My plan to prevent the same mishap from recurring is...

{20 }

{20 }

{20 }

{20 }
S M T W T F S
Today I mostly prospected:

L	DISCUSSIONS	B
	DAILY TRACKER	
	PRESENTATIONS	
	CLIENTS	
	CONTRACTS	
	TRANSACTIONS	

☐ Did not work today; instead, I:

{20 }
S M T W T F S
Today I mostly prospected:

L	DISCUSSIONS	B
	DAILY TRACKER	
	PRESENTATIONS	
	CLIENTS	
	CONTRACTS	
	TRANSACTIONS	

☐ Did not work today; instead, I:

{20 }
S M T W T F S
Today I mostly prospected:

L	DISCUSSIONS	B
	DAILY TRACKER	
	PRESENTATIONS	
	CLIENTS	
	CONTRACTS	
	TRANSACTIONS	

☐ Did not work today; instead, I:

Notes

{20 } MONTHLY ACTIVITY TRACKER (GOALS→RESULTS)

GOALS	ACTIVITY	WK 1	WK 2	WK 3	WK 4	WK 5	TOTAL RESULTS
	TRANSACTIONS (T)	L B	L B	L B	L B	L B	L B
	NEW CLIENTS (C)	L B	L B	L B	L B	L B	L B
	PRESENTATIONS (P)	L B	L B	L B	L B	L B	L B
	DISCUSSIONS (D)						
	DAYS WORKED (W)						
	DAILY DISCUSSIONS (D/W)	ACTUAL DAILY DISCUSSION AVERAGE				D/W	
$	GCI	$					

{20 } MONTHLY ACTIVITY TRACKER (GOALS→RESULTS)

GOALS	ACTIVITY	WK 1	WK 2	WK 3	WK 4	WK 5	TOTAL RESULTS
	TRANSACTIONS (T)	L B	L B	L B	L B	L B	L B
	NEW CLIENTS (C)	L B	L B	L B	L B	L B	L B
	PRESENTATIONS (P)	L B	L B	L B	L B	L B	L B
	DISCUSSIONS (D)						
	DAYS WORKED (W)						
	DAILY DISCUSSIONS (D/W)	ACTUAL DAILY DISCUSSION AVERAGE				D/W	
$	GCI	$					

{20 } MONTHLY ACTIVITY TRACKER (GOALS→RESULTS)

GOALS	ACTIVITY	WK 1	WK 2	WK 3	WK 4	WK 5	TOTAL RESULTS
	TRANSACTIONS (T)	L B	L B	L B	L B	L B	L B
	NEW CLIENTS (C)	L B	L B	L B	L B	L B	L B
	PRESENTATIONS (P)	L B	L B	L B	L B	L B	L B
	DISCUSSIONS (D)						
	DAYS WORKED (W)						
	DAILY DISCUSSIONS (D/W)	ACTUAL DAILY DISCUSSION AVERAGE				D/W	
$	GCI	$					

May

01

Today is Business Plan Day.[XVIII]
Review/revise yours, and contemplate the past/future.
What is your plan to improve upon last month's performance?

{20 }

{20 }

{20 }

{20 }

S M T W T F S

Today I mostly prospected:

	DISCUSSIONS	
L	DAILY TRACKER	B
	PRESENTATIONS	
	CLIENTS	
	CONTRACTS	
	TRANSACTIONS	

☐ Did not work today; instead, I:

{20 }

S M T W T F S

Today I mostly prospected:

	DISCUSSIONS	
L	DAILY TRACKER	B
	PRESENTATIONS	
	CLIENTS	
	CONTRACTS	
	TRANSACTIONS	

☐ Did not work today; instead, I:

{20 }

S M T W T F S

Today I mostly prospected:

	DISCUSSIONS	
L	DAILY TRACKER	B
	PRESENTATIONS	
	CLIENTS	
	CONTRACTS	
	TRANSACTIONS	

☐ Did not work today; instead, I:

02

May

List a good habit you wanna adopt this month. How will you implement and make it a permanent part of your routine? Has last month's habit stuck yet?

{20 }

{20 }

{20 }

{20 }

S M T W T F S

Today I mostly prospected:

	DISCUSSIONS	
L	DAILY TRACKER	B
	PRESENTATIONS	
	CLIENTS	
	CONTRACTS	
	TRANSACTIONS	

☐ Did not work today; instead, I:

{20 }

S M T W T F S

Today I mostly prospected:

	DISCUSSIONS	
L	DAILY TRACKER	B
	PRESENTATIONS	
	CLIENTS	
	CONTRACTS	
	TRANSACTIONS	

☐ Did not work today; instead, I:

{20 }

S M T W T F S

Today I mostly prospected:

	DISCUSSIONS	
L	DAILY TRACKER	B
	PRESENTATIONS	
	CLIENTS	
	CONTRACTS	
	TRANSACTIONS	

☐ Did not work today; instead, I:

May

03

List ten words that describe your scripts.
Which words would you like to change?
Which ones make you proud?

{20 }

{20 }

{20 }

{20 }

S M T W T F S

Today I mostly prospected:

	DISCUSSIONS	
L	DAILY TRACKER	B
	PRESENTATIONS	
	CLIENTS	
	CONTRACTS	
	TRANSACTIONS	

☐ Did not work today; instead, I:

{20 }

S M T W T F S

Today I mostly prospected:

	DISCUSSIONS	
L	DAILY TRACKER	B
	PRESENTATIONS	
	CLIENTS	
	CONTRACTS	
	TRANSACTIONS	

☐ Did not work today; instead, I:

{20 }

S M T W T F S

Today I mostly prospected:

	DISCUSSIONS	
L	DAILY TRACKER	B
	PRESENTATIONS	
	CLIENTS	
	CONTRACTS	
	TRANSACTIONS	

☐ Did not work today; instead, I:

04

May

What is the best advice you've recently received?
Have you implemented it into your life?

{20 } ______________________________

{20 } ______________________________

{20 } ______________________________

{20 }

S M T W T F S

Today I mostly prospected:

	DISCUSSIONS	
L	DAILY TRACKER	B
	PRESENTATIONS	
	CLIENTS	
	CONTRACTS	
	TRANSACTIONS	

☐ Did not work today; instead, I:

{20 }

S M T W T F S

Today I mostly prospected:

	DISCUSSIONS	
L	DAILY TRACKER	B
	PRESENTATIONS	
	CLIENTS	
	CONTRACTS	
	TRANSACTIONS	

☐ Did not work today; instead, I:

{20 }

S M T W T F S

Today I mostly prospected:

	DISCUSSIONS	
L	DAILY TRACKER	B
	PRESENTATIONS	
	CLIENTS	
	CONTRACTS	
	TRANSACTIONS	

☐ Did not work today; instead, I:

May

Describe a recent opportunity lost.
How could things have gone your way? Is there a system modification (or script) that will mitigate future recurrences?

{20 }

{20 }

{20 }

{20 }

S M T W T F S

Today I mostly prospected:

	DISCUSSIONS	
L	DAILY TRACKER	B
	PRESENTATIONS	
	CLIENTS	
	CONTRACTS	
	TRANSACTIONS	

☐ Did not work today; instead, I:

{20 }

S M T W T F S

Today I mostly prospected:

	DISCUSSIONS	
L	DAILY TRACKER	B
	PRESENTATIONS	
	CLIENTS	
	CONTRACTS	
	TRANSACTIONS	

☐ Did not work today; instead, I:

{20 }

S M T W T F S

Today I mostly prospected:

	DISCUSSIONS	
L	DAILY TRACKER	B
	PRESENTATIONS	
	CLIENTS	
	CONTRACTS	
	TRANSACTIONS	

☐ Did not work today; instead, I:

May

What does your physical appearance say to prospects/clients?[025]
Are you attracting or repelling opportunities?

{20 }

{20 }

{20 }

{20 }		
S M T W T F S		
Today I mostly prospected:		
	DISCUSSIONS	
L	DAILY TRACKER	B
	PRESENTATIONS	
	CLIENTS	
	CONTRACTS	
	TRANSACTIONS	
☐ Did not work today; instead, I:		

{20 }		
S M T W T F S		
Today I mostly prospected:		
	DISCUSSIONS	
L	DAILY TRACKER	B
	PRESENTATIONS	
	CLIENTS	
	CONTRACTS	
	TRANSACTIONS	
☐ Did not work today; instead, I:		

{20 }		
S M T W T F S		
Today I mostly prospected:		
	DISCUSSIONS	
L	DAILY TRACKER	B
	PRESENTATIONS	
	CLIENTS	
	CONTRACTS	
	TRANSACTIONS	
☐ Did not work today; instead, I:		

May

The three greatest reasons to hire me are...

{20 }

{20 }

{20 }

{20 }
S M T W T F S
Today I mostly prospected:
DISCUSSIONS
L · DAILY TRACKER · B
PRESENTATIONS
CLIENTS
CONTRACTS
TRANSACTIONS
☐ Did not work today; instead, I:

{20 }
S M T W T F S
Today I mostly prospected:
DISCUSSIONS
L · DAILY TRACKER · B
PRESENTATIONS
CLIENTS
CONTRACTS
TRANSACTIONS
☐ Did not work today; instead, I:

{20 }
S M T W T F S
Today I mostly prospected:
DISCUSSIONS
L · DAILY TRACKER · B
PRESENTATIONS
CLIENTS
CONTRACTS
TRANSACTIONS
☐ Did not work today; instead, I:

May

Write an affirmation to soothe your prospecting pains.
Otherwise, write one to encourage your enthusiasm.

{20 } ____

{20 } ____

{20 } ____

{20 }

S M T W T F S

Today I mostly prospected:

	DISCUSSIONS	
L	DAILY TRACKER	B
	PRESENTATIONS	
	CLIENTS	
	CONTRACTS	
	TRANSACTIONS	

☐ Did not work today; instead, I:

{20 }

S M T W T F S

Today I mostly prospected:

	DISCUSSIONS	
L	DAILY TRACKER	B
	PRESENTATIONS	
	CLIENTS	
	CONTRACTS	
	TRANSACTIONS	

☐ Did not work today; instead, I:

{20 }

S M T W T F S

Today I mostly prospected:

	DISCUSSIONS	
L	DAILY TRACKER	B
	PRESENTATIONS	
	CLIENTS	
	CONTRACTS	
	TRANSACTIONS	

☐ Did not work today; instead, I:

May

Do you sometimes take on clients
who are outside of your niche?[042]
Why do you do it? What have the results been?

{20 }

{20 }

{20 }

{20 }		
S M T W T F S		
Today I mostly prospected:		
	DISCUSSIONS	
L	DAILY TRACKER	B
	PRESENTATIONS	
	CLIENTS	
	CONTRACTS	
	TRANSACTIONS	
☐ Did not work today; instead, I:		

{20 }		
S M T W T F S		
Today I mostly prospected:		
	DISCUSSIONS	
L	DAILY TRACKER	B
	PRESENTATIONS	
	CLIENTS	
	CONTRACTS	
	TRANSACTIONS	
☐ Did not work today; instead, I:		

{20 }		
S M T W T F S		
Today I mostly prospected:		
	DISCUSSIONS	
L	DAILY TRACKER	B
	PRESENTATIONS	
	CLIENTS	
	CONTRACTS	
	TRANSACTIONS	
☐ Did not work today; instead, I:		

10

May

Is your listing presentation consistent?[196]
How would improving the structure/delivery[195]
improve your agent stats?[x]

{20 }

{20 }

{20 }

{20 }

S M T W T F S

Today I mostly prospected:

	DISCUSSIONS	
L	DAILY TRACKER	B
	PRESENTATIONS	
	CLIENTS	
	CONTRACTS	
	TRANSACTIONS	

☐ Did not work today; instead, I:

{20 }

S M T W T F S

Today I mostly prospected:

	DISCUSSIONS	
L	DAILY TRACKER	B
	PRESENTATIONS	
	CLIENTS	
	CONTRACTS	
	TRANSACTIONS	

☐ Did not work today; instead, I:

{20 }

S M T W T F S

Today I mostly prospected:

	DISCUSSIONS	
L	DAILY TRACKER	B
	PRESENTATIONS	
	CLIENTS	
	CONTRACTS	
	TRANSACTIONS	

☐ Did not work today; instead, I:

11

Name one thing that would improve your return on transactions (ROT).[XVI]

{20 }

{20 }

{20 }

{20 }

S M T W T F S

Today I mostly prospected:

	DISCUSSIONS	
L	DAILY TRACKER	B
	PRESENTATIONS	
	CLIENTS	
	CONTRACTS	
	TRANSACTIONS	

☐ Did not work today; instead, I:

{20 }

S M T W T F S

Today I mostly prospected:

	DISCUSSIONS	
L	DAILY TRACKER	B
	PRESENTATIONS	
	CLIENTS	
	CONTRACTS	
	TRANSACTIONS	

☐ Did not work today; instead, I:

{20 }

S M T W T F S

Today I mostly prospected:

	DISCUSSIONS	
L	DAILY TRACKER	B
	PRESENTATIONS	
	CLIENTS	
	CONTRACTS	
	TRANSACTIONS	

☐ Did not work today; instead, I:

12 May

How many different ways do you prospect for clients?[084]
Which ones provide the most presentations? ...the least?
Should you alter your strategy?[004]

{20 }

{20 }

{20 }

{20 }
S M T W T F S
Today I mostly prospected:

	DISCUSSIONS	
L	DAILY TRACKER	B
	PRESENTATIONS	
	CLIENTS	
	CONTRACTS	
	TRANSACTIONS	

☐ Did not work today; instead, I:

{20 }
S M T W T F S
Today I mostly prospected:

	DISCUSSIONS	
L	DAILY TRACKER	B
	PRESENTATIONS	
	CLIENTS	
	CONTRACTS	
	TRANSACTIONS	

☐ Did not work today; instead, I:

{20 }
S M T W T F S
Today I mostly prospected:

	DISCUSSIONS	
L	DAILY TRACKER	B
	PRESENTATIONS	
	CLIENTS	
	CONTRACTS	
	TRANSACTIONS	

☐ Did not work today; instead, I:

May

13

A funny (real estate related) thing happened recently...

{20 }

{20 }

{20 }

{20 }	{20 }	{20 }
S M T W T F S	S M T W T F S	S M T W T F S
Today I mostly prospected:	Today I mostly prospected:	Today I mostly prospected:
DISCUSSIONS	DISCUSSIONS	DISCUSSIONS
L · DAILY TRACKER · B	L · DAILY TRACKER · B	L · DAILY TRACKER · B
PRESENTATIONS	PRESENTATIONS	PRESENTATIONS
CLIENTS	CLIENTS	CLIENTS
CONTRACTS	CONTRACTS	CONTRACTS
TRANSACTIONS	TRANSACTIONS	TRANSACTIONS
☐ Did not work today; instead, I:	☐ Did not work today; instead, I:	☐ Did not work today; instead, I:

14

May

Write a script for this buyer objection: "First, I wanna find the house I want, then I'll talk to a loan officer."

{20 }

{20 }

{20 }

{20 }

S M T W T F S

Today I mostly prospected:

	DISCUSSIONS	
L	DAILY TRACKER	B
	PRESENTATIONS	
	CLIENTS	
	CONTRACTS	
	TRANSACTIONS	

☐ Did not work today; instead, I:

{20 }

S M T W T F S

Today I mostly prospected:

	DISCUSSIONS	
L	DAILY TRACKER	B
	PRESENTATIONS	
	CLIENTS	
	CONTRACTS	
	TRANSACTIONS	

☐ Did not work today; instead, I:

{20 }

S M T W T F S

Today I mostly prospected:

	DISCUSSIONS	
L	DAILY TRACKER	B
	PRESENTATIONS	
	CLIENTS	
	CONTRACTS	
	TRANSACTIONS	

☐ Did not work today; instead, I:

May

15

Are you falling behind (or surging ahead) on any monthly goals?
What's your plan to achieve them all?[XIX]
Adjust your activities now, so you will meet or exceed all.

{20 }

{20 }

{20 }

{20 }		
S M T W T F S		
Today I mostly prospected:		
	DISCUSSIONS	
L	DAILY TRACKER	B
	PRESENTATIONS	
	CLIENTS	
	CONTRACTS	
	TRANSACTIONS	
☐ Did not work today; instead, I:		

{20 }		
S M T W T F S		
Today I mostly prospected:		
	DISCUSSIONS	
L	DAILY TRACKER	B
	PRESENTATIONS	
	CLIENTS	
	CONTRACTS	
	TRANSACTIONS	
☐ Did not work today; instead, I:		

{20 }		
S M T W T F S		
Today I mostly prospected:		
	DISCUSSIONS	
L	DAILY TRACKER	B
	PRESENTATIONS	
	CLIENTS	
	CONTRACTS	
	TRANSACTIONS	
☐ Did not work today; instead, I:		

16

May

Today is Do the Right Thing Day.
When was the last time someone asked you to do wrong?
How did you handle it? Did you play by the rules?[036]

{20 }

{20 }

{20 }

{20 }

S M T W T F S

Today I mostly prospected:

	DISCUSSIONS	
L	DAILY TRACKER	B
	PRESENTATIONS	
	CLIENTS	
	CONTRACTS	
	TRANSACTIONS	

☐ Did not work today; instead, I:

{20 }

S M T W T F S

Today I mostly prospected:

	DISCUSSIONS	
L	DAILY TRACKER	B
	PRESENTATIONS	
	CLIENTS	
	CONTRACTS	
	TRANSACTIONS	

☐ Did not work today; instead, I:

{20 }

S M T W T F S

Today I mostly prospected:

	DISCUSSIONS	
L	DAILY TRACKER	B
	PRESENTATIONS	
	CLIENTS	
	CONTRACTS	
	TRANSACTIONS	

☐ Did not work today; instead, I:

May

17

Recall a recent class or educational session.
What was the number one thing you learned?
How will you implement it into your business?

{20 }

{20 }

{20 }

{20 }

S M T W T F S

Today I mostly prospected:

	DISCUSSIONS	
L	DAILY TRACKER	B
	PRESENTATIONS	
	CLIENTS	
	CONTRACTS	
	TRANSACTIONS	

☐ Did not work today; instead, I:

{20 }

S M T W T F S

Today I mostly prospected:

	DISCUSSIONS	
L	DAILY TRACKER	B
	PRESENTATIONS	
	CLIENTS	
	CONTRACTS	
	TRANSACTIONS	

☐ Did not work today; instead, I:

{20 }

S M T W T F S

Today I mostly prospected:

	DISCUSSIONS	
L	DAILY TRACKER	B
	PRESENTATIONS	
	CLIENTS	
	CONTRACTS	
	TRANSACTIONS	

☐ Did not work today; instead, I:

18

May

Today is Future You Day.
List three things you'd like to change about yourself.

{20 }

{20 }

{20 }

{20 }

S M T W T F S

Today I mostly prospected:

DISCUSSIONS

L DAILY TRACKER B

PRESENTATIONS

CLIENTS

CONTRACTS

TRANSACTIONS

☐ Did not work today; instead, I:

{20 }

S M T W T F S

Today I mostly prospected:

DISCUSSIONS

L DAILY TRACKER B

PRESENTATIONS

CLIENTS

CONTRACTS

TRANSACTIONS

☐ Did not work today; instead, I:

{20 }

S M T W T F S

Today I mostly prospected:

DISCUSSIONS

L DAILY TRACKER B

PRESENTATIONS

CLIENTS

CONTRACTS

TRANSACTIONS

☐ Did not work today; instead, I:

May

19

How many mentors do you embrace?[044]
What do you get from these people?
How do you repay them?

{20 }

{20 }

{20 }

{20 }
S M T W T F S
Today I mostly prospected:

L	DISCUSSIONS	B
	DAILY TRACKER	
	PRESENTATIONS	
	CLIENTS	
	CONTRACTS	
	TRANSACTIONS	

☐ Did not work today; instead, I:

{20 }
S M T W T F S
Today I mostly prospected:

L	DISCUSSIONS	B
	DAILY TRACKER	
	PRESENTATIONS	
	CLIENTS	
	CONTRACTS	
	TRANSACTIONS	

☐ Did not work today; instead, I:

{20 }
S M T W T F S
Today I mostly prospected:

L	DISCUSSIONS	B
	DAILY TRACKER	
	PRESENTATIONS	
	CLIENTS	
	CONTRACTS	
	TRANSACTIONS	

☐ Did not work today; instead, I:

20

May

Describe your Happy Place.[313]
How often do you go there?
What stresses you the most about real estate sales?

{20 }

{20 }

{20 }

{20 }
S M T W T F S
Today I mostly prospected:

	DISCUSSIONS	
L	DAILY TRACKER	B
	PRESENTATIONS	
	CLIENTS	
	CONTRACTS	
	TRANSACTIONS	

☐ Did not work today; instead, I:

{20 }
S M T W T F S
Today I mostly prospected:

	DISCUSSIONS	
L	DAILY TRACKER	B
	PRESENTATIONS	
	CLIENTS	
	CONTRACTS	
	TRANSACTIONS	

☐ Did not work today; instead, I:

{20 }
S M T W T F S
Today I mostly prospected:

	DISCUSSIONS	
L	DAILY TRACKER	B
	PRESENTATIONS	
	CLIENTS	
	CONTRACTS	
	TRANSACTIONS	

☐ Did not work today; instead, I:

May

21

*If your business was a dog,
would it be obedient and well-trained,
or would it soil the carpet? Explain yourself.*

{20 }

{20 }

{20 }

{20 }

S M T W T F S

Today I mostly prospected:

	DISCUSSIONS	
L	DAILY TRACKER	B
	PRESENTATIONS	
	CLIENTS	
	CONTRACTS	
	TRANSACTIONS	

☐ Did not work today; instead, I:

{20 }

S M T W T F S

Today I mostly prospected:

	DISCUSSIONS	
L	DAILY TRACKER	B
	PRESENTATIONS	
	CLIENTS	
	CONTRACTS	
	TRANSACTIONS	

☐ Did not work today; instead, I:

{20 }

S M T W T F S

Today I mostly prospected:

	DISCUSSIONS	
L	DAILY TRACKER	B
	PRESENTATIONS	
	CLIENTS	
	CONTRACTS	
	TRANSACTIONS	

☐ Did not work today; instead, I:

22

May

List twenty words that describe your negotiation techniques.[264]
Which of these words would you like to change?

{20 }

{20 }

{20 }

{20 }	{20 }	{20 }
S M T W T F S	S M T W T F S	S M T W T F S
Today I mostly prospected:	Today I mostly prospected:	Today I mostly prospected:
DISCUSSIONS	DISCUSSIONS	DISCUSSIONS
L DAILY TRACKER B	L DAILY TRACKER B	L DAILY TRACKER B
PRESENTATIONS	PRESENTATIONS	PRESENTATIONS
CLIENTS	CLIENTS	CLIENTS
CONTRACTS	CONTRACTS	CONTRACTS
TRANSACTIONS	TRANSACTIONS	TRANSACTIONS
☐ Did not work today; instead, I:	☐ Did not work today; instead, I:	☐ Did not work today; instead, I:

May

23

Are you tracking business expenses? How might you cut expenses without sacrificing your services?[283]

{20 }

{20 }

{20 }

{20 }
S M T W T F S
Today I mostly prospected:

	DISCUSSIONS	
L	DAILY TRACKER	B
	PRESENTATIONS	
	CLIENTS	
	CONTRACTS	
	TRANSACTIONS	

☐ Did not work today; instead, I:

{20 }
S M T W T F S
Today I mostly prospected:

	DISCUSSIONS	
L	DAILY TRACKER	B
	PRESENTATIONS	
	CLIENTS	
	CONTRACTS	
	TRANSACTIONS	

☐ Did not work today; instead, I:

{20 }
S M T W T F S
Today I mostly prospected:

	DISCUSSIONS	
L	DAILY TRACKER	B
	PRESENTATIONS	
	CLIENTS	
	CONTRACTS	
	TRANSACTIONS	

☐ Did not work today; instead, I:

24 May

Why did you choose the broker you're with?[028]
Why do you stay?

{20 }

{20 }

{20 }

{20 }
S M T W T F S
Today I mostly prospected:
DISCUSSIONS
L · DAILY TRACKER · B
PRESENTATIONS
CLIENTS
CONTRACTS
TRANSACTIONS
☐ Did not work today; instead, I:

{20 }
S M T W T F S
Today I mostly prospected:
DISCUSSIONS
L · DAILY TRACKER · B
PRESENTATIONS
CLIENTS
CONTRACTS
TRANSACTIONS
☐ Did not work today; instead, I:

{20 }
S M T W T F S
Today I mostly prospected:
DISCUSSIONS
L · DAILY TRACKER · B
PRESENTATIONS
CLIENTS
CONTRACTS
TRANSACTIONS
☐ Did not work today; instead, I:

May

25

How do you deal with frustrated sellers?[237]
When expiry of a listing draws near,[202]
do you employ specialized tactics? Explain.[203]

{20 }

{20 }

{20 }

{20 }	{20 }	{20 }
S M T W T F S	S M T W T F S	S M T W T F S
Today I mostly prospected:	Today I mostly prospected:	Today I mostly prospected:
DISCUSSIONS	DISCUSSIONS	DISCUSSIONS
L · DAILY TRACKER · B	L · DAILY TRACKER · B	L · DAILY TRACKER · B
PRESENTATIONS	PRESENTATIONS	PRESENTATIONS
CLIENTS	CLIENTS	CLIENTS
CONTRACTS	CONTRACTS	CONTRACTS
TRANSACTIONS	TRANSACTIONS	TRANSACTIONS
☐ Did not work today; instead, I:	☐ Did not work today; instead, I:	☐ Did not work today; instead, I:

May

Are you fluent in real estate lingo?[032]
Define a term you recently learned.

{20 }

{20 }

{20 }

{20 }

S M T W T F S

Today I mostly prospected:

	DISCUSSIONS	
L	DAILY TRACKER	B
	PRESENTATIONS	
	CLIENTS	
	CONTRACTS	
	TRANSACTIONS	

☐ Did not work today; instead, I:

{20 }

S M T W T F S

Today I mostly prospected:

	DISCUSSIONS	
L	DAILY TRACKER	B
	PRESENTATIONS	
	CLIENTS	
	CONTRACTS	
	TRANSACTIONS	

☐ Did not work today; instead, I:

{20 }

S M T W T F S

Today I mostly prospected:

	DISCUSSIONS	
L	DAILY TRACKER	B
	PRESENTATIONS	
	CLIENTS	
	CONTRACTS	
	TRANSACTIONS	

☐ Did not work today; instead, I:

27

What keeps you motivated to prospect?[300]

{20 }

{20 }

{20 }

{20 }
S M T W T F S
Today I mostly prospected:

	DISCUSSIONS	
L	DAILY TRACKER	B
	PRESENTATIONS	
	CLIENTS	
	CONTRACTS	
	TRANSACTIONS	

☐ Did not work today; instead, I:

{20 }
S M T W T F S
Today I mostly prospected:

	DISCUSSIONS	
L	DAILY TRACKER	B
	PRESENTATIONS	
	CLIENTS	
	CONTRACTS	
	TRANSACTIONS	

☐ Did not work today; instead, I:

{20 }
S M T W T F S
Today I mostly prospected:

	DISCUSSIONS	
L	DAILY TRACKER	B
	PRESENTATIONS	
	CLIENTS	
	CONTRACTS	
	TRANSACTIONS	

☐ Did not work today; instead, I:

May

How could you lower expenses without harming client services? Otherwise, how could you increase GCI *without raising expenses?*

{20 }

{20 }

{20 }

{20 }	{20 }	{20 }
S M T W T F S	S M T W T F S	S M T W T F S
Today I mostly prospected:	Today I mostly prospected:	Today I mostly prospected:

	DISCUSSIONS	
L	DAILY TRACKER	B
	PRESENTATIONS	
	CLIENTS	
	CONTRACTS	
	TRANSACTIONS	

☐ Did not work today; instead, I:

	DISCUSSIONS	
L	DAILY TRACKER	B
	PRESENTATIONS	
	CLIENTS	
	CONTRACTS	
	TRANSACTIONS	

☐ Did not work today; instead, I:

	DISCUSSIONS	
L	DAILY TRACKER	B
	PRESENTATIONS	
	CLIENTS	
	CONTRACTS	
	TRANSACTIONS	

☐ Did not work today; instead, I:

May

29

Write a script for this seller objection:
"Agents are paid too much.
I'm gonna try to sell it myself."

{20 }

{20 }

{20 }

{20 }

S M T W T F S

Today I mostly prospected:

	DISCUSSIONS	
L	DAILY TRACKER	B
	PRESENTATIONS	
	CLIENTS	
	CONTRACTS	
	TRANSACTIONS	

☐ Did not work today; instead, I:

{20 }

S M T W T F S

Today I mostly prospected:

	DISCUSSIONS	
L	DAILY TRACKER	B
	PRESENTATIONS	
	CLIENTS	
	CONTRACTS	
	TRANSACTIONS	

☐ Did not work today; instead, I:

{20 }

S M T W T F S

Today I mostly prospected:

	DISCUSSIONS	
L	DAILY TRACKER	B
	PRESENTATIONS	
	CLIENTS	
	CONTRACTS	
	TRANSACTIONS	

☐ Did not work today; instead, I:

30 May

My grandest achievement this month was...
My plan to repeat this victory is...

{20 }

{20 }

{20 }

{20 }

S M T W T F S

Today I mostly prospected:

	DISCUSSIONS	
L	DAILY TRACKER	B
	PRESENTATIONS	
	CLIENTS	
	CONTRACTS	
	TRANSACTIONS	

☐ Did not work today; instead, I:

{20 }

S M T W T F S

Today I mostly prospected:

	DISCUSSIONS	
L	DAILY TRACKER	B
	PRESENTATIONS	
	CLIENTS	
	CONTRACTS	
	TRANSACTIONS	

☐ Did not work today; instead, I:

{20 }

S M T W T F S

Today I mostly prospected:

	DISCUSSIONS	
L	DAILY TRACKER	B
	PRESENTATIONS	
	CLIENTS	
	CONTRACTS	
	TRANSACTIONS	

☐ Did not work today; instead, I:

May

31

The biggest mistake/misstep I made this month was...
My plan to prevent the same mishap from recurring is...

{20 }

{20 }

{20 }

{20 }

S M T W T F S

Today I mostly prospected:

	DISCUSSIONS	
L	DAILY TRACKER	B
	PRESENTATIONS	
	CLIENTS	
	CONTRACTS	
	TRANSACTIONS	

☐ Did not work today; instead, I:

{20 }

S M T W T F S

Today I mostly prospected:

	DISCUSSIONS	
L	DAILY TRACKER	B
	PRESENTATIONS	
	CLIENTS	
	CONTRACTS	
	TRANSACTIONS	

☐ Did not work today; instead, I:

{20 }

S M T W T F S

Today I mostly prospected:

	DISCUSSIONS	
L	DAILY TRACKER	B
	PRESENTATIONS	
	CLIENTS	
	CONTRACTS	
	TRANSACTIONS	

☐ Did not work today; instead, I:

{20 } MONTHLY ACTIVITY TRACKER (GOALS→RESULTS)

GOALS	ACTIVITY	WK 1	WK 2	WK 3	WK 4	WK 5	TOTAL RESULTS
	TRANSACTIONS (T)	L B	L B	L B	L B	L B	L B
	NEW CLIENTS (C)	L B	L B	L B	L B	L B	L B
	PRESENTATIONS (P)	L B	L B	L B	L B	L B	L B
	DISCUSSIONS (D)						
	DAYS WORKED (W)						
	DAILY DISCUSSIONS (D/W)	ACTUAL DAILY DISCUSSION AVERAGE				D/W	
$	GCI	$					

{20 } MONTHLY ACTIVITY TRACKER (GOALS→RESULTS)

GOALS	ACTIVITY	WK 1	WK 2	WK 3	WK 4	WK 5	TOTAL RESULTS
	TRANSACTIONS (T)	L B	L B	L B	L B	L B	L B
	NEW CLIENTS (C)	L B	L B	L B	L B	L B	L B
	PRESENTATIONS (P)	L B	L B	L B	L B	L B	L B
	DISCUSSIONS (D)						
	DAYS WORKED (W)						
	DAILY DISCUSSIONS (D/W)	ACTUAL DAILY DISCUSSION AVERAGE				D/W	
$	GCI	$					

{20 } MONTHLY ACTIVITY TRACKER (GOALS→RESULTS)

GOALS	ACTIVITY	WK 1	WK 2	WK 3	WK 4	WK 5	TOTAL RESULTS
	TRANSACTIONS (T)	L B	L B	L B	L B	L B	L B
	NEW CLIENTS (C)	L B	L B	L B	L B	L B	L B
	PRESENTATIONS (P)	L B	L B	L B	L B	L B	L B
	DISCUSSIONS (D)						
	DAYS WORKED (W)						
	DAILY DISCUSSIONS (D/W)	ACTUAL DAILY DISCUSSION AVERAGE				D/W	
$	GCI	$					

June

01

Today is Business Plan Day.[XVIII]
Review/revise yours, and contemplate the past/future.
What is your plan to improve upon last month's performance?

{20 }

{20 }

{20 }

{20 }

S M T W T F S

Today I mostly prospected:

	DISCUSSIONS	
L	DAILY TRACKER	B
	PRESENTATIONS	
	CLIENTS	
	CONTRACTS	
	TRANSACTIONS	

☐ Did not work today; instead, I:

{20 }

S M T W T F S

Today I mostly prospected:

	DISCUSSIONS	
L	DAILY TRACKER	B
	PRESENTATIONS	
	CLIENTS	
	CONTRACTS	
	TRANSACTIONS	

☐ Did not work today; instead, I:

{20 }

S M T W T F S

Today I mostly prospected:

	DISCUSSIONS	
L	DAILY TRACKER	B
	PRESENTATIONS	
	CLIENTS	
	CONTRACTS	
	TRANSACTIONS	

☐ Did not work today; instead, I:

02

June

List a good habit you wanna adopt this month. How will you implement and make it a permanent part of your routine? Has last month's habit stuck yet?

{20 } ____________________

{20 } ____________________

{20 } ____________________

{20 }

S M T W T F S

Today I mostly prospected:

L	DAILY TRACKER	B
	DISCUSSIONS	
	PRESENTATIONS	
	CLIENTS	
	CONTRACTS	
	TRANSACTIONS	

☐ Did not work today; instead, I:

{20 }

S M T W T F S

Today I mostly prospected:

L	DAILY TRACKER	B
	DISCUSSIONS	
	PRESENTATIONS	
	CLIENTS	
	CONTRACTS	
	TRANSACTIONS	

☐ Did not work today; instead, I:

{20 }

S M T W T F S

Today I mostly prospected:

L	DAILY TRACKER	B
	DISCUSSIONS	
	PRESENTATIONS	
	CLIENTS	
	CONTRACTS	
	TRANSACTIONS	

☐ Did not work today; instead, I:

June

03

List ten words that describe your real estate website.[071]
If asked again next month, which words should change?
Is it doing its job, or does it need some help?

{20 }

{20 }

{20 }

{20 }	{20 }	{20 }
S M T W T F S	S M T W T F S	S M T W T F S
Today I mostly prospected:	Today I mostly prospected:	Today I mostly prospected:
DISCUSSIONS	DISCUSSIONS	DISCUSSIONS
L · DAILY TRACKER · B	L · DAILY TRACKER · B	L · DAILY TRACKER · B
PRESENTATIONS	PRESENTATIONS	PRESENTATIONS
CLIENTS	CLIENTS	CLIENTS
CONTRACTS	CONTRACTS	CONTRACTS
TRANSACTIONS	TRANSACTIONS	TRANSACTIONS
☐ Did not work today; instead, I:	☐ Did not work today; instead, I:	☐ Did not work today; instead, I:

04

June

If real estate sales did not exist,
to what other job would your current skills transfer best?

{20 }

{20 }

{20 }

{20 }

S M T W T F S

Today I mostly prospected:

L	DISCUSSIONS	B
	DAILY TRACKER	
	PRESENTATIONS	
	CLIENTS	
	CONTRACTS	
	TRANSACTIONS	

☐ Did not work today; instead, I:

{20 }

S M T W T F S

Today I mostly prospected:

L	DISCUSSIONS	B
	DAILY TRACKER	
	PRESENTATIONS	
	CLIENTS	
	CONTRACTS	
	TRANSACTIONS	

☐ Did not work today; instead, I:

{20 }

S M T W T F S

Today I mostly prospected:

L	DISCUSSIONS	B
	DAILY TRACKER	
	PRESENTATIONS	
	CLIENTS	
	CONTRACTS	
	TRANSACTIONS	

☐ Did not work today; instead, I:

June

Name one thing about you that every client should know, then write a script about it.

05

{20 }

{20 }

{20 }

{20 }

S M T W T F S

Today I mostly prospected:

	DISCUSSIONS	
L	DAILY TRACKER	B
	PRESENTATIONS	
	CLIENTS	
	CONTRACTS	
	TRANSACTIONS	

☐ Did not work today; instead, I:

{20 }

S M T W T F S

Today I mostly prospected:

	DISCUSSIONS	
L	DAILY TRACKER	B
	PRESENTATIONS	
	CLIENTS	
	CONTRACTS	
	TRANSACTIONS	

☐ Did not work today; instead, I:

{20 }

S M T W T F S

Today I mostly prospected:

	DISCUSSIONS	
L	DAILY TRACKER	B
	PRESENTATIONS	
	CLIENTS	
	CONTRACTS	
	TRANSACTIONS	

☐ Did not work today; instead, I:

June

Which day of the week is best for prospecting?
How can you take advantage of this day?

{20 }

{20 }

{20 }

{20 }

S M T W T F S

Today I mostly prospected:

L	DAILY TRACKER	B
	DISCUSSIONS	
	PRESENTATIONS	
	CLIENTS	
	CONTRACTS	
	TRANSACTIONS	

☐ Did not work today; instead, I:

{20 }

S M T W T F S

Today I mostly prospected:

L	DAILY TRACKER	B
	DISCUSSIONS	
	PRESENTATIONS	
	CLIENTS	
	CONTRACTS	
	TRANSACTIONS	

☐ Did not work today; instead, I:

{20 }

S M T W T F S

Today I mostly prospected:

L	DAILY TRACKER	B
	DISCUSSIONS	
	PRESENTATIONS	
	CLIENTS	
	CONTRACTS	
	TRANSACTIONS	

☐ Did not work today; instead, I:

June

What is your system for handling buyer inquiries?[184]
Do you routinely pre-qualify before showing?[170]
Do you insist on a presentation and agency agreement?[186]

{20 } ______________________________

{20 } ______________________________

{20 } ______________________________

{20 }	{20 }	{20 }
S M T W T F S	S M T W T F S	S M T W T F S
Today I mostly prospected:	Today I mostly prospected:	Today I mostly prospected:
DISCUSSIONS	DISCUSSIONS	DISCUSSIONS
L · DAILY TRACKER · B	L · DAILY TRACKER · B	L · DAILY TRACKER · B
PRESENTATIONS	PRESENTATIONS	PRESENTATIONS
CLIENTS	CLIENTS	CLIENTS
CONTRACTS	CONTRACTS	CONTRACTS
TRANSACTIONS	TRANSACTIONS	TRANSACTIONS
☐ Did not work today; instead, I:	☐ Did not work today; instead, I:	☐ Did not work today; instead, I:

June

Give some advice to the you from last year.

{20 }

{20 }

{20 }

{20 }		
S M T W T F S		
Today I mostly prospected:		
	DISCUSSIONS	
L	DAILY TRACKER	B
	PRESENTATIONS	
	CLIENTS	
	CONTRACTS	
	TRANSACTIONS	
☐ Did not work today; instead, I:		

{20 }		
S M T W T F S		
Today I mostly prospected:		
	DISCUSSIONS	
L	DAILY TRACKER	B
	PRESENTATIONS	
	CLIENTS	
	CONTRACTS	
	TRANSACTIONS	
☐ Did not work today; instead, I:		

{20 }		
S M T W T F S		
Today I mostly prospected:		
	DISCUSSIONS	
L	DAILY TRACKER	B
	PRESENTATIONS	
	CLIENTS	
	CONTRACTS	
	TRANSACTIONS	
☐ Did not work today; instead, I:		

June

09

How do you leverage your posse (vendor relationships) to the benefit of clients?[179]

{20 }

{20 }

{20 }

{20 }		
S M T W T F S		
Today I mostly prospected:		
	DISCUSSIONS	
L	DAILY TRACKER	B
	PRESENTATIONS	
	CLIENTS	
	CONTRACTS	
	TRANSACTIONS	
☐ Did not work today; instead, I:		

{20 }		
S M T W T F S		
Today I mostly prospected:		
	DISCUSSIONS	
L	DAILY TRACKER	B
	PRESENTATIONS	
	CLIENTS	
	CONTRACTS	
	TRANSACTIONS	
☐ Did not work today; instead, I:		

{20 }		
S M T W T F S		
Today I mostly prospected:		
	DISCUSSIONS	
L	DAILY TRACKER	B
	PRESENTATIONS	
	CLIENTS	
	CONTRACTS	
	TRANSACTIONS	
☐ Did not work today; instead, I:		

10

June

Who (specifically) has been the single, most helpful person to your real estate business? How might you show the extent of your gratitude?

{20 }

{20 }

{20 }

{20 }

S M T W T F S

Today I mostly prospected:

	DISCUSSIONS	
L	DAILY TRACKER	B
	PRESENTATIONS	
	CLIENTS	
	CONTRACTS	
	TRANSACTIONS	

☐ Did not work today; instead, I:

{20 }

S M T W T F S

Today I mostly prospected:

	DISCUSSIONS	
L	DAILY TRACKER	B
	PRESENTATIONS	
	CLIENTS	
	CONTRACTS	
	TRANSACTIONS	

☐ Did not work today; instead, I:

{20 }

S M T W T F S

Today I mostly prospected:

	DISCUSSIONS	
L	DAILY TRACKER	B
	PRESENTATIONS	
	CLIENTS	
	CONTRACTS	
	TRANSACTIONS	

☐ Did not work today; instead, I:

June

11

Name one thing that would improve your presentation turnover rate (PTR).[XVI]

{20 }

{20 }

{20 }

{20 }

S M T W T F S

Today I mostly prospected:

	DISCUSSIONS	
L	DAILY TRACKER	B
	PRESENTATIONS	
	CLIENTS	
	CONTRACTS	
	TRANSACTIONS	

☐ Did not work today; instead, I:

{20 }

S M T W T F S

Today I mostly prospected:

	DISCUSSIONS	
L	DAILY TRACKER	B
	PRESENTATIONS	
	CLIENTS	
	CONTRACTS	
	TRANSACTIONS	

☐ Did not work today; instead, I:

{20 }

S M T W T F S

Today I mostly prospected:

	DISCUSSIONS	
L	DAILY TRACKER	B
	PRESENTATIONS	
	CLIENTS	
	CONTRACTS	
	TRANSACTIONS	

☐ Did not work today; instead, I:

12

June

Is your real estate glass half full or half empty?
Why do you say that?

{20 }

{20 }

{20 }

{20 }

S M T W T F S

Today I mostly prospected:

L	DAILY TRACKER	B
	DISCUSSIONS	
	PRESENTATIONS	
	CLIENTS	
	CONTRACTS	
	TRANSACTIONS	

☐ Did not work today; instead, I:

{20 }

S M T W T F S

Today I mostly prospected:

L	DAILY TRACKER	B
	DISCUSSIONS	
	PRESENTATIONS	
	CLIENTS	
	CONTRACTS	
	TRANSACTIONS	

☐ Did not work today; instead, I:

{20 }

S M T W T F S

Today I mostly prospected:

L	DAILY TRACKER	B
	DISCUSSIONS	
	PRESENTATIONS	
	CLIENTS	
	CONTRACTS	
	TRANSACTIONS	

☐ Did not work today; instead, I:

June

13

Do you have a written commission schedule?[181]
When (under what circumstances)
do you offer a discount?

{20 }

{20 }

{20 }

{20 }

S M T W T F S

Today I mostly prospected:

	DISCUSSIONS	
L	DAILY TRACKER	B
	PRESENTATIONS	
	CLIENTS	
	CONTRACTS	
	TRANSACTIONS	

☐ Did not work today; instead, I:

{20 }

S M T W T F S

Today I mostly prospected:

	DISCUSSIONS	
L	DAILY TRACKER	B
	PRESENTATIONS	
	CLIENTS	
	CONTRACTS	
	TRANSACTIONS	

☐ Did not work today; instead, I:

{20 }

S M T W T F S

Today I mostly prospected:

	DISCUSSIONS	
L	DAILY TRACKER	B
	PRESENTATIONS	
	CLIENTS	
	CONTRACTS	
	TRANSACTIONS	

☐ Did not work today; instead, I:

14

June

Write a script for this objection:
"I wanna talk to other real estate agents, before deciding which one to hire."

{20 }

{20 }

{20 }

{20 }		
S M T W T F S		
Today I mostly prospected:		
	DISCUSSIONS	
L	DAILY TRACKER	B
	PRESENTATIONS	
	CLIENTS	
	CONTRACTS	
	TRANSACTIONS	
☐ Did not work today; instead, I:		

{20 }		
S M T W T F S		
Today I mostly prospected:		
	DISCUSSIONS	
L	DAILY TRACKER	B
	PRESENTATIONS	
	CLIENTS	
	CONTRACTS	
	TRANSACTIONS	
☐ Did not work today; instead, I:		

{20 }		
S M T W T F S		
Today I mostly prospected:		
	DISCUSSIONS	
L	DAILY TRACKER	B
	PRESENTATIONS	
	CLIENTS	
	CONTRACTS	
	TRANSACTIONS	
☐ Did not work today; instead, I:		

June

15

Are you falling behind (or surging ahead) on any monthly goals?
What's your plan to achieve them all?[XIX]
Adjust your activities now, so you will meet or exceed all.

{20 }

{20 }

{20 }

{20 }

S M T W T F S

Today I mostly prospected:

	DISCUSSIONS	
L	DAILY TRACKER	B
	PRESENTATIONS	
	CLIENTS	
	CONTRACTS	
	TRANSACTIONS	

☐ Did not work today; instead, I:

{20 }

S M T W T F S

Today I mostly prospected:

	DISCUSSIONS	
L	DAILY TRACKER	B
	PRESENTATIONS	
	CLIENTS	
	CONTRACTS	
	TRANSACTIONS	

☐ Did not work today; instead, I:

{20 }

S M T W T F S

Today I mostly prospected:

	DISCUSSIONS	
L	DAILY TRACKER	B
	PRESENTATIONS	
	CLIENTS	
	CONTRACTS	
	TRANSACTIONS	

☐ Did not work today; instead, I:

16

June

Where else could you be looking for buyers and sellers? Name three new ways to meet prospects[084] and a plan to implement.

{20 }

{20 }

{20 }

{20 }	{20 }	{20 }
S M T W T F S	S M T W T F S	S M T W T F S
Today I mostly prospected:	Today I mostly prospected:	Today I mostly prospected:

	DISCUSSIONS	
L	DAILY TRACKER	B
	PRESENTATIONS	
	CLIENTS	
	CONTRACTS	
	TRANSACTIONS	

☐ Did not work today; instead, I:

	DISCUSSIONS	
L	DAILY TRACKER	B
	PRESENTATIONS	
	CLIENTS	
	CONTRACTS	
	TRANSACTIONS	

☐ Did not work today; instead, I:

	DISCUSSIONS	
L	DAILY TRACKER	B
	PRESENTATIONS	
	CLIENTS	
	CONTRACTS	
	TRANSACTIONS	

☐ Did not work today; instead, I:

June

17

Summer is heating up,
and your friends are happy to help.[106]
Who can you call for a referral?

{20 }

{20 }

{20 }

{20 }
S M T W T F S
Today I mostly prospected:

	DISCUSSIONS	
L	DAILY TRACKER	B
	PRESENTATIONS	
	CLIENTS	
	CONTRACTS	
	TRANSACTIONS	

☐ Did not work today; instead, I:

{20 }
S M T W T F S
Today I mostly prospected:

	DISCUSSIONS	
L	DAILY TRACKER	B
	PRESENTATIONS	
	CLIENTS	
	CONTRACTS	
	TRANSACTIONS	

☐ Did not work today; instead, I:

{20 }
S M T W T F S
Today I mostly prospected:

	DISCUSSIONS	
L	DAILY TRACKER	B
	PRESENTATIONS	
	CLIENTS	
	CONTRACTS	
	TRANSACTIONS	

☐ Did not work today; instead, I:

18 June

Today is Laugh It Off Day.
Recall a recent frustration and then let it go.[310]
What can you do to prevent its recurrence?

{20 }

{20 }

{20 }

{20 }
S M T W T F S
Today I mostly prospected:

	DISCUSSIONS	
L	DAILY TRACKER	B
	PRESENTATIONS	
	CLIENTS	
	CONTRACTS	
	TRANSACTIONS	

☐ Did not work today; instead, I:

{20 }
S M T W T F S
Today I mostly prospected:

	DISCUSSIONS	
L	DAILY TRACKER	B
	PRESENTATIONS	
	CLIENTS	
	CONTRACTS	
	TRANSACTIONS	

☐ Did not work today; instead, I:

{20 }
S M T W T F S
Today I mostly prospected:

	DISCUSSIONS	
L	DAILY TRACKER	B
	PRESENTATIONS	
	CLIENTS	
	CONTRACTS	
	TRANSACTIONS	

☐ Did not work today; instead, I:

June

19

*List three bad habits you'd like to lose.
Reward yourself with deadlines and
a plan to ditch each offending habit.*

{20 }

{20 }

{20 }

{20 }

S M T W T F S

Today I mostly prospected:

L		B
	DISCUSSIONS	
	DAILY TRACKER	
	PRESENTATIONS	
	CLIENTS	
	CONTRACTS	
	TRANSACTIONS	

☐ Did not work today; instead, I:

{20 }

S M T W T F S

Today I mostly prospected:

L		B
	DISCUSSIONS	
	DAILY TRACKER	
	PRESENTATIONS	
	CLIENTS	
	CONTRACTS	
	TRANSACTIONS	

☐ Did not work today; instead, I:

{20 }

S M T W T F S

Today I mostly prospected:

L		B
	DISCUSSIONS	
	DAILY TRACKER	
	PRESENTATIONS	
	CLIENTS	
	CONTRACTS	
	TRANSACTIONS	

☐ Did not work today; instead, I:

20 June

Describe your prospecting routine.[078]
How could it be improved to increase effectiveness/efficiency?

{20 }

{20 }

{20 }

{20 }	{20 }	{20 }
S M T W T F S	S M T W T F S	S M T W T F S
Today I mostly prospected:	Today I mostly prospected:	Today I mostly prospected:

	DISCUSSIONS	
L	DAILY TRACKER	B
	PRESENTATIONS	
	CLIENTS	
	CONTRACTS	
	TRANSACTIONS	

☐ Did not work today; instead, I:

	DISCUSSIONS	
L	DAILY TRACKER	B
	PRESENTATIONS	
	CLIENTS	
	CONTRACTS	
	TRANSACTIONS	

☐ Did not work today; instead, I:

	DISCUSSIONS	
L	DAILY TRACKER	B
	PRESENTATIONS	
	CLIENTS	
	CONTRACTS	
	TRANSACTIONS	

☐ Did not work today; instead, I:

June

21

Write a script for this seller objection:
"This offer is too low;
let's ignore them."

{20 }

{20 }

{20 }

{20 }
S M T W T F S
Today I mostly prospected:

	DISCUSSIONS	
L	DAILY TRACKER	B
	PRESENTATIONS	
	CLIENTS	
	CONTRACTS	
	TRANSACTIONS	

☐ Did not work today; instead, I:

{20 }
S M T W T F S
Today I mostly prospected:

	DISCUSSIONS	
L	DAILY TRACKER	B
	PRESENTATIONS	
	CLIENTS	
	CONTRACTS	
	TRANSACTIONS	

☐ Did not work today; instead, I:

{20 }
S M T W T F S
Today I mostly prospected:

	DISCUSSIONS	
L	DAILY TRACKER	B
	PRESENTATIONS	
	CLIENTS	
	CONTRACTS	
	TRANSACTIONS	

☐ Did not work today; instead, I:

22 June

List twenty words that describe your business creativity.[114]
Which ones would you like to change?

{20 }

{20 }

{20 }

{20 }	{20 }	{20 }
S M T W T F S	S M T W T F S	S M T W T F S
Today I mostly prospected:	Today I mostly prospected:	Today I mostly prospected:
DISCUSSIONS	DISCUSSIONS	DISCUSSIONS
L DAILY TRACKER B	L DAILY TRACKER B	L DAILY TRACKER B
PRESENTATIONS	PRESENTATIONS	PRESENTATIONS
CLIENTS	CLIENTS	CLIENTS
CONTRACTS	CONTRACTS	CONTRACTS
TRANSACTIONS	TRANSACTIONS	TRANSACTIONS
☐ Did not work today; instead, I:	☐ Did not work today; instead, I:	☐ Did not work today; instead, I:

June

23

How could you increase GCI *without adding time to your day? List three ways and a plan to implement.*

{20 }

{20 }

{20 }

{20 }	{20 }	{20 }
S M T W T F S	S M T W T F S	S M T W T F S
Today I mostly prospected:	Today I mostly prospected:	Today I mostly prospected:

L	DISCUSSIONS	B
	DAILY TRACKER	
	PRESENTATIONS	
	CLIENTS	
	CONTRACTS	
	TRANSACTIONS	

☐ Did not work today; instead, I:

L	DISCUSSIONS	B
	DAILY TRACKER	
	PRESENTATIONS	
	CLIENTS	
	CONTRACTS	
	TRANSACTIONS	

☐ Did not work today; instead, I:

L	DISCUSSIONS	B
	DAILY TRACKER	
	PRESENTATIONS	
	CLIENTS	
	CONTRACTS	
	TRANSACTIONS	

☐ Did not work today; instead, I:

24 June

What keeps you motivated to prospect?[300]
How could you find a new way
to make prospecting more fun?

{20 }

{20 }

{20 }

{20 }

S	M	T	W	T	F	S

Today I mostly prospected:

	DISCUSSIONS	
L	DAILY TRACKER	B
	PRESENTATIONS	
	CLIENTS	
	CONTRACTS	
	TRANSACTIONS	

☐ Did not work today; instead, I:

{20 }

S	M	T	W	T	F	S

Today I mostly prospected:

	DISCUSSIONS	
L	DAILY TRACKER	B
	PRESENTATIONS	
	CLIENTS	
	CONTRACTS	
	TRANSACTIONS	

☐ Did not work today; instead, I:

{20 }

S	M	T	W	T	F	S

Today I mostly prospected:

	DISCUSSIONS	
L	DAILY TRACKER	B
	PRESENTATIONS	
	CLIENTS	
	CONTRACTS	
	TRANSACTIONS	

☐ Did not work today; instead, I:

June

25

Name three systems that need improvement.[073]
What can you do to make them more effective/efficient?

{20 }

{20 }

{20 }

{20 }
S M T W T F S
Today I mostly prospected:

L	DISCUSSIONS	B
	DAILY TRACKER	
	PRESENTATIONS	
	CLIENTS	
	CONTRACTS	
	TRANSACTIONS	

☐ Did not work today; instead, I:

{20 }
S M T W T F S
Today I mostly prospected:

L	DISCUSSIONS	B
	DAILY TRACKER	
	PRESENTATIONS	
	CLIENTS	
	CONTRACTS	
	TRANSACTIONS	

☐ Did not work today; instead, I:

{20 }
S M T W T F S
Today I mostly prospected:

L	DISCUSSIONS	B
	DAILY TRACKER	
	PRESENTATIONS	
	CLIENTS	
	CONTRACTS	
	TRANSACTIONS	

☐ Did not work today; instead, I:

June

When was the last time you tried something new?
What was the result?
Would you do it again?

{20 } ______________________________

{20 } ______________________________

{20 } ______________________________

{20 }

S M T W T F S

Today I mostly prospected:

	DISCUSSIONS	
L	DAILY TRACKER	B
	PRESENTATIONS	
	CLIENTS	
	CONTRACTS	
	TRANSACTIONS	

☐ Did not work today; instead, I:

{20 }

S M T W T F S

Today I mostly prospected:

	DISCUSSIONS	
L	DAILY TRACKER	B
	PRESENTATIONS	
	CLIENTS	
	CONTRACTS	
	TRANSACTIONS	

☐ Did not work today; instead, I:

{20 }

S M T W T F S

Today I mostly prospected:

	DISCUSSIONS	
L	DAILY TRACKER	B
	PRESENTATIONS	
	CLIENTS	
	CONTRACTS	
	TRANSACTIONS	

☐ Did not work today; instead, I:

27

List three ways you could be a better boss to yourself.[060]

{20 } __________

{20 } __________

{20 } __________

{20 }

S M T W T F S

Today I mostly prospected:

L	DISCUSSIONS	B
	DAILY TRACKER	
	PRESENTATIONS	
	CLIENTS	
	CONTRACTS	
	TRANSACTIONS	

☐ Did not work today; instead, I:

{20 }

S M T W T F S

Today I mostly prospected:

L	DISCUSSIONS	B
	DAILY TRACKER	
	PRESENTATIONS	
	CLIENTS	
	CONTRACTS	
	TRANSACTIONS	

☐ Did not work today; instead, I:

{20 }

S M T W T F S

Today I mostly prospected:

L	DISCUSSIONS	B
	DAILY TRACKER	
	PRESENTATIONS	
	CLIENTS	
	CONTRACTS	
	TRANSACTIONS	

☐ Did not work today; instead, I:

28 June

My grandest achievement this month was...
My plan to repeat this victory is...

{20 }

{20 }

{20 }

{20 }

S M T W T F S

Today I mostly prospected:

L	DAILY TRACKER	B
	DISCUSSIONS	
	PRESENTATIONS	
	CLIENTS	
	CONTRACTS	
	TRANSACTIONS	

☐ Did not work today; instead, I:

{20 }

S M T W T F S

Today I mostly prospected:

L	DAILY TRACKER	B
	DISCUSSIONS	
	PRESENTATIONS	
	CLIENTS	
	CONTRACTS	
	TRANSACTIONS	

☐ Did not work today; instead, I:

{20 }

S M T W T F S

Today I mostly prospected:

L	DAILY TRACKER	B
	DISCUSSIONS	
	PRESENTATIONS	
	CLIENTS	
	CONTRACTS	
	TRANSACTIONS	

☐ Did not work today; instead, I:

June

29

Summarize the last three months with one word.
Given the opportunity, would you take a do-over?
Which parts would you like to forget?.. never forget?

{20 }

{20 }

{20 }

{20 }	{20 }	{20 }
S M T W T F S	S M T W T F S	S M T W T F S
Today I mostly prospected:	Today I mostly prospected:	Today I mostly prospected:
DISCUSSIONS	DISCUSSIONS	DISCUSSIONS
L · DAILY TRACKER · B	L · DAILY TRACKER · B	L · DAILY TRACKER · B
PRESENTATIONS	PRESENTATIONS	PRESENTATIONS
CLIENTS	CLIENTS	CLIENTS
CONTRACTS	CONTRACTS	CONTRACTS
TRANSACTIONS	TRANSACTIONS	TRANSACTIONS
☐ Did not work today; instead, I:	☐ Did not work today; instead, I:	☐ Did not work today; instead, I:

30

June

The biggest mistake/misstep I made this month was...
My plan to prevent the same mishap from recurring is...

{20 }

{20 }

{20 }

{20 }
S M T W T F S
Today I mostly prospected:

L	DAILY TRACKER	B
	DISCUSSIONS	
	PRESENTATIONS	
	CLIENTS	
	CONTRACTS	
	TRANSACTIONS	

☐ Did not work today; instead, I:

{20 }
S M T W T F S
Today I mostly prospected:

L	DAILY TRACKER	B
	DISCUSSIONS	
	PRESENTATIONS	
	CLIENTS	
	CONTRACTS	
	TRANSACTIONS	

☐ Did not work today; instead, I:

{20 }
S M T W T F S
Today I mostly prospected:

L	DAILY TRACKER	B
	DISCUSSIONS	
	PRESENTATIONS	
	CLIENTS	
	CONTRACTS	
	TRANSACTIONS	

☐ Did not work today; instead, I:

{20 }

MONTHLY ACTIVITY TRACKER (GOALS→RESULTS)

GOALS	ACTIVITY	WK 1	WK 2	WK 3	WK 4	WK 5	TOTAL RESULTS
	TRANSACTIONS (T)	L B	L B	L B	L B	L B	L B
	NEW CLIENTS (C)	L B	L B	L B	L B	L B	L B
	PRESENTATIONS (P)	L B	L B	L B	L B	L B	L B
	DISCUSSIONS (D)						
	DAYS WORKED (W)						
	DAILY DISCUSSIONS (D/W)	ACTUAL DAILY DISCUSSION AVERAGE				D/W	
$	GCI	$					

{20 }

MONTHLY ACTIVITY TRACKER (GOALS→RESULTS)

GOALS	ACTIVITY	WK 1	WK 2	WK 3	WK 4	WK 5	TOTAL RESULTS
	TRANSACTIONS (T)	L B	L B	L B	L B	L B	L B
	NEW CLIENTS (C)	L B	L B	L B	L B	L B	L B
	PRESENTATIONS (P)	L B	L B	L B	L B	L B	L B
	DISCUSSIONS (D)						
	DAYS WORKED (W)						
	DAILY DISCUSSIONS (D/W)	ACTUAL DAILY DISCUSSION AVERAGE				D/W	
$	GCI	$					

{20 }

MONTHLY ACTIVITY TRACKER (GOALS→RESULTS)

GOALS	ACTIVITY	WK 1	WK 2	WK 3	WK 4	WK 5	TOTAL RESULTS
	TRANSACTIONS (T)	L B	L B	L B	L B	L B	L B
	NEW CLIENTS (C)	L B	L B	L B	L B	L B	L B
	PRESENTATIONS (P)	L B	L B	L B	L B	L B	L B
	DISCUSSIONS (D)						
	DAYS WORKED (W)						
	DAILY DISCUSSIONS (D/W)	ACTUAL DAILY DISCUSSION AVERAGE				D/W	
$	GCI	$					

July

01

Today is Business Plan Day.[XVIII]
Review/revise yours, and contemplate the past/future.
What is your plan to improve upon last month's performance?

{20 }

{20 }

{20 }

{20 }
S M T W T F S
Today I mostly prospected:

	DISCUSSIONS	
L	DAILY TRACKER	B
	PRESENTATIONS	
	CLIENTS	
	CONTRACTS	
	TRANSACTIONS	

☐ Did not work today; instead, I:

{20 }
S M T W T F S
Today I mostly prospected:

	DISCUSSIONS	
L	DAILY TRACKER	B
	PRESENTATIONS	
	CLIENTS	
	CONTRACTS	
	TRANSACTIONS	

☐ Did not work today; instead, I:

{20 }
S M T W T F S
Today I mostly prospected:

	DISCUSSIONS	
L	DAILY TRACKER	B
	PRESENTATIONS	
	CLIENTS	
	CONTRACTS	
	TRANSACTIONS	

☐ Did not work today; instead, I:

02

July

List a good habit you wanna adopt this month. How will you implement and make it a permanent part of your routine? Has last month's habit stuck yet?

{20 }

{20 }

{20 }

{20 }

S M T W T F S

Today I mostly prospected:

	DISCUSSIONS	
L	DAILY TRACKER	B
	PRESENTATIONS	
	CLIENTS	
	CONTRACTS	
	TRANSACTIONS	

☐ Did not work today; instead, I:

{20 }

S M T W T F S

Today I mostly prospected:

	DISCUSSIONS	
L	DAILY TRACKER	B
	PRESENTATIONS	
	CLIENTS	
	CONTRACTS	
	TRANSACTIONS	

☐ Did not work today; instead, I:

{20 }

S M T W T F S

Today I mostly prospected:

	DISCUSSIONS	
L	DAILY TRACKER	B
	PRESENTATIONS	
	CLIENTS	
	CONTRACTS	
	TRANSACTIONS	

☐ Did not work today; instead, I:

July

03

What would make your prospecting efforts more efficient?[012]
How could your message reach more prospects in less time?
How could you increase your discussion turnover rate (DTR)?[XVI]

{20 }

{20 }

{20 }

{20 }

S	M	T	W	T	F	S

Today I mostly prospected:

	DISCUSSIONS	
L	DAILY TRACKER	B
	PRESENTATIONS	
	CLIENTS	
	CONTRACTS	
	TRANSACTIONS	

☐ Did not work today; instead, I:

{20 }

S	M	T	W	T	F	S

Today I mostly prospected:

	DISCUSSIONS	
L	DAILY TRACKER	B
	PRESENTATIONS	
	CLIENTS	
	CONTRACTS	
	TRANSACTIONS	

☐ Did not work today; instead, I:

{20 }

S	M	T	W	T	F	S

Today I mostly prospected:

	DISCUSSIONS	
L	DAILY TRACKER	B
	PRESENTATIONS	
	CLIENTS	
	CONTRACTS	
	TRANSACTIONS	

☐ Did not work today; instead, I:

04

July

Today is Independence Day.
How has your real estate business given you freedom?
How has it tied you up in chains?

{20 }

{20 }

{20 }

{20 }

S M T W T F S

Today I mostly prospected:

L	DISCUSSIONS	B
	DAILY TRACKER	
	PRESENTATIONS	
	CLIENTS	
	CONTRACTS	
	TRANSACTIONS	

☐ Did not work today; instead, I:

{20 }

S M T W T F S

Today I mostly prospected:

L	DISCUSSIONS	B
	DAILY TRACKER	
	PRESENTATIONS	
	CLIENTS	
	CONTRACTS	
	TRANSACTIONS	

☐ Did not work today; instead, I:

{20 }

S M T W T F S

Today I mostly prospected:

L	DISCUSSIONS	B
	DAILY TRACKER	
	PRESENTATIONS	
	CLIENTS	
	CONTRACTS	
	TRANSACTIONS	

☐ Did not work today; instead, I:

July

05

List ten words that describe your real estate systems.
Which words would you like to change?
Which will you never change?

{20 }

{20 }

{20 }

{20 }

S M T W T F S

Today I mostly prospected:

	DISCUSSIONS	
L	DAILY TRACKER	B
	PRESENTATIONS	
	CLIENTS	
	CONTRACTS	
	TRANSACTIONS	

☐ Did not work today; instead, I:

{20 }

S M T W T F S

Today I mostly prospected:

	DISCUSSIONS	
L	DAILY TRACKER	B
	PRESENTATIONS	
	CLIENTS	
	CONTRACTS	
	TRANSACTIONS	

☐ Did not work today; instead, I:

{20 }

S M T W T F S

Today I mostly prospected:

	DISCUSSIONS	
L	DAILY TRACKER	B
	PRESENTATIONS	
	CLIENTS	
	CONTRACTS	
	TRANSACTIONS	

☐ Did not work today; instead, I:

06

July

Describe your system for pre-qualifying seller prospects.[189]
Do you have any listing-client deal-breakers
(things that make you say NO*)? If so, what are they?*

{20 }

{20 }

{20 }

{20 }

S M T W T F S

Today I mostly prospected:

L	DISCUSSIONS	B
	DAILY TRACKER	
	PRESENTATIONS	
	CLIENTS	
	CONTRACTS	
	TRANSACTIONS	

☐ Did not work today; instead, I:

{20 }

S M T W T F S

Today I mostly prospected:

L	DISCUSSIONS	B
	DAILY TRACKER	
	PRESENTATIONS	
	CLIENTS	
	CONTRACTS	
	TRANSACTIONS	

☐ Did not work today; instead, I:

{20 }

S M T W T F S

Today I mostly prospected:

L	DISCUSSIONS	B
	DAILY TRACKER	
	PRESENTATIONS	
	CLIENTS	
	CONTRACTS	
	TRANSACTIONS	

☐ Did not work today; instead, I:

July

07

How do you deal with parachuting agents?[295]
Have you ever parachuted in on a deal?
How did the other agent react?

{20 }

{20 }

{20 }

{20 }

S M T W T F S

Today I mostly prospected:

	DISCUSSIONS	
L	DAILY TRACKER	B
	PRESENTATIONS	
	CLIENTS	
	CONTRACTS	
	TRANSACTIONS	

☐ Did not work today; instead, I:

{20 }

S M T W T F S

Today I mostly prospected:

	DISCUSSIONS	
L	DAILY TRACKER	B
	PRESENTATIONS	
	CLIENTS	
	CONTRACTS	
	TRANSACTIONS	

☐ Did not work today; instead, I:

{20 }

S M T W T F S

Today I mostly prospected:

	DISCUSSIONS	
L	DAILY TRACKER	B
	PRESENTATIONS	
	CLIENTS	
	CONTRACTS	
	TRANSACTIONS	

☐ Did not work today; instead, I:

08

July

What is your number one best tip for sellers?
How well are you communicating that to prospects?[094]

{20 }

{20 }

{20 }

{20 }	{20 }	{20 }
S M T W T F S	S M T W T F S	S M T W T F S
Today I mostly prospected:	Today I mostly prospected:	Today I mostly prospected:
DISCUSSIONS	DISCUSSIONS	DISCUSSIONS
L · DAILY TRACKER · B	L · DAILY TRACKER · B	L · DAILY TRACKER · B
PRESENTATIONS	PRESENTATIONS	PRESENTATIONS
CLIENTS	CLIENTS	CLIENTS
CONTRACTS	CONTRACTS	CONTRACTS
TRANSACTIONS	TRANSACTIONS	TRANSACTIONS
☐ Did not work today; instead, I:	☐ Did not work today; instead, I:	☐ Did not work today; instead, I:

July

09

How could today have gone better?
Even if it was great, what would have made it the best day ever?

{20 }

{20 }

{20 }

{20 }

S M T W T F S

Today I mostly prospected:

	DISCUSSIONS	
L	DAILY TRACKER	B
	PRESENTATIONS	
	CLIENTS	
	CONTRACTS	
	TRANSACTIONS	

☐ Did not work today; instead, I:

{20 }

S M T W T F S

Today I mostly prospected:

	DISCUSSIONS	
L	DAILY TRACKER	B
	PRESENTATIONS	
	CLIENTS	
	CONTRACTS	
	TRANSACTIONS	

☐ Did not work today; instead, I:

{20 }

S M T W T F S

Today I mostly prospected:

	DISCUSSIONS	
L	DAILY TRACKER	B
	PRESENTATIONS	
	CLIENTS	
	CONTRACTS	
	TRANSACTIONS	

☐ Did not work today; instead, I:

10

July

How many different ways do you prospect for clients?[084]
Which ones provide the most presentations? ...the least?
Should you alter your strategy?[004]

{20 }

{20 }

{20 }

{20 }

S M T W T F S

Today I mostly prospected:

	DISCUSSIONS	
L	DAILY TRACKER	B
	PRESENTATIONS	
	CLIENTS	
	CONTRACTS	
	TRANSACTIONS	

☐ Did not work today; instead, I:

{20 }

S M T W T F S

Today I mostly prospected:

	DISCUSSIONS	
L	DAILY TRACKER	B
	PRESENTATIONS	
	CLIENTS	
	CONTRACTS	
	TRANSACTIONS	

☐ Did not work today; instead, I:

{20 }

S M T W T F S

Today I mostly prospected:

	DISCUSSIONS	
L	DAILY TRACKER	B
	PRESENTATIONS	
	CLIENTS	
	CONTRACTS	
	TRANSACTIONS	

☐ Did not work today; instead, I:

July

11

List three systems that need improvement.[070]
Reward yourself with deadlines.

{20 }

{20 }

{20 }

{20 }	{20 }	{20 }
S M T W T F S	S M T W T F S	S M T W T F S
Today I mostly prospected:	Today I mostly prospected:	Today I mostly prospected:

	DISCUSSIONS			DISCUSSIONS			DISCUSSIONS	
L	DAILY TRACKER	B	L	DAILY TRACKER	B	L	DAILY TRACKER	B
	PRESENTATIONS			PRESENTATIONS			PRESENTATIONS	
	CLIENTS			CLIENTS			CLIENTS	
	CONTRACTS			CONTRACTS			CONTRACTS	
	TRANSACTIONS			TRANSACTIONS			TRANSACTIONS	

☐ Did not work today; instead, I:

☐ Did not work today; instead, I:

☐ Did not work today; instead, I:

12

July

Are you keeping your database clean and organized?[089]
What value are you giving to its members?[090]
Who can you call for a referral?

{20 }

{20 }

{20 }

{20 }
S M T W T F S
Today I mostly prospected:

L	DISCUSSIONS	B
	DAILY TRACKER	
	PRESENTATIONS	
	CLIENTS	
	CONTRACTS	
	TRANSACTIONS	

☐ Did not work today; instead, I:

{20 }
S M T W T F S
Today I mostly prospected:

L	DISCUSSIONS	B
	DAILY TRACKER	
	PRESENTATIONS	
	CLIENTS	
	CONTRACTS	
	TRANSACTIONS	

☐ Did not work today; instead, I:

{20 }
S M T W T F S
Today I mostly prospected:

L	DISCUSSIONS	B
	DAILY TRACKER	
	PRESENTATIONS	
	CLIENTS	
	CONTRACTS	
	TRANSACTIONS	

☐ Did not work today; instead, I:

July

13

What could you do tomorrow to get a well-priced listing?[098]
How would doing so impact your business?
...impact your life?

{20 }

{20 }

{20 }

{20 }

S M T W T F S

Today I mostly prospected:

	DISCUSSIONS	
L	DAILY TRACKER	B
	PRESENTATIONS	
	CLIENTS	
	CONTRACTS	
	TRANSACTIONS	

☐ Did not work today; instead, I:

{20 }

S M T W T F S

Today I mostly prospected:

	DISCUSSIONS	
L	DAILY TRACKER	B
	PRESENTATIONS	
	CLIENTS	
	CONTRACTS	
	TRANSACTIONS	

☐ Did not work today; instead, I:

{20 }

S M T W T F S

Today I mostly prospected:

	DISCUSSIONS	
L	DAILY TRACKER	B
	PRESENTATIONS	
	CLIENTS	
	CONTRACTS	
	TRANSACTIONS	

☐ Did not work today; instead, I:

14

July

What is currently your biggest bottleneck (slowdown in the transaction process)? [VII]
What are you doing to improve that turnover rate? [XVI]

{20 }

{20 }

{20 }

{20 }

S M T W T F S

Today I mostly prospected:

	DISCUSSIONS	
L	DAILY TRACKER	B
	PRESENTATIONS	
	CLIENTS	
	CONTRACTS	
	TRANSACTIONS	

☐ Did not work today; instead, I:

{20 }

S M T W T F S

Today I mostly prospected:

	DISCUSSIONS	
L	DAILY TRACKER	B
	PRESENTATIONS	
	CLIENTS	
	CONTRACTS	
	TRANSACTIONS	

☐ Did not work today; instead, I:

{20 }

S M T W T F S

Today I mostly prospected:

	DISCUSSIONS	
L	DAILY TRACKER	B
	PRESENTATIONS	
	CLIENTS	
	CONTRACTS	
	TRANSACTIONS	

☐ Did not work today; instead, I:

July

15

Are you proud of your real estate stats?[XI]
If YES: *how do you share your stats with prospects?*
If NO: *name three ways to improve your datapoints.*[X]

{20 } ______________________________

{20 } ______________________________

{20 } ______________________________

{20 }

S M T W T F S

Today I mostly prospected:

	DISCUSSIONS	
L	DAILY TRACKER	B
	PRESENTATIONS	
	CLIENTS	
	CONTRACTS	
	TRANSACTIONS	

☐ Did not work today; instead, I:

{20 }

S M T W T F S

Today I mostly prospected:

	DISCUSSIONS	
L	DAILY TRACKER	B
	PRESENTATIONS	
	CLIENTS	
	CONTRACTS	
	TRANSACTIONS	

☐ Did not work today; instead, I:

{20 }

S M T W T F S

Today I mostly prospected:

	DISCUSSIONS	
L	DAILY TRACKER	B
	PRESENTATIONS	
	CLIENTS	
	CONTRACTS	
	TRANSACTIONS	

☐ Did not work today; instead, I:

16

July

Are you falling behind (or surging ahead) on any monthly goals? What's your plan to achieve them all?[XIX] *Adjust your activities now, so you will meet or exceed all.*

{20 }

{20 }

{20 }

{20 }
S M T W T F S
Today I mostly prospected:

	DISCUSSIONS	
L	DAILY TRACKER	B
	PRESENTATIONS	
	CLIENTS	
	CONTRACTS	
	TRANSACTIONS	

☐ Did not work today; instead, I:

{20 }
S M T W T F S
Today I mostly prospected:

	DISCUSSIONS	
L	DAILY TRACKER	B
	PRESENTATIONS	
	CLIENTS	
	CONTRACTS	
	TRANSACTIONS	

☐ Did not work today; instead, I:

{20 }
S M T W T F S
Today I mostly prospected:

	DISCUSSIONS	
L	DAILY TRACKER	B
	PRESENTATIONS	
	CLIENTS	
	CONTRACTS	
	TRANSACTIONS	

☐ Did not work today; instead, I:

July

17

Do you utilize testimonials?[314]
If NO: *why not?*
If YES: *how are you leveraging them to your advantage?*

{20 }

{20 }

{20 }

{20 }		
S M T W T F S		
Today I mostly prospected:		
	DISCUSSIONS	
L	DAILY TRACKER	B
	PRESENTATIONS	
	CLIENTS	
	CONTRACTS	
	TRANSACTIONS	
☐ Did not work today; instead, I:		

{20 }		
S M T W T F S		
Today I mostly prospected:		
	DISCUSSIONS	
L	DAILY TRACKER	B
	PRESENTATIONS	
	CLIENTS	
	CONTRACTS	
	TRANSACTIONS	
☐ Did not work today; instead, I:		

{20 }		
S M T W T F S		
Today I mostly prospected:		
	DISCUSSIONS	
L	DAILY TRACKER	B
	PRESENTATIONS	
	CLIENTS	
	CONTRACTS	
	TRANSACTIONS	
☐ Did not work today; instead, I:		

18

July

If your business was a dream,
would it be lucid, confusing to explain, or a pure nightmare?
Explain yourself.

{20 }

{20 }

{20 }

{20 }		
S M T W T F S		
Today I mostly prospected:		
	DISCUSSIONS	
L	DAILY TRACKER	B
	PRESENTATIONS	
	CLIENTS	
	CONTRACTS	
	TRANSACTIONS	
☐ Did not work today; instead, I:		

{20 }		
S M T W T F S		
Today I mostly prospected:		
	DISCUSSIONS	
L	DAILY TRACKER	B
	PRESENTATIONS	
	CLIENTS	
	CONTRACTS	
	TRANSACTIONS	
☐ Did not work today; instead, I:		

{20 }		
S M T W T F S		
Today I mostly prospected:		
	DISCUSSIONS	
L	DAILY TRACKER	B
	PRESENTATIONS	
	CLIENTS	
	CONTRACTS	
	TRANSACTIONS	
☐ Did not work today; instead, I:		

July

19

What makes your service superior to other agents? How do you communicate this to prospects/clients (and how often)?

{20 }

{20 }

{20 }

{20 }

S M T W T F S

Today I mostly prospected:

	DISCUSSIONS	
L	DAILY TRACKER	B
	PRESENTATIONS	
	CLIENTS	
	CONTRACTS	
	TRANSACTIONS	

☐ Did not work today; instead, I:

{20 }

S M T W T F S

Today I mostly prospected:

	DISCUSSIONS	
L	DAILY TRACKER	B
	PRESENTATIONS	
	CLIENTS	
	CONTRACTS	
	TRANSACTIONS	

☐ Did not work today; instead, I:

{20 }

S M T W T F S

Today I mostly prospected:

	DISCUSSIONS	
L	DAILY TRACKER	B
	PRESENTATIONS	
	CLIENTS	
	CONTRACTS	
	TRANSACTIONS	

☐ Did not work today; instead, I:

20 July

Today is Kick the Habit Day.
Name three things you'd like to stop doing.
How would kicking these habits change your life?

{20 }

{20 }

{20 }

{20 }
S M T W T F S
Today I mostly prospected:

	DISCUSSIONS	
L	DAILY TRACKER	B
	PRESENTATIONS	
	CLIENTS	
	CONTRACTS	
	TRANSACTIONS	

☐ Did not work today; instead, I:

{20 }
S M T W T F S
Today I mostly prospected:

	DISCUSSIONS	
L	DAILY TRACKER	B
	PRESENTATIONS	
	CLIENTS	
	CONTRACTS	
	TRANSACTIONS	

☐ Did not work today; instead, I:

{20 }
S M T W T F S
Today I mostly prospected:

	DISCUSSIONS	
L	DAILY TRACKER	B
	PRESENTATIONS	
	CLIENTS	
	CONTRACTS	
	TRANSACTIONS	

☐ Did not work today; instead, I:

July

21

Recall a recent class or educational session.
What was the number one thing you learned?
How will you implement it into your business?

{20 }

{20 }

{20 }

{20 }

S M T W T F S

Today I mostly prospected:

	DISCUSSIONS	
L	DAILY TRACKER	B
	PRESENTATIONS	
	CLIENTS	
	CONTRACTS	
	TRANSACTIONS	

☐ Did not work today; instead, I:

{20 }

S M T W T F S

Today I mostly prospected:

	DISCUSSIONS	
L	DAILY TRACKER	B
	PRESENTATIONS	
	CLIENTS	
	CONTRACTS	
	TRANSACTIONS	

☐ Did not work today; instead, I:

{20 }

S M T W T F S

Today I mostly prospected:

	DISCUSSIONS	
L	DAILY TRACKER	B
	PRESENTATIONS	
	CLIENTS	
	CONTRACTS	
	TRANSACTIONS	

☐ Did not work today; instead, I:

22

July

Write a script for this seller objection:
"Another agent will list it for less,
so I should list with her."

{20 }

{20 }

{20 }

{20 }

S	M	T	W	T	F	S

Today I mostly prospected:

L	DISCUSSIONS	B
	DAILY TRACKER	
	PRESENTATIONS	
	CLIENTS	
	CONTRACTS	
	TRANSACTIONS	

☐ Did not work today; instead, I:

{20 }

S	M	T	W	T	F	S

Today I mostly prospected:

L	DISCUSSIONS	B
	DAILY TRACKER	
	PRESENTATIONS	
	CLIENTS	
	CONTRACTS	
	TRANSACTIONS	

☐ Did not work today; instead, I:

{20 }

S	M	T	W	T	F	S

Today I mostly prospected:

L	DISCUSSIONS	B
	DAILY TRACKER	
	PRESENTATIONS	
	CLIENTS	
	CONTRACTS	
	TRANSACTIONS	

☐ Did not work today; instead, I:

July

23

*Rank your business health on a scale of one to ten.
List one thing you could do to improve
and a plan to achieve.*

{20 }

{20 }

{20 }

{20 }

S M T W T F S

Today I mostly prospected:

	DISCUSSIONS	
L	DAILY TRACKER	B
	PRESENTATIONS	
	CLIENTS	
	CONTRACTS	
	TRANSACTIONS	

☐ Did not work today; instead, I:

{20 }

S M T W T F S

Today I mostly prospected:

	DISCUSSIONS	
L	DAILY TRACKER	B
	PRESENTATIONS	
	CLIENTS	
	CONTRACTS	
	TRANSACTIONS	

☐ Did not work today; instead, I:

{20 }

S M T W T F S

Today I mostly prospected:

	DISCUSSIONS	
L	DAILY TRACKER	B
	PRESENTATIONS	
	CLIENTS	
	CONTRACTS	
	TRANSACTIONS	

☐ Did not work today; instead, I:

24

July

List twenty words that describe your marketing efforts.[224]
Which words would you like to change?

{20 }

{20 }

{20 }

{20 }	{20 }	{20 }
S M T W T F S	S M T W T F S	S M T W T F S
Today I mostly prospected:	Today I mostly prospected:	Today I mostly prospected:
DISCUSSIONS	DISCUSSIONS	DISCUSSIONS
L · DAILY TRACKER · B	L · DAILY TRACKER · B	L · DAILY TRACKER · B
PRESENTATIONS	PRESENTATIONS	PRESENTATIONS
CLIENTS	CLIENTS	CLIENTS
CONTRACTS	CONTRACTS	CONTRACTS
TRANSACTIONS	TRANSACTIONS	TRANSACTIONS
☐ Did not work today; instead, I:	☐ Did not work today; instead, I:	☐ Did not work today; instead, I:

July

25

If your business was a spouse, what kind of relationship would you have? Would you kiss and canoodle, or sleep on the couch? Justify your response.

{20 }

{20 }

{20 }

{20 }

S M T W T F S

Today I mostly prospected:

	DISCUSSIONS	
L	DAILY TRACKER	B
	PRESENTATIONS	
	CLIENTS	
	CONTRACTS	
	TRANSACTIONS	

☐ Did not work today; instead, I:

{20 }

S M T W T F S

Today I mostly prospected:

	DISCUSSIONS	
L	DAILY TRACKER	B
	PRESENTATIONS	
	CLIENTS	
	CONTRACTS	
	TRANSACTIONS	

☐ Did not work today; instead, I:

{20 }

S M T W T F S

Today I mostly prospected:

	DISCUSSIONS	
L	DAILY TRACKER	B
	PRESENTATIONS	
	CLIENTS	
	CONTRACTS	
	TRANSACTIONS	

☐ Did not work today; instead, I:

July

Name one thing that would improve your sales price to list price ratio (SP/LP).[XVI]

{20 }

{20 }

{20 }

{20 }	{20 }	{20 }
S M T W T F S	S M T W T F S	S M T W T F S
Today I mostly prospected:	Today I mostly prospected:	Today I mostly prospected:
DISCUSSIONS	DISCUSSIONS	DISCUSSIONS
L / DAILY TRACKER / B	L / DAILY TRACKER / B	L / DAILY TRACKER / B
PRESENTATIONS	PRESENTATIONS	PRESENTATIONS
CLIENTS	CLIENTS	CLIENTS
CONTRACTS	CONTRACTS	CONTRACTS
TRANSACTIONS	TRANSACTIONS	TRANSACTIONS
☐ Did not work today; instead, I:	☐ Did not work today; instead, I:	☐ Did not work today; instead, I:

July

27

Write a recipe for the perfect real estate day.
How could you live (and re-live) this day often?
How would doing so change your life?

{20 }

{20 }

{20 }

{20 }

S M T W T F S

Today I mostly prospected:

	DISCUSSIONS	
L	DAILY TRACKER	B
	PRESENTATIONS	
	CLIENTS	
	CONTRACTS	
	TRANSACTIONS	

☐ Did not work today; instead, I:

{20 }

S M T W T F S

Today I mostly prospected:

	DISCUSSIONS	
L	DAILY TRACKER	B
	PRESENTATIONS	
	CLIENTS	
	CONTRACTS	
	TRANSACTIONS	

☐ Did not work today; instead, I:

{20 }

S M T W T F S

Today I mostly prospected:

	DISCUSSIONS	
L	DAILY TRACKER	B
	PRESENTATIONS	
	CLIENTS	
	CONTRACTS	
	TRANSACTIONS	

☐ Did not work today; instead, I:

28 July

How effective are your buyer needs analysis skills?[174]
On average, how many properties do you show before your buyer clients choose one?

{20 }

{20 }

{20 }

{20 }	{20 }	{20 }
S M T W T F S	S M T W T F S	S M T W T F S
Today I mostly prospected:	Today I mostly prospected:	Today I mostly prospected:
DISCUSSIONS	DISCUSSIONS	DISCUSSIONS
L · DAILY TRACKER · B	L · DAILY TRACKER · B	L · DAILY TRACKER · B
PRESENTATIONS	PRESENTATIONS	PRESENTATIONS
CLIENTS	CLIENTS	CLIENTS
CONTRACTS	CONTRACTS	CONTRACTS
TRANSACTIONS	TRANSACTIONS	TRANSACTIONS
☐ Did not work today; instead, I:	☐ Did not work today; instead, I:	☐ Did not work today; instead, I:

July

29

Write a script for this objection:
"We're not ready to sell yet;
first we must fix it up."

{20 }

{20 }

{20 }

{20 }

S M T W T F S

Today I mostly prospected:

	DISCUSSIONS	
L	DAILY TRACKER	B
	PRESENTATIONS	
	CLIENTS	
	CONTRACTS	
	TRANSACTIONS	

☐ Did not work today; instead, I:

{20 }

S M T W T F S

Today I mostly prospected:

	DISCUSSIONS	
L	DAILY TRACKER	B
	PRESENTATIONS	
	CLIENTS	
	CONTRACTS	
	TRANSACTIONS	

☐ Did not work today; instead, I:

{20 }

S M T W T F S

Today I mostly prospected:

	DISCUSSIONS	
L	DAILY TRACKER	B
	PRESENTATIONS	
	CLIENTS	
	CONTRACTS	
	TRANSACTIONS	

☐ Did not work today; instead, I:

30

July

My grandest achievement this month was...
My plan to repeat this victory is...

{20 }

{20 }

{20 }

{20 }

S M T W T F S

Today I mostly prospected:

	DISCUSSIONS	
L	DAILY TRACKER	B
	PRESENTATIONS	
	CLIENTS	
	CONTRACTS	
	TRANSACTIONS	

☐ Did not work today; instead, I:

{20 }

S M T W T F S

Today I mostly prospected:

	DISCUSSIONS	
L	DAILY TRACKER	B
	PRESENTATIONS	
	CLIENTS	
	CONTRACTS	
	TRANSACTIONS	

☐ Did not work today; instead, I:

{20 }

S M T W T F S

Today I mostly prospected:

	DISCUSSIONS	
L	DAILY TRACKER	B
	PRESENTATIONS	
	CLIENTS	
	CONTRACTS	
	TRANSACTIONS	

☐ Did not work today; instead, I:

July

31

The biggest mistake/misstep I made this month was...
My plan to prevent the same mishap from recurring is...

{20 }

{20 }

{20 }

{20 }	{20 }	{20 }
S M T W T F S	S M T W T F S	S M T W T F S
Today I mostly prospected:	Today I mostly prospected:	Today I mostly prospected:
DISCUSSIONS	DISCUSSIONS	DISCUSSIONS
L · DAILY TRACKER · B	L · DAILY TRACKER · B	L · DAILY TRACKER · B
PRESENTATIONS	PRESENTATIONS	PRESENTATIONS
CLIENTS	CLIENTS	CLIENTS
CONTRACTS	CONTRACTS	CONTRACTS
TRANSACTIONS	TRANSACTIONS	TRANSACTIONS
☐ Did not work today; instead, I:	☐ Did not work today; instead, I:	☐ Did not work today; instead, I:

{20 }

MONTHLY ACTIVITY TRACKER (GOALS→RESULTS)

GOALS	ACTIVITY	WK 1	WK 2	WK 3	WK 4	WK 5	TOTAL RESULTS
	TRANSACTIONS (T)	L : B	L : B	L : B	L : B	L : B	L : B
	NEW CLIENTS (C)	L : B	L : B	L : B	L : B	L : B	L : B
	PRESENTATIONS (P)	L : B	L : B	L : B	L : B	L : B	L : B
	DISCUSSIONS (D)						
	DAYS WORKED (W)						
	DAILY DISCUSSIONS (D/W)	**ACTUAL DAILY DISCUSSION AVERAGE**				**D/W**	
$	**GCI**	$					

{20 }

MONTHLY ACTIVITY TRACKER (GOALS→RESULTS)

GOALS	ACTIVITY	WK 1	WK 2	WK 3	WK 4	WK 5	TOTAL RESULTS
	TRANSACTIONS (T)	L : B	L : B	L : B	L : B	L : B	L : B
	NEW CLIENTS (C)	L : B	L : B	L : B	L : B	L : B	L : B
	PRESENTATIONS (P)	L : B	L : B	L : B	L : B	L : B	L : B
	DISCUSSIONS (D)						
	DAYS WORKED (W)						
	DAILY DISCUSSIONS (D/W)	**ACTUAL DAILY DISCUSSION AVERAGE**				**D/W**	
$	**GCI**	$					

{20 }

MONTHLY ACTIVITY TRACKER (GOALS→RESULTS)

GOALS	ACTIVITY	WK 1	WK 2	WK 3	WK 4	WK 5	TOTAL RESULTS
	TRANSACTIONS (T)	L : B	L : B	L : B	L : B	L : B	L : B
	NEW CLIENTS (C)	L : B	L : B	L : B	L : B	L : B	L : B
	PRESENTATIONS (P)	L : B	L : B	L : B	L : B	L : B	L : B
	DISCUSSIONS (D)						
	DAYS WORKED (W)						
	DAILY DISCUSSIONS (D/W)	**ACTUAL DAILY DISCUSSION AVERAGE**				**D/W**	
$	**GCI**	$					

August

01

Today is Business Plan Day.[XVIII]
Review/revise yours, and contemplate the past/future.
What is your plan to improve upon last month's performance?

{20 }

{20 }

{20 }

{20 }

S M T W T F S

Today I mostly prospected:

	DISCUSSIONS	
L	DAILY TRACKER	B
	PRESENTATIONS	
	CLIENTS	
	CONTRACTS	
	TRANSACTIONS	

☐ Did not work today; instead, I:

{20 }

S M T W T F S

Today I mostly prospected:

	DISCUSSIONS	
L	DAILY TRACKER	B
	PRESENTATIONS	
	CLIENTS	
	CONTRACTS	
	TRANSACTIONS	

☐ Did not work today; instead, I:

{20 }

S M T W T F S

Today I mostly prospected:

	DISCUSSIONS	
L	DAILY TRACKER	B
	PRESENTATIONS	
	CLIENTS	
	CONTRACTS	
	TRANSACTIONS	

☐ Did not work today; instead, I:

02

August

*List a good habit you wanna adopt this month.
How will you implement and make it a permanent part
of your routine? Has last month's habit stuck yet?*

{20 }

{20 }

{20 }

{20 }

S M T W T F S

Today I mostly prospected:

	DISCUSSIONS	
L	DAILY TRACKER	B
	PRESENTATIONS	
	CLIENTS	
	CONTRACTS	
	TRANSACTIONS	

☐ Did not work today; instead, I:

{20 }

S M T W T F S

Today I mostly prospected:

	DISCUSSIONS	
L	DAILY TRACKER	B
	PRESENTATIONS	
	CLIENTS	
	CONTRACTS	
	TRANSACTIONS	

☐ Did not work today; instead, I:

{20 }

S M T W T F S

Today I mostly prospected:

	DISCUSSIONS	
L	DAILY TRACKER	B
	PRESENTATIONS	
	CLIENTS	
	CONTRACTS	
	TRANSACTIONS	

☐ Did not work today; instead, I:

August

03

List ten words that describe your habits.
Which words would you like to change?
Which ones should stay with you forever?

{20 }

{20 }

{20 }

{20 }

S M T W T F S

Today I mostly prospected:

	DISCUSSIONS	
L	DAILY TRACKER	B
	PRESENTATIONS	
	CLIENTS	
	CONTRACTS	
	TRANSACTIONS	

☐ Did not work today; instead, I:

{20 }

S M T W T F S

Today I mostly prospected:

	DISCUSSIONS	
L	DAILY TRACKER	B
	PRESENTATIONS	
	CLIENTS	
	CONTRACTS	
	TRANSACTIONS	

☐ Did not work today; instead, I:

{20 }

S M T W T F S

Today I mostly prospected:

	DISCUSSIONS	
L	DAILY TRACKER	B
	PRESENTATIONS	
	CLIENTS	
	CONTRACTS	
	TRANSACTIONS	

☐ Did not work today; instead, I:

04

August

What is the best advice you've recently received?
Have you implemented it into your life?

{20 }

{20 }

{20 }

{20 }
S M T W T F S
Today I mostly prospected:

	DISCUSSIONS	
L	DAILY TRACKER	B
	PRESENTATIONS	
	CLIENTS	
	CONTRACTS	
	TRANSACTIONS	

☐ Did not work today; instead, I:

{20 }
S M T W T F S
Today I mostly prospected:

	DISCUSSIONS	
L	DAILY TRACKER	B
	PRESENTATIONS	
	CLIENTS	
	CONTRACTS	
	TRANSACTIONS	

☐ Did not work today; instead, I:

{20 }
S M T W T F S
Today I mostly prospected:

	DISCUSSIONS	
L	DAILY TRACKER	B
	PRESENTATIONS	
	CLIENTS	
	CONTRACTS	
	TRANSACTIONS	

☐ Did not work today; instead, I:

August

05

Recall a recent time when disclosure either saved your ass or exposed it for a spanking.[180]

{20 }

{20 }

{20 }

{20 }

S M T W T F S

Today I mostly prospected:

	DISCUSSIONS	
L	DAILY TRACKER	B
	PRESENTATIONS	
	CLIENTS	
	CONTRACTS	
	TRANSACTIONS	

☐ Did not work today; instead, I:

{20 }

S M T W T F S

Today I mostly prospected:

	DISCUSSIONS	
L	DAILY TRACKER	B
	PRESENTATIONS	
	CLIENTS	
	CONTRACTS	
	TRANSACTIONS	

☐ Did not work today; instead, I:

{20 }

S M T W T F S

Today I mostly prospected:

	DISCUSSIONS	
L	DAILY TRACKER	B
	PRESENTATIONS	
	CLIENTS	
	CONTRACTS	
	TRANSACTIONS	

☐ Did not work today; instead, I:

06

August

Which part of your job are you the most passionate?
Explain yourself.

{20 }

{20 }

{20 }

{20 }

S M T W T F S

Today I mostly prospected:

	DISCUSSIONS	
L	DAILY TRACKER	B
	PRESENTATIONS	
	CLIENTS	
	CONTRACTS	
	TRANSACTIONS	

☐ Did not work today; instead, I:

{20 }

S M T W T F S

Today I mostly prospected:

	DISCUSSIONS	
L	DAILY TRACKER	B
	PRESENTATIONS	
	CLIENTS	
	CONTRACTS	
	TRANSACTIONS	

☐ Did not work today; instead, I:

{20 }

S M T W T F S

Today I mostly prospected:

	DISCUSSIONS	
L	DAILY TRACKER	B
	PRESENTATIONS	
	CLIENTS	
	CONTRACTS	
	TRANSACTIONS	

☐ Did not work today; instead, I:

August

07

How could you lower expenses without harming client services? Otherwise, how could you increase GCI *without raising expenses?*

{20 }

{20 }

{20 }

{20 }

S M T W T F S

Today I mostly prospected:

	DISCUSSIONS	
L	DAILY TRACKER	B
	PRESENTATIONS	
	CLIENTS	
	CONTRACTS	
	TRANSACTIONS	

☐ Did not work today; instead, I:

{20 }

S M T W T F S

Today I mostly prospected:

	DISCUSSIONS	
L	DAILY TRACKER	B
	PRESENTATIONS	
	CLIENTS	
	CONTRACTS	
	TRANSACTIONS	

☐ Did not work today; instead, I:

{20 }

S M T W T F S

Today I mostly prospected:

	DISCUSSIONS	
L	DAILY TRACKER	B
	PRESENTATIONS	
	CLIENTS	
	CONTRACTS	
	TRANSACTIONS	

☐ Did not work today; instead, I:

08

August

How often do you cut your commission to 'make a deal work'? How could you avoid such situations?

{20 }

{20 }

{20 }

{20 }
S M T W T F S
Today I mostly prospected:

	DISCUSSIONS	
L	DAILY TRACKER	B
	PRESENTATIONS	
	CLIENTS	
	CONTRACTS	
	TRANSACTIONS	

☐ Did not work today; instead, I:

{20 }
S M T W T F S
Today I mostly prospected:

	DISCUSSIONS	
L	DAILY TRACKER	B
	PRESENTATIONS	
	CLIENTS	
	CONTRACTS	
	TRANSACTIONS	

☐ Did not work today; instead, I:

{20 }
S M T W T F S
Today I mostly prospected:

	DISCUSSIONS	
L	DAILY TRACKER	B
	PRESENTATIONS	
	CLIENTS	
	CONTRACTS	
	TRANSACTIONS	

☐ Did not work today; instead, I:

August

09

What is your biggest challenge to staying on-task? Otherwise, what do you attribute to staying on-task?[300]

{20 }

{20 }

{20 }

{20 }
S M T W T F S
Today I mostly prospected:

	DISCUSSIONS	
L	DAILY TRACKER	B
	PRESENTATIONS	
	CLIENTS	
	CONTRACTS	
	TRANSACTIONS	

☐ Did not work today; instead, I:

{20 }
S M T W T F S
Today I mostly prospected:

	DISCUSSIONS	
L	DAILY TRACKER	B
	PRESENTATIONS	
	CLIENTS	
	CONTRACTS	
	TRANSACTIONS	

☐ Did not work today; instead, I:

{20 }
S M T W T F S
Today I mostly prospected:

	DISCUSSIONS	
L	DAILY TRACKER	B
	PRESENTATIONS	
	CLIENTS	
	CONTRACTS	
	TRANSACTIONS	

☐ Did not work today; instead, I:

10

August

Write a script for this buyer objection:
"I don't wanna sign an agency agreement; I just wanna look at some houses. Besides, other agents don't insist on it."

{20 }

{20 }

{20 }

{20 }
S M T W T F S
Today I mostly prospected:

	DISCUSSIONS	
L	DAILY TRACKER	B
	PRESENTATIONS	
	CLIENTS	
	CONTRACTS	
	TRANSACTIONS	

☐ Did not work today; instead, I:

{20 }
S M T W T F S
Today I mostly prospected:

	DISCUSSIONS	
L	DAILY TRACKER	B
	PRESENTATIONS	
	CLIENTS	
	CONTRACTS	
	TRANSACTIONS	

☐ Did not work today; instead, I:

{20 }
S M T W T F S
Today I mostly prospected:

	DISCUSSIONS	
L	DAILY TRACKER	B
	PRESENTATIONS	
	CLIENTS	
	CONTRACTS	
	TRANSACTIONS	

☐ Did not work today; instead, I:

August

11

Name one thing that would improve your return on clients (ROC).[XVI]

{20 }

{20 }

{20 }

{20 }
S M T W T F S
Today I mostly prospected:

	DISCUSSIONS	
L	DAILY TRACKER	B
	PRESENTATIONS	
	CLIENTS	
	CONTRACTS	
	TRANSACTIONS	

☐ Did not work today; instead, I:

{20 }
S M T W T F S
Today I mostly prospected:

	DISCUSSIONS	
L	DAILY TRACKER	B
	PRESENTATIONS	
	CLIENTS	
	CONTRACTS	
	TRANSACTIONS	

☐ Did not work today; instead, I:

{20 }
S M T W T F S
Today I mostly prospected:

	DISCUSSIONS	
L	DAILY TRACKER	B
	PRESENTATIONS	
	CLIENTS	
	CONTRACTS	
	TRANSACTIONS	

☐ Did not work today; instead, I:

12

August

Write an affirmation to soothe your prospecting pains. Otherwise, write one to encourage your enthusiasm.

{20 }

{20 }

{20 }

{20 }

S M T W T F S

Today I mostly prospected:

	DISCUSSIONS	
L	DAILY TRACKER	B
	PRESENTATIONS	
	CLIENTS	
	CONTRACTS	
	TRANSACTIONS	

☐ Did not work today; instead, I:

{20 }

S M T W T F S

Today I mostly prospected:

	DISCUSSIONS	
L	DAILY TRACKER	B
	PRESENTATIONS	
	CLIENTS	
	CONTRACTS	
	TRANSACTIONS	

☐ Did not work today; instead, I:

{20 }

S M T W T F S

Today I mostly prospected:

	DISCUSSIONS	
L	DAILY TRACKER	B
	PRESENTATIONS	
	CLIENTS	
	CONTRACTS	
	TRANSACTIONS	

☐ Did not work today; instead, I:

August

13

Recall a recent time when you delivered extraordinary service to a client.[245]
What was their reaction?

{20 }

{20 }

{20 }

{20 }

S M T W T F S

Today I mostly prospected:

	DISCUSSIONS	
L	DAILY TRACKER	B
	PRESENTATIONS	
	CLIENTS	
	CONTRACTS	
	TRANSACTIONS	

☐ Did not work today; instead, I:

{20 }

S M T W T F S

Today I mostly prospected:

	DISCUSSIONS	
L	DAILY TRACKER	B
	PRESENTATIONS	
	CLIENTS	
	CONTRACTS	
	TRANSACTIONS	

☐ Did not work today; instead, I:

{20 }

S M T W T F S

Today I mostly prospected:

	DISCUSSIONS	
L	DAILY TRACKER	B
	PRESENTATIONS	
	CLIENTS	
	CONTRACTS	
	TRANSACTIONS	

☐ Did not work today; instead, I:

14

August

Where else could you be looking for buyers and sellers? Name three new ways to meet prospects[084] and a plan to implement.

{20 } ______________________________

{20 } ______________________________

{20 } ______________________________

{20 }

S M T W T F S

Today I mostly prospected:

L	DISCUSSIONS	B
	DAILY TRACKER	
	PRESENTATIONS	
	CLIENTS	
	CONTRACTS	
	TRANSACTIONS	

☐ Did not work today; instead, I:

{20 }

S M T W T F S

Today I mostly prospected:

L	DISCUSSIONS	B
	DAILY TRACKER	
	PRESENTATIONS	
	CLIENTS	
	CONTRACTS	
	TRANSACTIONS	

☐ Did not work today; instead, I:

{20 }

S M T W T F S

Today I mostly prospected:

L	DISCUSSIONS	B
	DAILY TRACKER	
	PRESENTATIONS	
	CLIENTS	
	CONTRACTS	
	TRANSACTIONS	

☐ Did not work today; instead, I:

August

15

Are you falling behind (or surging ahead) on any monthly goals?
What's your plan to achieve them all?[XIX]
Adjust your activities now, so you will meet or exceed all.

{20 }

{20 }

{20 }

{20 }

S M T W T F S

Today I mostly prospected:

	DISCUSSIONS	
L	DAILY TRACKER	B
	PRESENTATIONS	
	CLIENTS	
	CONTRACTS	
	TRANSACTIONS	

☐ Did not work today; instead, I:

{20 }

S M T W T F S

Today I mostly prospected:

	DISCUSSIONS	
L	DAILY TRACKER	B
	PRESENTATIONS	
	CLIENTS	
	CONTRACTS	
	TRANSACTIONS	

☐ Did not work today; instead, I:

{20 }

S M T W T F S

Today I mostly prospected:

	DISCUSSIONS	
L	DAILY TRACKER	B
	PRESENTATIONS	
	CLIENTS	
	CONTRACTS	
	TRANSACTIONS	

☐ Did not work today; instead, I:

16

August

What inspired you today (or most recently)?
How can you keep that feeling?

{20 }

{20 }

{20 }

{20 }

S M T W T F S

Today I mostly prospected:

	DISCUSSIONS	
L	DAILY TRACKER	B
	PRESENTATIONS	
	CLIENTS	
	CONTRACTS	
	TRANSACTIONS	

☐ Did not work today; instead, I:

{20 }

S M T W T F S

Today I mostly prospected:

	DISCUSSIONS	
L	DAILY TRACKER	B
	PRESENTATIONS	
	CLIENTS	
	CONTRACTS	
	TRANSACTIONS	

☐ Did not work today; instead, I:

{20 }

S M T W T F S

Today I mostly prospected:

	DISCUSSIONS	
L	DAILY TRACKER	B
	PRESENTATIONS	
	CLIENTS	
	CONTRACTS	
	TRANSACTIONS	

☐ Did not work today; instead, I:

August

17

Are you happy with your turnover rates? [XVI]
Which is the best and which is the worst?
What are you doing to improve them?

{20 }

{20 }

{20 }

{20 }

S M T W T F S

Today I mostly prospected:

	DISCUSSIONS	
L	DAILY TRACKER	B
	PRESENTATIONS	
	CLIENTS	
	CONTRACTS	
	TRANSACTIONS	

☐ Did not work today; instead, I:

{20 }

S M T W T F S

Today I mostly prospected:

	DISCUSSIONS	
L	DAILY TRACKER	B
	PRESENTATIONS	
	CLIENTS	
	CONTRACTS	
	TRANSACTIONS	

☐ Did not work today; instead, I:

{20 }

S M T W T F S

Today I mostly prospected:

	DISCUSSIONS	
L	DAILY TRACKER	B
	PRESENTATIONS	
	CLIENTS	
	CONTRACTS	
	TRANSACTIONS	

☐ Did not work today; instead, I:

18

August

List twenty words that describe your mental state.[309]
Which ones would you like to change?
Which do you hope last forever?

{20 } ______________________________

{20 } ______________________________

{20 } ______________________________

{20 }

S M T W T F S

Today I mostly prospected:

L	DISCUSSIONS	B
	DAILY TRACKER	
	PRESENTATIONS	
	CLIENTS	
	CONTRACTS	
	TRANSACTIONS	

☐ Did not work today; instead, I:

{20 }

S M T W T F S

Today I mostly prospected:

L	DISCUSSIONS	B
	DAILY TRACKER	
	PRESENTATIONS	
	CLIENTS	
	CONTRACTS	
	TRANSACTIONS	

☐ Did not work today; instead, I:

{20 }

S M T W T F S

Today I mostly prospected:

L	DISCUSSIONS	B
	DAILY TRACKER	
	PRESENTATIONS	
	CLIENTS	
	CONTRACTS	
	TRANSACTIONS	

☐ Did not work today; instead, I:

August

19

What is your best online resource for real estate?
Are you going to the source?[006]
Justify your response.

{20 } ______________________________

{20 } ______________________________

{20 } ______________________________

{20 }	{20 }	{20 }
S M T W T F S	S M T W T F S	S M T W T F S
Today I mostly prospected:	Today I mostly prospected:	Today I mostly prospected:
DISCUSSIONS	DISCUSSIONS	DISCUSSIONS
L · DAILY TRACKER · B	L · DAILY TRACKER · B	L · DAILY TRACKER · B
PRESENTATIONS	PRESENTATIONS	PRESENTATIONS
CLIENTS	CLIENTS	CLIENTS
CONTRACTS	CONTRACTS	CONTRACTS
TRANSACTIONS	TRANSACTIONS	TRANSACTIONS
☐ Did not work today; instead, I:	☐ Did not work today; instead, I:	☐ Did not work today; instead, I:

20 August

What is the biggest challenge to your growth?
How are you seeking to resolve your hurdles?

{20 }

{20 }

{20 }

{20 }
S M T W T F S
Today I mostly prospected:

	DISCUSSIONS	
L	DAILY TRACKER	B
	PRESENTATIONS	
	CLIENTS	
	CONTRACTS	
	TRANSACTIONS	

☐ Did not work today; instead, I:

{20 }
S M T W T F S
Today I mostly prospected:

	DISCUSSIONS	
L	DAILY TRACKER	B
	PRESENTATIONS	
	CLIENTS	
	CONTRACTS	
	TRANSACTIONS	

☐ Did not work today; instead, I:

{20 }
S M T W T F S
Today I mostly prospected:

	DISCUSSIONS	
L	DAILY TRACKER	B
	PRESENTATIONS	
	CLIENTS	
	CONTRACTS	
	TRANSACTIONS	

☐ Did not work today; instead, I:

21

Write about the last time you implemented newfound knowledge and it resulted in money/success (whether it induced/saved a transaction or client signing). Have you adopted this practice into your systems?

{20 }

{20 }

{20 }

{20 }

S M T W T F S

Today I mostly prospected:

	DISCUSSIONS	
L	DAILY TRACKER	B
	PRESENTATIONS	
	CLIENTS	
	CONTRACTS	
	TRANSACTIONS	

☐ Did not work today; instead, I:

{20 }

S M T W T F S

Today I mostly prospected:

	DISCUSSIONS	
L	DAILY TRACKER	B
	PRESENTATIONS	
	CLIENTS	
	CONTRACTS	
	TRANSACTIONS	

☐ Did not work today; instead, I:

{20 }

S M T W T F S

Today I mostly prospected:

	DISCUSSIONS	
L	DAILY TRACKER	B
	PRESENTATIONS	
	CLIENTS	
	CONTRACTS	
	TRANSACTIONS	

☐ Did not work today; instead, I:

22

August

Are you achieving your daily/weekly/monthly goals? What keeps you on/off track?

{20 }

{20 }

{20 }

{20 }

S M T W T F S

Today I mostly prospected:

	DISCUSSIONS	
L	DAILY TRACKER	B
	PRESENTATIONS	
	CLIENTS	
	CONTRACTS	
	TRANSACTIONS	

☐ Did not work today; instead, I:

{20 }

S M T W T F S

Today I mostly prospected:

	DISCUSSIONS	
L	DAILY TRACKER	B
	PRESENTATIONS	
	CLIENTS	
	CONTRACTS	
	TRANSACTIONS	

☐ Did not work today; instead, I:

{20 }

S M T W T F S

Today I mostly prospected:

	DISCUSSIONS	
L	DAILY TRACKER	B
	PRESENTATIONS	
	CLIENTS	
	CONTRACTS	
	TRANSACTIONS	

☐ Did not work today; instead, I:

August

23

Today is Come Clean Day.
Confess your biggest regret/downfall/neglect to your business.
How will you make things right?

{20 }

{20 }

{20 }

{20 }

S M T W T F S

Today I mostly prospected:

		DISCUSSIONS
L	DAILY TRACKER	B
	PRESENTATIONS	
	CLIENTS	
	CONTRACTS	
	TRANSACTIONS	

☐ Did not work today; instead, I:

{20 }

S M T W T F S

Today I mostly prospected:

		DISCUSSIONS
L	DAILY TRACKER	B
	PRESENTATIONS	
	CLIENTS	
	CONTRACTS	
	TRANSACTIONS	

☐ Did not work today; instead, I:

{20 }

S M T W T F S

Today I mostly prospected:

		DISCUSSIONS
L	DAILY TRACKER	B
	PRESENTATIONS	
	CLIENTS	
	CONTRACTS	
	TRANSACTIONS	

☐ Did not work today; instead, I:

24 August

A funny (real estate related) thing happened recently...

{20 }

{20 }

{20 }

{20 }		
S M T W T F S		
Today I mostly prospected:		
	DISCUSSIONS	
L	DAILY TRACKER	B
	PRESENTATIONS	
	CLIENTS	
	CONTRACTS	
	TRANSACTIONS	
☐ Did not work today; instead, I:		

{20 }		
S M T W T F S		
Today I mostly prospected:		
	DISCUSSIONS	
L	DAILY TRACKER	B
	PRESENTATIONS	
	CLIENTS	
	CONTRACTS	
	TRANSACTIONS	
☐ Did not work today; instead, I:		

{20 }		
S M T W T F S		
Today I mostly prospected:		
	DISCUSSIONS	
L	DAILY TRACKER	B
	PRESENTATIONS	
	CLIENTS	
	CONTRACTS	
	TRANSACTIONS	
☐ Did not work today; instead, I:		

August

25

Do you utilize testimonials of your service?[314]
If YES: to what extent? How effective are they?
If NO: why not?

{20 }

{20 }

{20 }

{20 }		
S M T W T F S		
Today I mostly prospected:		
	DISCUSSIONS	
L	DAILY TRACKER	B
	PRESENTATIONS	
	CLIENTS	
	CONTRACTS	
	TRANSACTIONS	
☐ Did not work today; instead, I:		

{20 }		
S M T W T F S		
Today I mostly prospected:		
	DISCUSSIONS	
L	DAILY TRACKER	B
	PRESENTATIONS	
	CLIENTS	
	CONTRACTS	
	TRANSACTIONS	
☐ Did not work today; instead, I:		

{20 }		
S M T W T F S		
Today I mostly prospected:		
	DISCUSSIONS	
L	DAILY TRACKER	B
	PRESENTATIONS	
	CLIENTS	
	CONTRACTS	
	TRANSACTIONS	
☐ Did not work today; instead, I:		

August

If you could outsource one aspect of your business,[286] *what would it be and why?*

{20 }

{20 }

{20 }

{20 }

S M T W T F S

Today I mostly prospected:

	DISCUSSIONS	
L	DAILY TRACKER	B
	PRESENTATIONS	
	CLIENTS	
	CONTRACTS	
	TRANSACTIONS	

☐ Did not work today; instead, I:

{20 }

S M T W T F S

Today I mostly prospected:

	DISCUSSIONS	
L	DAILY TRACKER	B
	PRESENTATIONS	
	CLIENTS	
	CONTRACTS	
	TRANSACTIONS	

☐ Did not work today; instead, I:

{20 }

S M T W T F S

Today I mostly prospected:

	DISCUSSIONS	
L	DAILY TRACKER	B
	PRESENTATIONS	
	CLIENTS	
	CONTRACTS	
	TRANSACTIONS	

☐ Did not work today; instead, I:

August

27

Write a script for this objection:
"I cannot afford to pay your commission,
so I'll have to hire someone else."

{20 }

{20 }

{20 }

{20 }		
S M T W T F S		
Today I mostly prospected:		
	DISCUSSIONS	
L	DAILY TRACKER	B
	PRESENTATIONS	
	CLIENTS	
	CONTRACTS	
	TRANSACTIONS	
☐ Did not work today; instead, I:		

{20 }		
S M T W T F S		
Today I mostly prospected:		
	DISCUSSIONS	
L	DAILY TRACKER	B
	PRESENTATIONS	
	CLIENTS	
	CONTRACTS	
	TRANSACTIONS	
☐ Did not work today; instead, I:		

{20 }		
S M T W T F S		
Today I mostly prospected:		
	DISCUSSIONS	
L	DAILY TRACKER	B
	PRESENTATIONS	
	CLIENTS	
	CONTRACTS	
	TRANSACTIONS	
☐ Did not work today; instead, I:		

28 August

How often do you take a day off?[306]
Describe your perfect day off,
then make it happen.

{20 }

{20 }

{20 }

{20 }	{20 }	{20 }
S M T W T F S	S M T W T F S	S M T W T F S
Today I mostly prospected:	Today I mostly prospected:	Today I mostly prospected:

	DISCUSSIONS			DISCUSSIONS			DISCUSSIONS	
L	DAILY TRACKER	B	L	DAILY TRACKER	B	L	DAILY TRACKER	B
	PRESENTATIONS			PRESENTATIONS			PRESENTATIONS	
	CLIENTS			CLIENTS			CLIENTS	
	CONTRACTS			CONTRACTS			CONTRACTS	
	TRANSACTIONS			TRANSACTIONS			TRANSACTIONS	

☐ Did not work today; instead, I: ☐ Did not work today; instead, I: ☐ Did not work today; instead, I:

August

29

Do you have a written list of client services?[173]
Do your clients know what they're paying for?
How do you communicate your services?

{20 }

{20 }

{20 }

{20 }

S M T W T F S

Today I mostly prospected:

	DISCUSSIONS	
L	DAILY TRACKER	B
	PRESENTATIONS	
	CLIENTS	
	CONTRACTS	
	TRANSACTIONS	

☐ Did not work today; instead, I:

{20 }

S M T W T F S

Today I mostly prospected:

	DISCUSSIONS	
L	DAILY TRACKER	B
	PRESENTATIONS	
	CLIENTS	
	CONTRACTS	
	TRANSACTIONS	

☐ Did not work today; instead, I:

{20 }

S M T W T F S

Today I mostly prospected:

	DISCUSSIONS	
L	DAILY TRACKER	B
	PRESENTATIONS	
	CLIENTS	
	CONTRACTS	
	TRANSACTIONS	

☐ Did not work today; instead, I:

30

August

My grandest achievement this month was...
My plan to repeat this victory is...

{20 }

{20 }

{20 }

{20 }

S M T W T F S

Today I mostly prospected:

L	DAILY TRACKER	B
	DISCUSSIONS	
	PRESENTATIONS	
	CLIENTS	
	CONTRACTS	
	TRANSACTIONS	

☐ Did not work today; instead, I:

{20 }

S M T W T F S

Today I mostly prospected:

L	DAILY TRACKER	B
	DISCUSSIONS	
	PRESENTATIONS	
	CLIENTS	
	CONTRACTS	
	TRANSACTIONS	

☐ Did not work today; instead, I:

{20 }

S M T W T F S

Today I mostly prospected:

L	DAILY TRACKER	B
	DISCUSSIONS	
	PRESENTATIONS	
	CLIENTS	
	CONTRACTS	
	TRANSACTIONS	

☐ Did not work today; instead, I:

August

31

The biggest mistake/misstep I made this month was...
My plan to prevent the same mishap from recurring is...

{20 } ______________________________

{20 } ______________________________

{20 } ______________________________

{20 }

S M T W T F S

Today I mostly prospected:

	DISCUSSIONS	
L	DAILY TRACKER	B
	PRESENTATIONS	
	CLIENTS	
	CONTRACTS	
	TRANSACTIONS	

☐ Did not work today; instead, I:

{20 }

S M T W T F S

Today I mostly prospected:

	DISCUSSIONS	
L	DAILY TRACKER	B
	PRESENTATIONS	
	CLIENTS	
	CONTRACTS	
	TRANSACTIONS	

☐ Did not work today; instead, I:

{20 }

S M T W T F S

Today I mostly prospected:

	DISCUSSIONS	
L	DAILY TRACKER	B
	PRESENTATIONS	
	CLIENTS	
	CONTRACTS	
	TRANSACTIONS	

☐ Did not work today; instead, I:

{20 }

MONTHLY ACTIVITY TRACKER (GOALS→RESULTS)

GOALS	ACTIVITY	WK 1	WK 2	WK 3	WK 4	WK 5	TOTAL RESULTS
	TRANSACTIONS (T)	L B	L B	L B	L B	L B	L B
	NEW CLIENTS (C)	L B	L B	L B	L B	L B	L B
	PRESENTATIONS (P)	L B	L B	L B	L B	L B	L B
	DISCUSSIONS (D)						
	DAYS WORKED (W)						
	DAILY DISCUSSIONS (D/W)	**ACTUAL DAILY DISCUSSION AVERAGE**				**D/W**	
$	**GCI**	$					

{20 }

MONTHLY ACTIVITY TRACKER (GOALS→RESULTS)

GOALS	ACTIVITY	WK 1	WK 2	WK 3	WK 4	WK 5	TOTAL RESULTS
	TRANSACTIONS (T)	L B	L B	L B	L B	L B	L B
	NEW CLIENTS (C)	L B	L B	L B	L B	L B	L B
	PRESENTATIONS (P)	L B	L B	L B	L B	L B	L B
	DISCUSSIONS (D)						
	DAYS WORKED (W)						
	DAILY DISCUSSIONS (D/W)	**ACTUAL DAILY DISCUSSION AVERAGE**				**D/W**	
$	**GCI**	$					

{20 }

MONTHLY ACTIVITY TRACKER (GOALS→RESULTS)

GOALS	ACTIVITY	WK 1	WK 2	WK 3	WK 4	WK 5	TOTAL RESULTS
	TRANSACTIONS (T)	L B	L B	L B	L B	L B	L B
	NEW CLIENTS (C)	L B	L B	L B	L B	L B	L B
	PRESENTATIONS (P)	L B	L B	L B	L B	L B	L B
	DISCUSSIONS (D)						
	DAYS WORKED (W)						
	DAILY DISCUSSIONS (D/W)	**ACTUAL DAILY DISCUSSION AVERAGE**				**D/W**	
$	**GCI**	$					

September

01

Today is Business Plan Day. [XVIII]
Review/revise yours, and contemplate the past/future.
What is your plan to improve upon last month's performance?

{20 }

{20 }

{20 }

{20 }
S M T W T F S
Today I mostly prospected:

	DISCUSSIONS	
L	DAILY TRACKER	B
	PRESENTATIONS	
	CLIENTS	
	CONTRACTS	
	TRANSACTIONS	

☐ Did not work today; instead, I:

{20 }
S M T W T F S
Today I mostly prospected:

	DISCUSSIONS	
L	DAILY TRACKER	B
	PRESENTATIONS	
	CLIENTS	
	CONTRACTS	
	TRANSACTIONS	

☐ Did not work today; instead, I:

{20 }
S M T W T F S
Today I mostly prospected:

	DISCUSSIONS	
L	DAILY TRACKER	B
	PRESENTATIONS	
	CLIENTS	
	CONTRACTS	
	TRANSACTIONS	

☐ Did not work today; instead, I:

02

September

List a good habit you wanna adopt this month.
How will you implement and make it a permanent part of your routine? Has last month's habit stuck yet?

{20 }

{20 }

{20 }

{20 }	{20 }	{20 }
S M T W T F S	S M T W T F S	S M T W T F S
Today I mostly prospected:	Today I mostly prospected:	Today I mostly prospected:
DISCUSSIONS	DISCUSSIONS	DISCUSSIONS
L · DAILY TRACKER · B	L · DAILY TRACKER · B	L · DAILY TRACKER · B
PRESENTATIONS	PRESENTATIONS	PRESENTATIONS
CLIENTS	CLIENTS	CLIENTS
CONTRACTS	CONTRACTS	CONTRACTS
TRANSACTIONS	TRANSACTIONS	TRANSACTIONS
☐ Did not work today; instead, I:	☐ Did not work today; instead, I:	☐ Did not work today; instead, I:

September

03

Recall a recent class or educational session.
What was the number one thing you learned?
How will you implement it into your business?

{20 }

{20 }

{20 }

{20 }

S M T W T F S

Today I mostly prospected:

	DISCUSSIONS	
L	DAILY TRACKER	B
	PRESENTATIONS	
	CLIENTS	
	CONTRACTS	
	TRANSACTIONS	

☐ Did not work today; instead, I:

{20 }

S M T W T F S

Today I mostly prospected:

	DISCUSSIONS	
L	DAILY TRACKER	B
	PRESENTATIONS	
	CLIENTS	
	CONTRACTS	
	TRANSACTIONS	

☐ Did not work today; instead, I:

{20 }

S M T W T F S

Today I mostly prospected:

	DISCUSSIONS	
L	DAILY TRACKER	B
	PRESENTATIONS	
	CLIENTS	
	CONTRACTS	
	TRANSACTIONS	

☐ Did not work today; instead, I:

04

September

Do you hold any real estate grudges?
(think carefully about it)
Do these grudges help or hurt your clients?

{20 }

{20 }

{20 }

{20 }

S M T W T F S

Today I mostly prospected:

	DISCUSSIONS	
L	DAILY TRACKER	B
	PRESENTATIONS	
	CLIENTS	
	CONTRACTS	
	TRANSACTIONS	

☐ Did not work today; instead, I:

{20 }

S M T W T F S

Today I mostly prospected:

	DISCUSSIONS	
L	DAILY TRACKER	B
	PRESENTATIONS	
	CLIENTS	
	CONTRACTS	
	TRANSACTIONS	

☐ Did not work today; instead, I:

{20 }

S M T W T F S

Today I mostly prospected:

	DISCUSSIONS	
L	DAILY TRACKER	B
	PRESENTATIONS	
	CLIENTS	
	CONTRACTS	
	TRANSACTIONS	

☐ Did not work today; instead, I:

September

05

How does prospecting make you feel?
Do you love it or would you rather leave it?
How could prospecting be more fun?[114]

{20 }

{20 }

{20 }

{20 }

S M T W T F S

Today I mostly prospected:

	DISCUSSIONS	
L	DAILY TRACKER	B
	PRESENTATIONS	
	CLIENTS	
	CONTRACTS	
	TRANSACTIONS	

☐ Did not work today; instead, I:

{20 }

S M T W T F S

Today I mostly prospected:

	DISCUSSIONS	
L	DAILY TRACKER	B
	PRESENTATIONS	
	CLIENTS	
	CONTRACTS	
	TRANSACTIONS	

☐ Did not work today; instead, I:

{20 }

S M T W T F S

Today I mostly prospected:

	DISCUSSIONS	
L	DAILY TRACKER	B
	PRESENTATIONS	
	CLIENTS	
	CONTRACTS	
	TRANSACTIONS	

☐ Did not work today; instead, I:

06 September

List ten words that describe your thoughts on the future. What will you do to ensure the good ones happen and the bad ones never surface?

{20 }

{20 }

{20 }

{20 }

S M T W T F S

Today I mostly prospected:

	DISCUSSIONS	
L	DAILY TRACKER	B
	PRESENTATIONS	
	CLIENTS	
	CONTRACTS	
	TRANSACTIONS	

☐ Did not work today; instead, I:

{20 }

S M T W T F S

Today I mostly prospected:

	DISCUSSIONS	
L	DAILY TRACKER	B
	PRESENTATIONS	
	CLIENTS	
	CONTRACTS	
	TRANSACTIONS	

☐ Did not work today; instead, I:

{20 }

S M T W T F S

Today I mostly prospected:

	DISCUSSIONS	
L	DAILY TRACKER	B
	PRESENTATIONS	
	CLIENTS	
	CONTRACTS	
	TRANSACTIONS	

☐ Did not work today; instead, I:

September

How could you increase GCI *without adding time to your day?*
List three ways and a plan to implement.

{20 }

{20 }

{20 }

{20 }

S M T W T F S

Today I mostly prospected:

	DISCUSSIONS	
L	DAILY TRACKER	B
	PRESENTATIONS	
	CLIENTS	
	CONTRACTS	
	TRANSACTIONS	

☐ Did not work today; instead, I:

{20 }

S M T W T F S

Today I mostly prospected:

	DISCUSSIONS	
L	DAILY TRACKER	B
	PRESENTATIONS	
	CLIENTS	
	CONTRACTS	
	TRANSACTIONS	

☐ Did not work today; instead, I:

{20 }

S M T W T F S

Today I mostly prospected:

	DISCUSSIONS	
L	DAILY TRACKER	B
	PRESENTATIONS	
	CLIENTS	
	CONTRACTS	
	TRANSACTIONS	

☐ Did not work today; instead, I:

08

September

Recall the last time you encountered buyer's remorse.[188] *How did you handle it? What was the outcome?*

{20 }

{20 }

{20 }

{20 }

S M T W T F S

Today I mostly prospected:

	DISCUSSIONS	
L	DAILY TRACKER	B
	PRESENTATIONS	
	CLIENTS	
	CONTRACTS	
	TRANSACTIONS	

☐ Did not work today; instead, I:

{20 }

S M T W T F S

Today I mostly prospected:

	DISCUSSIONS	
L	DAILY TRACKER	B
	PRESENTATIONS	
	CLIENTS	
	CONTRACTS	
	TRANSACTIONS	

☐ Did not work today; instead, I:

{20 }

S M T W T F S

Today I mostly prospected:

	DISCUSSIONS	
L	DAILY TRACKER	B
	PRESENTATIONS	
	CLIENTS	
	CONTRACTS	
	TRANSACTIONS	

☐ Did not work today; instead, I:

September

09

Name the number one objection you hear from buyer prospects. What is your best script to overcome this objection?

{20 } ____________________

{20 } ____________________

{20 } ____________________

{20 }

S M T W T F S

Today I mostly prospected:

	DISCUSSIONS	
L	DAILY TRACKER	B
	PRESENTATIONS	
	CLIENTS	
	CONTRACTS	
	TRANSACTIONS	

☐ Did not work today; instead, I:

{20 }

S M T W T F S

Today I mostly prospected:

	DISCUSSIONS	
L	DAILY TRACKER	B
	PRESENTATIONS	
	CLIENTS	
	CONTRACTS	
	TRANSACTIONS	

☐ Did not work today; instead, I:

{20 }

S M T W T F S

Today I mostly prospected:

	DISCUSSIONS	
L	DAILY TRACKER	B
	PRESENTATIONS	
	CLIENTS	
	CONTRACTS	
	TRANSACTIONS	

☐ Did not work today; instead, I:

10

September

Write a script for this seller objection:
"I won't pay for the buyer's closing costs,
because I paid my own when I bought this place."

{20 }

{20 }

{20 }

{20 }	{20 }	{20 }
S M T W T F S	S M T W T F S	S M T W T F S
Today I mostly prospected:	Today I mostly prospected:	Today I mostly prospected:

	DISCUSSIONS	
L	DAILY TRACKER	B
	PRESENTATIONS	
	CLIENTS	
	CONTRACTS	
	TRANSACTIONS	

	DISCUSSIONS	
L	DAILY TRACKER	B
	PRESENTATIONS	
	CLIENTS	
	CONTRACTS	
	TRANSACTIONS	

	DISCUSSIONS	
L	DAILY TRACKER	B
	PRESENTATIONS	
	CLIENTS	
	CONTRACTS	
	TRANSACTIONS	

☐ Did not work today; instead, I:

☐ Did not work today; instead, I:

☐ Did not work today; instead, I:

September

11

Name one thing that would improve your client turnover rate (CTR).[XVI]

{20 }

{20 }

{20 }

{20 }

S M T W T F S

Today I mostly prospected:

	DISCUSSIONS	
L	DAILY TRACKER	B
	PRESENTATIONS	
	CLIENTS	
	CONTRACTS	
	TRANSACTIONS	

☐ Did not work today; instead, I:

{20 }

S M T W T F S

Today I mostly prospected:

	DISCUSSIONS	
L	DAILY TRACKER	B
	PRESENTATIONS	
	CLIENTS	
	CONTRACTS	
	TRANSACTIONS	

☐ Did not work today; instead, I:

{20 }

S M T W T F S

Today I mostly prospected:

	DISCUSSIONS	
L	DAILY TRACKER	B
	PRESENTATIONS	
	CLIENTS	
	CONTRACTS	
	TRANSACTIONS	

☐ Did not work today; instead, I:

12 September

What keeps you motivated to prospect?[300]
How would your extra effort today payoff tomorrow?

{20 }

{20 }

{20 }

{20 }		
S M T W T F S		
Today I mostly prospected:		
	DISCUSSIONS	
L	DAILY TRACKER	B
	PRESENTATIONS	
	CLIENTS	
	CONTRACTS	
	TRANSACTIONS	
☐ Did not work today; instead, I:		

{20 }		
S M T W T F S		
Today I mostly prospected:		
	DISCUSSIONS	
L	DAILY TRACKER	B
	PRESENTATIONS	
	CLIENTS	
	CONTRACTS	
	TRANSACTIONS	
☐ Did not work today; instead, I:		

{20 }		
S M T W T F S		
Today I mostly prospected:		
	DISCUSSIONS	
L	DAILY TRACKER	B
	PRESENTATIONS	
	CLIENTS	
	CONTRACTS	
	TRANSACTIONS	
☐ Did not work today; instead, I:		

September

13

When was the last time you tried something new?
What was the result?
Would you do it again?

{20 }

{20 }

{20 }

{20 }	{20 }	{20 }
S M T W T F S	S M T W T F S	S M T W T F S
Today I mostly prospected:	Today I mostly prospected:	Today I mostly prospected:

	DISCUSSIONS	
L	DAILY TRACKER	B
	PRESENTATIONS	
	CLIENTS	
	CONTRACTS	
	TRANSACTIONS	

☐ Did not work today; instead, I:

	DISCUSSIONS	
L	DAILY TRACKER	B
	PRESENTATIONS	
	CLIENTS	
	CONTRACTS	
	TRANSACTIONS	

☐ Did not work today; instead, I:

	DISCUSSIONS	
L	DAILY TRACKER	B
	PRESENTATIONS	
	CLIENTS	
	CONTRACTS	
	TRANSACTIONS	

☐ Did not work today; instead, I:

14 September

Are you falling behind (or surging ahead) on any monthly goals?
What's your plan to achieve them all?[XIX]
Adjust your activities now, so you will meet or exceed all.

{20 }

{20 }

{20 }

{20 }

S M T W T F S

Today I mostly prospected:

	DISCUSSIONS	
L	DAILY TRACKER	B
	PRESENTATIONS	
	CLIENTS	
	CONTRACTS	
	TRANSACTIONS	

☐ Did not work today; instead, I:

{20 }

S M T W T F S

Today I mostly prospected:

	DISCUSSIONS	
L	DAILY TRACKER	B
	PRESENTATIONS	
	CLIENTS	
	CONTRACTS	
	TRANSACTIONS	

☐ Did not work today; instead, I:

{20 }

S M T W T F S

Today I mostly prospected:

	DISCUSSIONS	
L	DAILY TRACKER	B
	PRESENTATIONS	
	CLIENTS	
	CONTRACTS	
	TRANSACTIONS	

☐ Did not work today; instead, I:

September

15

How many different ways do you prospect for clients?[084]
Which ones provide the most presentations? ...the least?
Should you alter your strategy?[004]

{20 } ______________________________

{20 } ______________________________

{20 } ______________________________

{20 }

S M T W T F S

Today I mostly prospected:

	DISCUSSIONS	
L	DAILY TRACKER	B
	PRESENTATIONS	
	CLIENTS	
	CONTRACTS	
	TRANSACTIONS	

☐ Did not work today; instead, I:

{20 }

S M T W T F S

Today I mostly prospected:

	DISCUSSIONS	
L	DAILY TRACKER	B
	PRESENTATIONS	
	CLIENTS	
	CONTRACTS	
	TRANSACTIONS	

☐ Did not work today; instead, I:

{20 }

S M T W T F S

Today I mostly prospected:

	DISCUSSIONS	
L	DAILY TRACKER	B
	PRESENTATIONS	
	CLIENTS	
	CONTRACTS	
	TRANSACTIONS	

☐ Did not work today; instead, I:

16

September

Autumn has befallen.
How do you keep relationships alive?[086]
Who can you call for a referral?

{20 }

{20 }

{20 }

{20 }

S M T W T F S

Today I mostly prospected:

	DISCUSSIONS	
L	DAILY TRACKER	B
	PRESENTATIONS	
	CLIENTS	
	CONTRACTS	
	TRANSACTIONS	

☐ Did not work today; instead, I:

{20 }

S M T W T F S

Today I mostly prospected:

	DISCUSSIONS	
L	DAILY TRACKER	B
	PRESENTATIONS	
	CLIENTS	
	CONTRACTS	
	TRANSACTIONS	

☐ Did not work today; instead, I:

{20 }

S M T W T F S

Today I mostly prospected:

	DISCUSSIONS	
L	DAILY TRACKER	B
	PRESENTATIONS	
	CLIENTS	
	CONTRACTS	
	TRANSACTIONS	

☐ Did not work today; instead, I:

September

17

Write a script for this objection:
"Another agent told me that you're a jerk,
so I should work with someone else."

{20 } ______

{20 } ______

{20 } ______

{20 }

S M T W T F S

Today I mostly prospected:

L	DISCUSSIONS	B
	DAILY TRACKER	
	PRESENTATIONS	
	CLIENTS	
	CONTRACTS	
	TRANSACTIONS	

☐ Did not work today; instead, I:

{20 }

S M T W T F S

Today I mostly prospected:

L	DISCUSSIONS	B
	DAILY TRACKER	
	PRESENTATIONS	
	CLIENTS	
	CONTRACTS	
	TRANSACTIONS	

☐ Did not work today; instead, I:

{20 }

S M T W T F S

Today I mostly prospected:

L	DISCUSSIONS	B
	DAILY TRACKER	
	PRESENTATIONS	
	CLIENTS	
	CONTRACTS	
	TRANSACTIONS	

☐ Did not work today; instead, I:

18 September

Today is Scripts Are Your Friends Day.[046]
What is your favorite script (and how often do you say it)?
How often do you practice/create new scripts?[050]

{20 }

{20 }

{20 }

{20 }	{20 }	{20 }
S M T W T F S	S M T W T F S	S M T W T F S
Today I mostly prospected:	Today I mostly prospected:	Today I mostly prospected:
DISCUSSIONS	DISCUSSIONS	DISCUSSIONS
L · DAILY TRACKER · B	L · DAILY TRACKER · B	L · DAILY TRACKER · B
PRESENTATIONS	PRESENTATIONS	PRESENTATIONS
CLIENTS	CLIENTS	CLIENTS
CONTRACTS	CONTRACTS	CONTRACTS
TRANSACTIONS	TRANSACTIONS	TRANSACTIONS
☐ Did not work today; instead, I:	☐ Did not work today; instead, I:	☐ Did not work today; instead, I:

September

19

Rank your physical health on a scale of one to ten. List one thing you could do to improve and a plan to achieve.

{20 }

{20 }

{20 }

{20 }

S M T W T F S

Today I mostly prospected:

L	DISCUSSIONS	B
	DAILY TRACKER	
	PRESENTATIONS	
	CLIENTS	
	CONTRACTS	
	TRANSACTIONS	

☐ Did not work today; instead, I:

{20 }

S M T W T F S

Today I mostly prospected:

L	DISCUSSIONS	B
	DAILY TRACKER	
	PRESENTATIONS	
	CLIENTS	
	CONTRACTS	
	TRANSACTIONS	

☐ Did not work today; instead, I:

{20 }

S M T W T F S

Today I mostly prospected:

L	DISCUSSIONS	B
	DAILY TRACKER	
	PRESENTATIONS	
	CLIENTS	
	CONTRACTS	
	TRANSACTIONS	

☐ Did not work today; instead, I:

20 September

How would you like to be remembered by past clients (what do you hope they say about you)?[086]
How might you encourage them to think about you this way?

{20 }

{20 }

{20 }

{20 }
S M T W T F S
Today I mostly prospected:

	DISCUSSIONS	
L	DAILY TRACKER	B
	PRESENTATIONS	
	CLIENTS	
	CONTRACTS	
	TRANSACTIONS	

☐ Did not work today; instead, I:

{20 }
S M T W T F S
Today I mostly prospected:

	DISCUSSIONS	
L	DAILY TRACKER	B
	PRESENTATIONS	
	CLIENTS	
	CONTRACTS	
	TRANSACTIONS	

☐ Did not work today; instead, I:

{20 }
S M T W T F S
Today I mostly prospected:

	DISCUSSIONS	
L	DAILY TRACKER	B
	PRESENTATIONS	
	CLIENTS	
	CONTRACTS	
	TRANSACTIONS	

☐ Did not work today; instead, I:

September

21

List twenty words that describe your bedside manner.[214]
Which ones would you like to change?

{20 }

{20 }

{20 }

{20 }

S M T W T F S

Today I mostly prospected:

L	DISCUSSIONS	B
	DAILY TRACKER	
	PRESENTATIONS	
	CLIENTS	
	CONTRACTS	
	TRANSACTIONS	

☐ Did not work today; instead, I:

{20 }

S M T W T F S

Today I mostly prospected:

L	DISCUSSIONS	B
	DAILY TRACKER	
	PRESENTATIONS	
	CLIENTS	
	CONTRACTS	
	TRANSACTIONS	

☐ Did not work today; instead, I:

{20 }

S M T W T F S

Today I mostly prospected:

L	DISCUSSIONS	B
	DAILY TRACKER	
	PRESENTATIONS	
	CLIENTS	
	CONTRACTS	
	TRANSACTIONS	

☐ Did not work today; instead, I:

22 September

If your business was a boat,
would it cut smoothly through the water, or has it sprang a leak?
Explain yourself.

{20 }

{20 }

{20 }

{20 }

S M T W T F S

Today I mostly prospected:

	DISCUSSIONS	
L	DAILY TRACKER	B
	PRESENTATIONS	
	CLIENTS	
	CONTRACTS	
	TRANSACTIONS	

☐ Did not work today; instead, I:

{20 }

S M T W T F S

Today I mostly prospected:

	DISCUSSIONS	
L	DAILY TRACKER	B
	PRESENTATIONS	
	CLIENTS	
	CONTRACTS	
	TRANSACTIONS	

☐ Did not work today; instead, I:

{20 }

S M T W T F S

Today I mostly prospected:

	DISCUSSIONS	
L	DAILY TRACKER	B
	PRESENTATIONS	
	CLIENTS	
	CONTRACTS	
	TRANSACTIONS	

☐ Did not work today; instead, I:

September

23

List three admirable qualities of other agents' businesses. How can you be more like them?[068]

{20 }

{20 }

{20 }

{20 }		
S M T W T F S		
Today I mostly prospected:		
	DISCUSSIONS	
L	DAILY TRACKER	B
	PRESENTATIONS	
	CLIENTS	
	CONTRACTS	
	TRANSACTIONS	
☐ Did not work today; instead, I:		

{20 }		
S M T W T F S		
Today I mostly prospected:		
	DISCUSSIONS	
L	DAILY TRACKER	B
	PRESENTATIONS	
	CLIENTS	
	CONTRACTS	
	TRANSACTIONS	
☐ Did not work today; instead, I:		

{20 }		
S M T W T F S		
Today I mostly prospected:		
	DISCUSSIONS	
L	DAILY TRACKER	B
	PRESENTATIONS	
	CLIENTS	
	CONTRACTS	
	TRANSACTIONS	
☐ Did not work today; instead, I:		

24 September

Write a note to yourself concerning your business growth.

{20 } ________________________

{20 } ________________________

{20 } ________________________

{20 }

S M T W T F S

Today I mostly prospected:

L	DISCUSSIONS	B
	DAILY TRACKER	
	PRESENTATIONS	
	CLIENTS	
	CONTRACTS	
	TRANSACTIONS	

☐ Did not work today; instead, I:

{20 }

S M T W T F S

Today I mostly prospected:

L	DISCUSSIONS	B
	DAILY TRACKER	
	PRESENTATIONS	
	CLIENTS	
	CONTRACTS	
	TRANSACTIONS	

☐ Did not work today; instead, I:

{20 }

S M T W T F S

Today I mostly prospected:

L	DISCUSSIONS	B
	DAILY TRACKER	
	PRESENTATIONS	
	CLIENTS	
	CONTRACTS	
	TRANSACTIONS	

☐ Did not work today; instead, I:

September

25

What are your thoughts on showing feedback?[242]
Do you think it hurts or helps your clients?

{20 }

{20 }

{20 }

{20 }		
S M T W T F S		
Today I mostly prospected:		
	DISCUSSIONS	
L	DAILY TRACKER	B
	PRESENTATIONS	
	CLIENTS	
	CONTRACTS	
	TRANSACTIONS	
☐ Did not work today; instead, I:		

{20 }		
S M T W T F S		
Today I mostly prospected:		
	DISCUSSIONS	
L	DAILY TRACKER	B
	PRESENTATIONS	
	CLIENTS	
	CONTRACTS	
	TRANSACTIONS	
☐ Did not work today; instead, I:		

{20 }		
S M T W T F S		
Today I mostly prospected:		
	DISCUSSIONS	
L	DAILY TRACKER	B
	PRESENTATIONS	
	CLIENTS	
	CONTRACTS	
	TRANSACTIONS	
☐ Did not work today; instead, I:		

26 September

List three ways you could increase your physical health; reward yourself with a plan to adopt.

{20 }

{20 }

{20 }

{20 }	{20 }	{20 }
S M T W T F S	S M T W T F S	S M T W T F S
Today I mostly prospected:	Today I mostly prospected:	Today I mostly prospected:
DISCUSSIONS	DISCUSSIONS	DISCUSSIONS
L · DAILY TRACKER · B	L · DAILY TRACKER · B	L · DAILY TRACKER · B
PRESENTATIONS	PRESENTATIONS	PRESENTATIONS
CLIENTS	CLIENTS	CLIENTS
CONTRACTS	CONTRACTS	CONTRACTS
TRANSACTIONS	TRANSACTIONS	TRANSACTIONS
☐ Did not work today; instead, I:	☐ Did not work today; instead, I:	☐ Did not work today; instead, I:

September

27

List three ways you could be a better employee to yourself.[060]

{20 }

{20 }

{20 }

{20 }

S M T W T F S

Today I mostly prospected:

	DISCUSSIONS	
L	DAILY TRACKER	B
	PRESENTATIONS	
	CLIENTS	
	CONTRACTS	
	TRANSACTIONS	

☐ Did not work today; instead, I:

{20 }

S M T W T F S

Today I mostly prospected:

	DISCUSSIONS	
L	DAILY TRACKER	B
	PRESENTATIONS	
	CLIENTS	
	CONTRACTS	
	TRANSACTIONS	

☐ Did not work today; instead, I:

{20 }

S M T W T F S

Today I mostly prospected:

	DISCUSSIONS	
L	DAILY TRACKER	B
	PRESENTATIONS	
	CLIENTS	
	CONTRACTS	
	TRANSACTIONS	

☐ Did not work today; instead, I:

28 September

My grandest achievement this month was...
My plan to repeat this victory is...

{20 }

{20 }

{20 }

{20 }

S M T W T F S

Today I mostly prospected:

L	DAILY TRACKER	B
	DISCUSSIONS	
	PRESENTATIONS	
	CLIENTS	
	CONTRACTS	
	TRANSACTIONS	

☐ Did not work today; instead, I:

{20 }

S M T W T F S

Today I mostly prospected:

L	DAILY TRACKER	B
	DISCUSSIONS	
	PRESENTATIONS	
	CLIENTS	
	CONTRACTS	
	TRANSACTIONS	

☐ Did not work today; instead, I:

{20 }

S M T W T F S

Today I mostly prospected:

L	DAILY TRACKER	B
	DISCUSSIONS	
	PRESENTATIONS	
	CLIENTS	
	CONTRACTS	
	TRANSACTIONS	

☐ Did not work today; instead, I:

September

29

Summarize the last three months with one word.
Given the opportunity, would you take a do-over?
Which parts would you like to forget?.. never forget?

{20 }

{20 }

{20 }

{20 }

S	M	T	W	T	F	S

Today I mostly prospected:

	DISCUSSIONS	
L	DAILY TRACKER	B
	PRESENTATIONS	
	CLIENTS	
	CONTRACTS	
	TRANSACTIONS	

☐ Did not work today; instead, I:

{20 }

S	M	T	W	T	F	S

Today I mostly prospected:

	DISCUSSIONS	
L	DAILY TRACKER	B
	PRESENTATIONS	
	CLIENTS	
	CONTRACTS	
	TRANSACTIONS	

☐ Did not work today; instead, I:

{20 }

S	M	T	W	T	F	S

Today I mostly prospected:

	DISCUSSIONS	
L	DAILY TRACKER	B
	PRESENTATIONS	
	CLIENTS	
	CONTRACTS	
	TRANSACTIONS	

☐ Did not work today; instead, I:

30 September

The biggest mistake/misstep I made this month was...
My plan to prevent the same mishap from recurring is...

{20 }

{20 }

{20 }

{20 }

S M T W T F S

Today I mostly prospected:

	DISCUSSIONS	
L	DAILY TRACKER	B
	PRESENTATIONS	
	CLIENTS	
	CONTRACTS	
	TRANSACTIONS	

☐ Did not work today; instead, I:

{20 }

S M T W T F S

Today I mostly prospected:

	DISCUSSIONS	
L	DAILY TRACKER	B
	PRESENTATIONS	
	CLIENTS	
	CONTRACTS	
	TRANSACTIONS	

☐ Did not work today; instead, I:

{20 }

S M T W T F S

Today I mostly prospected:

	DISCUSSIONS	
L	DAILY TRACKER	B
	PRESENTATIONS	
	CLIENTS	
	CONTRACTS	
	TRANSACTIONS	

☐ Did not work today; instead, I:

{20 } MONTHLY ACTIVITY TRACKER (GOALS→RESULTS)

GOALS	ACTIVITY	WK 1	WK 2	WK 3	WK 4	WK 5	TOTAL RESULTS
	TRANSACTIONS (T)	L B	L B	L B	L B	L B	L B
	NEW CLIENTS (C)	L B	L B	L B	L B	L B	L B
	PRESENTATIONS (P)	L B	L B	L B	L B	L B	L B
	DISCUSSIONS (D)						
	DAYS WORKED (W)						
	DAILY DISCUSSIONS (D/W)	ACTUAL DAILY DISCUSSION AVERAGE				D/W	
$	GCI	$					

{20 } MONTHLY ACTIVITY TRACKER (GOALS→RESULTS)

GOALS	ACTIVITY	WK 1	WK 2	WK 3	WK 4	WK 5	TOTAL RESULTS
	TRANSACTIONS (T)	L B	L B	L B	L B	L B	L B
	NEW CLIENTS (C)	L B	L B	L B	L B	L B	L B
	PRESENTATIONS (P)	L B	L B	L B	L B	L B	L B
	DISCUSSIONS (D)						
	DAYS WORKED (W)						
	DAILY DISCUSSIONS (D/W)	ACTUAL DAILY DISCUSSION AVERAGE				D/W	
$	GCI	$					

{20 } MONTHLY ACTIVITY TRACKER (GOALS→RESULTS)

GOALS	ACTIVITY	WK 1	WK 2	WK 3	WK 4	WK 5	TOTAL RESULTS
	TRANSACTIONS (T)	L B	L B	L B	L B	L B	L B
	NEW CLIENTS (C)	L B	L B	L B	L B	L B	L B
	PRESENTATIONS (P)	L B	L B	L B	L B	L B	L B
	DISCUSSIONS (D)						
	DAYS WORKED (W)						
	DAILY DISCUSSIONS (D/W)	ACTUAL DAILY DISCUSSION AVERAGE				D/W	
$	GCI	$					

October

01

Today is Business Plan Day.[XVIII]
Review/revise yours, and contemplate the past/future.
What is your plan to improve upon last month's performance?

{20 }

{20 }

{20 }

{20 }

S M T W T F S

Today I mostly prospected:

	DISCUSSIONS	
L	DAILY TRACKER	B
	PRESENTATIONS	
	CLIENTS	
	CONTRACTS	
	TRANSACTIONS	

☐ Did not work today; instead, I:

{20 }

S M T W T F S

Today I mostly prospected:

	DISCUSSIONS	
L	DAILY TRACKER	B
	PRESENTATIONS	
	CLIENTS	
	CONTRACTS	
	TRANSACTIONS	

☐ Did not work today; instead, I:

{20 }

S M T W T F S

Today I mostly prospected:

	DISCUSSIONS	
L	DAILY TRACKER	B
	PRESENTATIONS	
	CLIENTS	
	CONTRACTS	
	TRANSACTIONS	

☐ Did not work today; instead, I:

02

October

List a good habit you wanna adopt this month. How will you implement and make it a permanent part of your routine? Has last month's habit stuck yet?

{20 }

{20 }

{20 }

{20 }

S M T W T F S

Today I mostly prospected:

	DISCUSSIONS	
L	DAILY TRACKER	B
	PRESENTATIONS	
	CLIENTS	
	CONTRACTS	
	TRANSACTIONS	

☐ Did not work today; instead, I:

{20 }

S M T W T F S

Today I mostly prospected:

	DISCUSSIONS	
L	DAILY TRACKER	B
	PRESENTATIONS	
	CLIENTS	
	CONTRACTS	
	TRANSACTIONS	

☐ Did not work today; instead, I:

{20 }

S M T W T F S

Today I mostly prospected:

	DISCUSSIONS	
L	DAILY TRACKER	B
	PRESENTATIONS	
	CLIENTS	
	CONTRACTS	
	TRANSACTIONS	

☐ Did not work today; instead, I:

October

03

What would make your prospecting efforts more efficient? [012]
How could your message reach more prospects in less time?
How could you increase your discussion turnover rate (DTR)*?* [XVI]

{20 }

{20 }

{20 }

{20 }		
S M T W T F S		
Today I mostly prospected:		
	DISCUSSIONS	
L	DAILY TRACKER	B
	PRESENTATIONS	
	CLIENTS	
	CONTRACTS	
	TRANSACTIONS	
☐ Did not work today; instead, I:		

{20 }		
S M T W T F S		
Today I mostly prospected:		
	DISCUSSIONS	
L	DAILY TRACKER	B
	PRESENTATIONS	
	CLIENTS	
	CONTRACTS	
	TRANSACTIONS	
☐ Did not work today; instead, I:		

{20 }		
S M T W T F S		
Today I mostly prospected:		
	DISCUSSIONS	
L	DAILY TRACKER	B
	PRESENTATIONS	
	CLIENTS	
	CONTRACTS	
	TRANSACTIONS	
☐ Did not work today; instead, I:		

04 October

Today is Makeover Day.
What does your look say about you?[025]

{20 }

{20 }

{20 }

{20 }		
S M T W T F S		
Today I mostly prospected:		
	DISCUSSIONS	
L	DAILY TRACKER	B
	PRESENTATIONS	
	CLIENTS	
	CONTRACTS	
	TRANSACTIONS	
☐ Did not work today; instead, I:		

{20 }		
S M T W T F S		
Today I mostly prospected:		
	DISCUSSIONS	
L	DAILY TRACKER	B
	PRESENTATIONS	
	CLIENTS	
	CONTRACTS	
	TRANSACTIONS	
☐ Did not work today; instead, I:		

{20 }		
S M T W T F S		
Today I mostly prospected:		
	DISCUSSIONS	
L	DAILY TRACKER	B
	PRESENTATIONS	
	CLIENTS	
	CONTRACTS	
	TRANSACTIONS	
☐ Did not work today; instead, I:		

October

05

The three biggest troubles with my business are...
My plan to correct each one is...

{20 }

{20 }

{20 }

{20 }	{20 }	{20 }
S M T W T F S	S M T W T F S	S M T W T F S
Today I mostly prospected:	Today I mostly prospected:	Today I mostly prospected:
DISCUSSIONS	DISCUSSIONS	DISCUSSIONS
L · DAILY TRACKER · B	L · DAILY TRACKER · B	L · DAILY TRACKER · B
PRESENTATIONS	PRESENTATIONS	PRESENTATIONS
CLIENTS	CLIENTS	CLIENTS
CONTRACTS	CONTRACTS	CONTRACTS
TRANSACTIONS	TRANSACTIONS	TRANSACTIONS
☐ Did not work today; instead, I:	☐ Did not work today; instead, I:	☐ Did not work today; instead, I:

06 October

List ten words that describe your ideal client.
Where could you find such people?
How will you encourage them to work with you?

{20 }

{20 }

{20 }

{20 }	{20 }	{20 }
S M T W T F S	S M T W T F S	S M T W T F S
Today I mostly prospected:	Today I mostly prospected:	Today I mostly prospected:

	DISCUSSIONS	
L	DAILY TRACKER	B
	PRESENTATIONS	
	CLIENTS	
	CONTRACTS	
	TRANSACTIONS	

☐ Did not work today; instead, I:

	DISCUSSIONS	
L	DAILY TRACKER	B
	PRESENTATIONS	
	CLIENTS	
	CONTRACTS	
	TRANSACTIONS	

☐ Did not work today; instead, I:

	DISCUSSIONS	
L	DAILY TRACKER	B
	PRESENTATIONS	
	CLIENTS	
	CONTRACTS	
	TRANSACTIONS	

☐ Did not work today; instead, I:

October

07

Do you routinely insist buyers sit for a presentation?[186] *How could your presentation become more efficient, thereby saving time in the field?*

{20 }

{20 }

{20 }

{20 }
S M T W T F S
Today I mostly prospected:

	DISCUSSIONS	
L	DAILY TRACKER	B
	PRESENTATIONS	
	CLIENTS	
	CONTRACTS	
	TRANSACTIONS	

☐ Did not work today; instead, I:

{20 }
S M T W T F S
Today I mostly prospected:

	DISCUSSIONS	
L	DAILY TRACKER	B
	PRESENTATIONS	
	CLIENTS	
	CONTRACTS	
	TRANSACTIONS	

☐ Did not work today; instead, I:

{20 }
S M T W T F S
Today I mostly prospected:

	DISCUSSIONS	
L	DAILY TRACKER	B
	PRESENTATIONS	
	CLIENTS	
	CONTRACTS	
	TRANSACTIONS	

☐ Did not work today; instead, I:

08 October

Write a script for this seller objection:
"I don't wanna reduce the price of my listing;
I'm not gonna give it away."

{20 }

{20 }

{20 }

{20 }

S M T W T F S

Today I mostly prospected:

	DISCUSSIONS	
L	DAILY TRACKER	B
	PRESENTATIONS	
	CLIENTS	
	CONTRACTS	
	TRANSACTIONS	

☐ Did not work today; instead, I:

{20 }

S M T W T F S

Today I mostly prospected:

	DISCUSSIONS	
L	DAILY TRACKER	B
	PRESENTATIONS	
	CLIENTS	
	CONTRACTS	
	TRANSACTIONS	

☐ Did not work today; instead, I:

{20 }

S M T W T F S

Today I mostly prospected:

	DISCUSSIONS	
L	DAILY TRACKER	B
	PRESENTATIONS	
	CLIENTS	
	CONTRACTS	
	TRANSACTIONS	

☐ Did not work today; instead, I:

October

09

List three bad habits you'd like to lose. Reward yourself with deadlines and a plan to ditch each offending habit.

{20 }

{20 }

{20 }

{20 }

S M T W T F S

Today I mostly prospected:

	DISCUSSIONS	
L	DAILY TRACKER	B
	PRESENTATIONS	
	CLIENTS	
	CONTRACTS	
	TRANSACTIONS	

☐ Did not work today; instead, I:

{20 }

S M T W T F S

Today I mostly prospected:

	DISCUSSIONS	
L	DAILY TRACKER	B
	PRESENTATIONS	
	CLIENTS	
	CONTRACTS	
	TRANSACTIONS	

☐ Did not work today; instead, I:

{20 }

S M T W T F S

Today I mostly prospected:

	DISCUSSIONS	
L	DAILY TRACKER	B
	PRESENTATIONS	
	CLIENTS	
	CONTRACTS	
	TRANSACTIONS	

☐ Did not work today; instead, I:

10 October

What is currently your biggest bottleneck (slowdown in the transaction process)? [VII]
What are you doing to improve that turnover rate? [XVI]

{20 }

{20 }

{20 }

{20 }	{20 }	{20 }
S M T W T F S	S M T W T F S	S M T W T F S
Today I mostly prospected:	Today I mostly prospected:	Today I mostly prospected:

	DISCUSSIONS			DISCUSSIONS			DISCUSSIONS	
L	DAILY TRACKER	B	L	DAILY TRACKER	B	L	DAILY TRACKER	B
	PRESENTATIONS			PRESENTATIONS			PRESENTATIONS	
	CLIENTS			CLIENTS			CLIENTS	
	CONTRACTS			CONTRACTS			CONTRACTS	
	TRANSACTIONS			TRANSACTIONS			TRANSACTIONS	

☐ Did not work today; instead, I:

☐ Did not work today; instead, I:

☐ Did not work today; instead, I:

October

11

What could you do tomorrow to get a well-priced listing?[098]
How would doing so impact your business?
...impact your life?

{20 }

{20 }

{20 }

{20 }

S M T W T F S

Today I mostly prospected:

	DISCUSSIONS	
L	DAILY TRACKER	B
	PRESENTATIONS	
	CLIENTS	
	CONTRACTS	
	TRANSACTIONS	

☐ Did not work today; instead, I:

{20 }

S M T W T F S

Today I mostly prospected:

	DISCUSSIONS	
L	DAILY TRACKER	B
	PRESENTATIONS	
	CLIENTS	
	CONTRACTS	
	TRANSACTIONS	

☐ Did not work today; instead, I:

{20 }

S M T W T F S

Today I mostly prospected:

	DISCUSSIONS	
L	DAILY TRACKER	B
	PRESENTATIONS	
	CLIENTS	
	CONTRACTS	
	TRANSACTIONS	

☐ Did not work today; instead, I:

12

October

Describe your last 'perfect' day?
When was it? What happened?

{20 }

{20 }

{20 }

{20 }	{20 }	{20 }
S M T W T F S	S M T W T F S	S M T W T F S
Today I mostly prospected:	Today I mostly prospected:	Today I mostly prospected:
DISCUSSIONS	DISCUSSIONS	DISCUSSIONS

L	DAILY TRACKER	B	L	DAILY TRACKER	B	L	DAILY TRACKER	B
	PRESENTATIONS			PRESENTATIONS			PRESENTATIONS	
	CLIENTS			CLIENTS			CLIENTS	
	CONTRACTS			CONTRACTS			CONTRACTS	
	TRANSACTIONS			TRANSACTIONS			TRANSACTIONS	

☐ Did not work today; instead, I: ☐ Did not work today; instead, I: ☐ Did not work today; instead, I:

October

13

Name one thing that would improve your average listing days on market (DOM).[XVI]

{20 }

{20 }

{20 }

{20 }
S M T W T F S
Today I mostly prospected:

	DISCUSSIONS	
L	DAILY TRACKER	B
	PRESENTATIONS	
	CLIENTS	
	CONTRACTS	
	TRANSACTIONS	

☐ Did not work today; instead, I:

{20 }
S M T W T F S
Today I mostly prospected:

	DISCUSSIONS	
L	DAILY TRACKER	B
	PRESENTATIONS	
	CLIENTS	
	CONTRACTS	
	TRANSACTIONS	

☐ Did not work today; instead, I:

{20 }
S M T W T F S
Today I mostly prospected:

	DISCUSSIONS	
L	DAILY TRACKER	B
	PRESENTATIONS	
	CLIENTS	
	CONTRACTS	
	TRANSACTIONS	

☐ Did not work today; instead, I:

14 October

Are you proud of your real estate stats?[XI]
If YES: *how do you share your stats with prospects?*
If NO: *name three ways to improve your datapoints.*[X]

{20 }

{20 }

{20 }

{20 }

S M T W T F S

Today I mostly prospected:

	DISCUSSIONS	
L	DAILY TRACKER	B
	PRESENTATIONS	
	CLIENTS	
	CONTRACTS	
	TRANSACTIONS	

☐ Did not work today; instead, I:

{20 }

S M T W T F S

Today I mostly prospected:

	DISCUSSIONS	
L	DAILY TRACKER	B
	PRESENTATIONS	
	CLIENTS	
	CONTRACTS	
	TRANSACTIONS	

☐ Did not work today; instead, I:

{20 }

S M T W T F S

Today I mostly prospected:

	DISCUSSIONS	
L	DAILY TRACKER	B
	PRESENTATIONS	
	CLIENTS	
	CONTRACTS	
	TRANSACTIONS	

☐ Did not work today; instead, I:

October

15

Are you falling behind (or surging ahead) on any monthly goals?
What's your plan to achieve them all?[XIX]
Adjust your activities now, so you will meet or exceed all.

{20 }

{20 }

{20 }

{20 }	{20 }	{20 }
S M T W T F S	S M T W T F S	S M T W T F S
Today I mostly prospected:	Today I mostly prospected:	Today I mostly prospected:
DISCUSSIONS	DISCUSSIONS	DISCUSSIONS
L · DAILY TRACKER · B	L · DAILY TRACKER · B	L · DAILY TRACKER · B
PRESENTATIONS	PRESENTATIONS	PRESENTATIONS
CLIENTS	CLIENTS	CLIENTS
CONTRACTS	CONTRACTS	CONTRACTS
TRANSACTIONS	TRANSACTIONS	TRANSACTIONS
☐ Did not work today; instead, I:	☐ Did not work today; instead, I:	☐ Did not work today; instead, I:

16 October

Rank your business health on a scale of one to ten. List one thing you could do to improve and a plan to achieve.

{20 }

{20 }

{20 }

{20 }

S M T W T F S

Today I mostly prospected:

	DISCUSSIONS	
L	DAILY TRACKER	B
	PRESENTATIONS	
	CLIENTS	
	CONTRACTS	
	TRANSACTIONS	

☐ Did not work today; instead, I:

{20 }

S M T W T F S

Today I mostly prospected:

	DISCUSSIONS	
L	DAILY TRACKER	B
	PRESENTATIONS	
	CLIENTS	
	CONTRACTS	
	TRANSACTIONS	

☐ Did not work today; instead, I:

{20 }

S M T W T F S

Today I mostly prospected:

	DISCUSSIONS	
L	DAILY TRACKER	B
	PRESENTATIONS	
	CLIENTS	
	CONTRACTS	
	TRANSACTIONS	

☐ Did not work today; instead, I:

October

17

Are you keeping your database clean and organized?[089]
What value are you giving to its members?[090]
Who can you call for a referral?

{20 }

{20 }

{20 }

{20 }

S M T W T F S

Today I mostly prospected:

	DISCUSSIONS	
L	DAILY TRACKER	B
	PRESENTATIONS	
	CLIENTS	
	CONTRACTS	
	TRANSACTIONS	

☐ Did not work today; instead, I:

{20 }

S M T W T F S

Today I mostly prospected:

	DISCUSSIONS	
L	DAILY TRACKER	B
	PRESENTATIONS	
	CLIENTS	
	CONTRACTS	
	TRANSACTIONS	

☐ Did not work today; instead, I:

{20 }

S M T W T F S

Today I mostly prospected:

	DISCUSSIONS	
L	DAILY TRACKER	B
	PRESENTATIONS	
	CLIENTS	
	CONTRACTS	
	TRANSACTIONS	

☐ Did not work today; instead, I:

October

Do you have a strategy for sellers who wanna make repairs before listing?[200] *How do your systems manage their improvements?*

{20 }

{20 }

{20 }

{20 }
S M T W T F S
Today I mostly prospected:

L	DISCUSSIONS	B
	DAILY TRACKER	
	PRESENTATIONS	
	CLIENTS	
	CONTRACTS	
	TRANSACTIONS	

☐ Did not work today; instead, I:

{20 }
S M T W T F S
Today I mostly prospected:

L	DISCUSSIONS	B
	DAILY TRACKER	
	PRESENTATIONS	
	CLIENTS	
	CONTRACTS	
	TRANSACTIONS	

☐ Did not work today; instead, I:

{20 }
S M T W T F S
Today I mostly prospected:

L	DISCUSSIONS	B
	DAILY TRACKER	
	PRESENTATIONS	
	CLIENTS	
	CONTRACTS	
	TRANSACTIONS	

☐ Did not work today; instead, I:

October

19

Where else could you be looking for buyers and sellers? Name three new ways to meet prospects[084] *and a plan to implement.*

{20 }

{20 }

{20 }

{20 }

S M T W T F S

Today I mostly prospected:

	DISCUSSIONS	
L	DAILY TRACKER	B
	PRESENTATIONS	
	CLIENTS	
	CONTRACTS	
	TRANSACTIONS	

☐ Did not work today; instead, I:

{20 }

S M T W T F S

Today I mostly prospected:

	DISCUSSIONS	
L	DAILY TRACKER	B
	PRESENTATIONS	
	CLIENTS	
	CONTRACTS	
	TRANSACTIONS	

☐ Did not work today; instead, I:

{20 }

S M T W T F S

Today I mostly prospected:

	DISCUSSIONS	
L	DAILY TRACKER	B
	PRESENTATIONS	
	CLIENTS	
	CONTRACTS	
	TRANSACTIONS	

☐ Did not work today; instead, I:

20 October

List three systems that need improvement.[070]
Reward yourself with deadlines.

{20 }

{20 }

{20 }

{20 }

S M T W T F S

Today I mostly prospected:

	DISCUSSIONS	
L	DAILY TRACKER	B
	PRESENTATIONS	
	CLIENTS	
	CONTRACTS	
	TRANSACTIONS	

☐ Did not work today; instead, I:

{20 }

S M T W T F S

Today I mostly prospected:

	DISCUSSIONS	
L	DAILY TRACKER	B
	PRESENTATIONS	
	CLIENTS	
	CONTRACTS	
	TRANSACTIONS	

☐ Did not work today; instead, I:

{20 }

S M T W T F S

Today I mostly prospected:

	DISCUSSIONS	
L	DAILY TRACKER	B
	PRESENTATIONS	
	CLIENTS	
	CONTRACTS	
	TRANSACTIONS	

☐ Did not work today; instead, I:

October

21

List twenty words that describe your state of affairs (including finances).

{20 }

{20 }

{20 }

{20 }
S M T W T F S
Today I mostly prospected:

L	DAILY TRACKER	B
	DISCUSSIONS	
	PRESENTATIONS	
	CLIENTS	
	CONTRACTS	
	TRANSACTIONS	

☐ Did not work today; instead, I:

{20 }
S M T W T F S
Today I mostly prospected:

L	DAILY TRACKER	B
	DISCUSSIONS	
	PRESENTATIONS	
	CLIENTS	
	CONTRACTS	
	TRANSACTIONS	

☐ Did not work today; instead, I:

{20 }
S M T W T F S
Today I mostly prospected:

L	DAILY TRACKER	B
	DISCUSSIONS	
	PRESENTATIONS	
	CLIENTS	
	CONTRACTS	
	TRANSACTIONS	

☐ Did not work today; instead, I:

22 October

Today is Get Off the Fence Day.
Describe a current dilemma and choose a side.

{20 }

{20 }

{20 }

{20 }

S M T W T F S

Today I mostly prospected:

	DISCUSSIONS	
L	DAILY TRACKER	B
	PRESENTATIONS	
	CLIENTS	
	CONTRACTS	
	TRANSACTIONS	

☐ Did not work today; instead, I:

{20 }

S M T W T F S

Today I mostly prospected:

	DISCUSSIONS	
L	DAILY TRACKER	B
	PRESENTATIONS	
	CLIENTS	
	CONTRACTS	
	TRANSACTIONS	

☐ Did not work today; instead, I:

{20 }

S M T W T F S

Today I mostly prospected:

	DISCUSSIONS	
L	DAILY TRACKER	B
	PRESENTATIONS	
	CLIENTS	
	CONTRACTS	
	TRANSACTIONS	

☐ Did not work today; instead, I:

October

23

Write a script for this objection:
"I've never heard of your company.
I should hire an agent with a brand I recognize."

{20 }

{20 }

{20 }

{20 }

S M T W T F S

Today I mostly prospected:

	DISCUSSIONS	
L	DAILY TRACKER	B
	PRESENTATIONS	
	CLIENTS	
	CONTRACTS	
	TRANSACTIONS	

☐ Did not work today; instead, I:

{20 }

S M T W T F S

Today I mostly prospected:

	DISCUSSIONS	
L	DAILY TRACKER	B
	PRESENTATIONS	
	CLIENTS	
	CONTRACTS	
	TRANSACTIONS	

☐ Did not work today; instead, I:

{20 }

S M T W T F S

Today I mostly prospected:

	DISCUSSIONS	
L	DAILY TRACKER	B
	PRESENTATIONS	
	CLIENTS	
	CONTRACTS	
	TRANSACTIONS	

☐ Did not work today; instead, I:

24 October

If your business had a nickname, what would it be? Explain yourself.

{20 }

{20 }

{20 }

{20 }

S M T W T F S

Today I mostly prospected:

L	DAILY TRACKER	B
	DISCUSSIONS	
	PRESENTATIONS	
	CLIENTS	
	CONTRACTS	
	TRANSACTIONS	

☐ Did not work today; instead, I:

{20 }

S M T W T F S

Today I mostly prospected:

L	DAILY TRACKER	B
	DISCUSSIONS	
	PRESENTATIONS	
	CLIENTS	
	CONTRACTS	
	TRANSACTIONS	

☐ Did not work today; instead, I:

{20 }

S M T W T F S

Today I mostly prospected:

L	DAILY TRACKER	B
	DISCUSSIONS	
	PRESENTATIONS	
	CLIENTS	
	CONTRACTS	
	TRANSACTIONS	

☐ Did not work today; instead, I:

October

25

How often are you reducing the prices of your listings?[202]
What would make the endeavor less of a hassle?

{20 }

{20 }

{20 }

{20 }

S M T W T F S

Today I mostly prospected:

	DISCUSSIONS	
L	DAILY TRACKER	B
	PRESENTATIONS	
	CLIENTS	
	CONTRACTS	
	TRANSACTIONS	

☐ Did not work today; instead, I:

{20 }

S M T W T F S

Today I mostly prospected:

	DISCUSSIONS	
L	DAILY TRACKER	B
	PRESENTATIONS	
	CLIENTS	
	CONTRACTS	
	TRANSACTIONS	

☐ Did not work today; instead, I:

{20 }

S M T W T F S

Today I mostly prospected:

	DISCUSSIONS	
L	DAILY TRACKER	B
	PRESENTATIONS	
	CLIENTS	
	CONTRACTS	
	TRANSACTIONS	

☐ Did not work today; instead, I:

October

What advice would you give to the you from last year?

{20 }

{20 }

{20 }

{20 }

S M T W T F S

Today I mostly prospected:

	DISCUSSIONS	
L	DAILY TRACKER	B
	PRESENTATIONS	
	CLIENTS	
	CONTRACTS	
	TRANSACTIONS	

☐ Did not work today; instead, I:

{20 }

S M T W T F S

Today I mostly prospected:

	DISCUSSIONS	
L	DAILY TRACKER	B
	PRESENTATIONS	
	CLIENTS	
	CONTRACTS	
	TRANSACTIONS	

☐ Did not work today; instead, I:

{20 }

S M T W T F S

Today I mostly prospected:

	DISCUSSIONS	
L	DAILY TRACKER	B
	PRESENTATIONS	
	CLIENTS	
	CONTRACTS	
	TRANSACTIONS	

☐ Did not work today; instead, I:

October

27

Write a script for this objection:
"We're gonna list after the holidays."

{20 }

{20 }

{20 }

{20 }	{20 }	{20 }
S M T W T F S	S M T W T F S	S M T W T F S
Today I mostly prospected:	Today I mostly prospected:	Today I mostly prospected:

	DISCUSSIONS	
L	DAILY TRACKER	B
	PRESENTATIONS	
	CLIENTS	
	CONTRACTS	
	TRANSACTIONS	

	DISCUSSIONS	
L	DAILY TRACKER	B
	PRESENTATIONS	
	CLIENTS	
	CONTRACTS	
	TRANSACTIONS	

	DISCUSSIONS	
L	DAILY TRACKER	B
	PRESENTATIONS	
	CLIENTS	
	CONTRACTS	
	TRANSACTIONS	

☐ Did not work today; instead, I:

☐ Did not work today; instead, I:

☐ Did not work today; instead, I:

28 October

Do you have any trick shots?[305]
Describe your current favorite.
Otherwise, where might a new one prove handy?

{20 }

{20 }

{20 }

{20 }		
S M T W T F S		
Today I mostly prospected:		
	DISCUSSIONS	
L	DAILY TRACKER	B
	PRESENTATIONS	
	CLIENTS	
	CONTRACTS	
	TRANSACTIONS	
☐ Did not work today; instead, I:		

{20 }		
S M T W T F S		
Today I mostly prospected:		
	DISCUSSIONS	
L	DAILY TRACKER	B
	PRESENTATIONS	
	CLIENTS	
	CONTRACTS	
	TRANSACTIONS	
☐ Did not work today; instead, I:		

{20 }		
S M T W T F S		
Today I mostly prospected:		
	DISCUSSIONS	
L	DAILY TRACKER	B
	PRESENTATIONS	
	CLIENTS	
	CONTRACTS	
	TRANSACTIONS	
☐ Did not work today; instead, I:		

October

29

My grandest achievement this month was...
My plan to repeat this victory is...

{20 }

{20 }

{20 }

{20 }

S M T W T F S

Today I mostly prospected:

	DISCUSSIONS	
L	DAILY TRACKER	B
	PRESENTATIONS	
	CLIENTS	
	CONTRACTS	
	TRANSACTIONS	

☐ Did not work today; instead, I:

{20 }

S M T W T F S

Today I mostly prospected:

	DISCUSSIONS	
L	DAILY TRACKER	B
	PRESENTATIONS	
	CLIENTS	
	CONTRACTS	
	TRANSACTIONS	

☐ Did not work today; instead, I:

{20 }

S M T W T F S

Today I mostly prospected:

	DISCUSSIONS	
L	DAILY TRACKER	B
	PRESENTATIONS	
	CLIENTS	
	CONTRACTS	
	TRANSACTIONS	

☐ Did not work today; instead, I:

30 October

The biggest mistake/misstep I made this month was...
My plan to prevent the same mishap from recurring is...

{20 }

{20 }

{20 }

{20 }
S M T W T F S
Today I mostly prospected:

	DISCUSSIONS	
L	DAILY TRACKER	B
	PRESENTATIONS	
	CLIENTS	
	CONTRACTS	
	TRANSACTIONS	

☐ Did not work today; instead, I:

{20 }
S M T W T F S
Today I mostly prospected:

	DISCUSSIONS	
L	DAILY TRACKER	B
	PRESENTATIONS	
	CLIENTS	
	CONTRACTS	
	TRANSACTIONS	

☐ Did not work today; instead, I:

{20 }
S M T W T F S
Today I mostly prospected:

	DISCUSSIONS	
L	DAILY TRACKER	B
	PRESENTATIONS	
	CLIENTS	
	CONTRACTS	
	TRANSACTIONS	

☐ Did not work today; instead, I:

October

31

Today is Halloween.
Which part of your business is the most scary (something you dread doing)? How can you overcome this fear?

{20 }

{20 }

{20 }

{20 }

S M T W T F S

Today I mostly prospected:

	DISCUSSIONS	
L	DAILY TRACKER	B
	PRESENTATIONS	
	CLIENTS	
	CONTRACTS	
	TRANSACTIONS	

☐ Did not work today; instead, I:

{20 }

S M T W T F S

Today I mostly prospected:

	DISCUSSIONS	
L	DAILY TRACKER	B
	PRESENTATIONS	
	CLIENTS	
	CONTRACTS	
	TRANSACTIONS	

☐ Did not work today; instead, I:

{20 }

S M T W T F S

Today I mostly prospected:

	DISCUSSIONS	
L	DAILY TRACKER	B
	PRESENTATIONS	
	CLIENTS	
	CONTRACTS	
	TRANSACTIONS	

☐ Did not work today; instead, I:

{20 }

MONTHLY ACTIVITY TRACKER (GOALS→RESULTS)

GOALS	ACTIVITY	WK 1	WK 2	WK 3	WK 4	WK 5	TOTAL RESULTS
	TRANSACTIONS (T)	L B	L B	L B	L B	L B	L B
	NEW CLIENTS (C)	L B	L B	L B	L B	L B	L B
	PRESENTATIONS (P)	L B	L B	L B	L B	L B	L B
	DISCUSSIONS (D)						
	DAYS WORKED (W)						
	DAILY DISCUSSIONS (D/W)	ACTUAL DAILY DISCUSSION AVERAGE				D/W	
$	GCI	$					

{20 }

MONTHLY ACTIVITY TRACKER (GOALS→RESULTS)

GOALS	ACTIVITY	WK 1	WK 2	WK 3	WK 4	WK 5	TOTAL RESULTS
	TRANSACTIONS (T)	L B	L B	L B	L B	L B	L B
	NEW CLIENTS (C)	L B	L B	L B	L B	L B	L B
	PRESENTATIONS (P)	L B	L B	L B	L B	L B	L B
	DISCUSSIONS (D)						
	DAYS WORKED (W)						
	DAILY DISCUSSIONS (D/W)	ACTUAL DAILY DISCUSSION AVERAGE				D/W	
$	GCI	$					

{20 }

MONTHLY ACTIVITY TRACKER (GOALS→RESULTS)

GOALS	ACTIVITY	WK 1	WK 2	WK 3	WK 4	WK 5	TOTAL RESULTS
	TRANSACTIONS (T)	L B	L B	L B	L B	L B	L B
	NEW CLIENTS (C)	L B	L B	L B	L B	L B	L B
	PRESENTATIONS (P)	L B	L B	L B	L B	L B	L B
	DISCUSSIONS (D)						
	DAYS WORKED (W)						
	DAILY DISCUSSIONS (D/W)	ACTUAL DAILY DISCUSSION AVERAGE				D/W	
$	GCI	$					

November

01

Today is Business Plan Day.[XVIII]
Review/revise yours, and contemplate the past/future.
What is your plan to improve upon last month's performance?

{20 }

{20 }

{20 }

{20 }

S M T W T F S

Today I mostly prospected:

	DISCUSSIONS	
L	DAILY TRACKER	B
	PRESENTATIONS	
	CLIENTS	
	CONTRACTS	
	TRANSACTIONS	

☐ Did not work today; instead, I:

{20 }

S M T W T F S

Today I mostly prospected:

	DISCUSSIONS	
L	DAILY TRACKER	B
	PRESENTATIONS	
	CLIENTS	
	CONTRACTS	
	TRANSACTIONS	

☐ Did not work today; instead, I:

{20 }

S M T W T F S

Today I mostly prospected:

	DISCUSSIONS	
L	DAILY TRACKER	B
	PRESENTATIONS	
	CLIENTS	
	CONTRACTS	
	TRANSACTIONS	

☐ Did not work today; instead, I:

02

November

List a good habit you wanna adopt this month. How will you implement and make it a permanent part of your routine? Has last month's habit stuck yet?

{20 }

{20 }

{20 }

{20 }
S M T W T F S
Today I mostly prospected:

	DISCUSSIONS	
L	DAILY TRACKER	B
	PRESENTATIONS	
	CLIENTS	
	CONTRACTS	
	TRANSACTIONS	

☐ Did not work today; instead, I:

{20 }
S M T W T F S
Today I mostly prospected:

	DISCUSSIONS	
L	DAILY TRACKER	B
	PRESENTATIONS	
	CLIENTS	
	CONTRACTS	
	TRANSACTIONS	

☐ Did not work today; instead, I:

{20 }
S M T W T F S
Today I mostly prospected:

	DISCUSSIONS	
L	DAILY TRACKER	B
	PRESENTATIONS	
	CLIENTS	
	CONTRACTS	
	TRANSACTIONS	

☐ Did not work today; instead, I:

November

Do you utilize a pre-listing package?[193]
What format do you use? What's included? Does it need an update?
What has been the reaction of prospects?

{20 }

{20 }

{20 }

{20 }		
S M T W T F S		
Today I mostly prospected:		
	DISCUSSIONS	
L	DAILY TRACKER	B
	PRESENTATIONS	
	CLIENTS	
	CONTRACTS	
	TRANSACTIONS	
☐ Did not work today; instead, I:		

{20 }		
S M T W T F S		
Today I mostly prospected:		
	DISCUSSIONS	
L	DAILY TRACKER	B
	PRESENTATIONS	
	CLIENTS	
	CONTRACTS	
	TRANSACTIONS	
☐ Did not work today; instead, I:		

{20 }		
S M T W T F S		
Today I mostly prospected:		
	DISCUSSIONS	
L	DAILY TRACKER	B
	PRESENTATIONS	
	CLIENTS	
	CONTRACTS	
	TRANSACTIONS	
☐ Did not work today; instead, I:		

04 November

List ten words to describe your conversion ratios/turnover rates.
Would you share your list with others?
Of which are you the most proud? disappointed?

{20 } ____________________

{20 } ____________________

{20 } ____________________

{20 }	{20 }	{20 }
S M T W T F S	S M T W T F S	S M T W T F S
Today I mostly prospected:	Today I mostly prospected:	Today I mostly prospected:
DISCUSSIONS	DISCUSSIONS	DISCUSSIONS
L : DAILY TRACKER : B	L : DAILY TRACKER : B	L : DAILY TRACKER : B
PRESENTATIONS	PRESENTATIONS	PRESENTATIONS
CLIENTS	CLIENTS	CLIENTS
CONTRACTS	CONTRACTS	CONTRACTS
TRANSACTIONS	TRANSACTIONS	TRANSACTIONS
☐ Did not work today; instead, I:	☐ Did not work today; instead, I:	☐ Did not work today; instead, I:

November

05

How many different ways do you prospect for clients?[084]
Which ones provide the most presentations? ...the least?
Should you alter your strategy?[004]

{20 }

{20 }

{20 }

{20 }
S M T W T F S
Today I mostly prospected:

	DISCUSSIONS	
L	DAILY TRACKER	B
	PRESENTATIONS	
	CLIENTS	
	CONTRACTS	
	TRANSACTIONS	

☐ Did not work today; instead, I:

{20 }
S M T W T F S
Today I mostly prospected:

	DISCUSSIONS	
L	DAILY TRACKER	B
	PRESENTATIONS	
	CLIENTS	
	CONTRACTS	
	TRANSACTIONS	

☐ Did not work today; instead, I:

{20 }
S M T W T F S
Today I mostly prospected:

	DISCUSSIONS	
L	DAILY TRACKER	B
	PRESENTATIONS	
	CLIENTS	
	CONTRACTS	
	TRANSACTIONS	

☐ Did not work today; instead, I:

06

November

Do you have a real estate coach?[043]
If YES: *how has the coach helped you?*
If NO: *which part of your business would benefit from coaching?*

{20 } ______

{20 } ______

{20 } ______

{20 }		
S M T W T F S		
Today I mostly prospected:		
	DISCUSSIONS	
L	DAILY TRACKER	B
	PRESENTATIONS	
	CLIENTS	
	CONTRACTS	
	TRANSACTIONS	
☐ Did not work today; instead, I:		

{20 }		
S M T W T F S		
Today I mostly prospected:		
	DISCUSSIONS	
L	DAILY TRACKER	B
	PRESENTATIONS	
	CLIENTS	
	CONTRACTS	
	TRANSACTIONS	
☐ Did not work today; instead, I:		

{20 }		
S M T W T F S		
Today I mostly prospected:		
	DISCUSSIONS	
L	DAILY TRACKER	B
	PRESENTATIONS	
	CLIENTS	
	CONTRACTS	
	TRANSACTIONS	
☐ Did not work today; instead, I:		

November

07

What is your favorite part of real estate sales?
What is your least favorite?
Explain yourself.

{20 }

{20 }

{20 }

{20 }

S M T W T F S

Today I mostly prospected:

	DISCUSSIONS	
L	DAILY TRACKER	B
	PRESENTATIONS	
	CLIENTS	
	CONTRACTS	
	TRANSACTIONS	

☐ Did not work today; instead, I:

{20 }

S M T W T F S

Today I mostly prospected:

	DISCUSSIONS	
L	DAILY TRACKER	B
	PRESENTATIONS	
	CLIENTS	
	CONTRACTS	
	TRANSACTIONS	

☐ Did not work today; instead, I:

{20 }

S M T W T F S

Today I mostly prospected:

	DISCUSSIONS	
L	DAILY TRACKER	B
	PRESENTATIONS	
	CLIENTS	
	CONTRACTS	
	TRANSACTIONS	

☐ Did not work today; instead, I:

08

November

Write a script for this expired seller objection:
"If you're so great, then why didn't you sell it when it was listed with my last agent."

{20 }

{20 }

{20 }

{20 }

S M T W T F S

Today I mostly prospected:

	DISCUSSIONS	
L	DAILY TRACKER	B
	PRESENTATIONS	
	CLIENTS	
	CONTRACTS	
	TRANSACTIONS	

☐ Did not work today; instead, I:

{20 }

S M T W T F S

Today I mostly prospected:

	DISCUSSIONS	
L	DAILY TRACKER	B
	PRESENTATIONS	
	CLIENTS	
	CONTRACTS	
	TRANSACTIONS	

☐ Did not work today; instead, I:

{20 }

S M T W T F S

Today I mostly prospected:

	DISCUSSIONS	
L	DAILY TRACKER	B
	PRESENTATIONS	
	CLIENTS	
	CONTRACTS	
	TRANSACTIONS	

☐ Did not work today; instead, I:

November

09

Name one thing that would lower your lost opportunity differential (LOD).[XVII]

{20 }

{20 }

{20 }

{20 }

S M T W T F S

Today I mostly prospected:

L	DAILY TRACKER	B
	DISCUSSIONS	
	PRESENTATIONS	
	CLIENTS	
	CONTRACTS	
	TRANSACTIONS	

☐ Did not work today; instead, I:

{20 }

S M T W T F S

Today I mostly prospected:

L	DAILY TRACKER	B
	DISCUSSIONS	
	PRESENTATIONS	
	CLIENTS	
	CONTRACTS	
	TRANSACTIONS	

☐ Did not work today; instead, I:

{20 }

S M T W T F S

Today I mostly prospected:

L	DAILY TRACKER	B
	DISCUSSIONS	
	PRESENTATIONS	
	CLIENTS	
	CONTRACTS	
	TRANSACTIONS	

☐ Did not work today; instead, I:

10

November

Rank your open house attendance on a scale of one to ten.[240]
How could you improve attendance?

{20 }

{20 }

{20 }

{20 }	{20 }	{20 }
S M T W T F S	S M T W T F S	S M T W T F S
Today I mostly prospected:	Today I mostly prospected:	Today I mostly prospected:
DISCUSSIONS	DISCUSSIONS	DISCUSSIONS
L · DAILY TRACKER · B	L · DAILY TRACKER · B	L · DAILY TRACKER · B
PRESENTATIONS	PRESENTATIONS	PRESENTATIONS
CLIENTS	CLIENTS	CLIENTS
CONTRACTS	CONTRACTS	CONTRACTS
TRANSACTIONS	TRANSACTIONS	TRANSACTIONS
☐ Did not work today; instead, I:	☐ Did not work today; instead, I:	☐ Did not work today; instead, I:

November

11

Today is Veterans Day.
How do you show your appreciation?
What kind of war are you currently waging?

{20 }

{20 }

{20 }

{20 }

S M T W T F S

Today I mostly prospected:

	DISCUSSIONS	
L	DAILY TRACKER	B
	PRESENTATIONS	
	CLIENTS	
	CONTRACTS	
	TRANSACTIONS	

☐ Did not work today; instead, I:

{20 }

S M T W T F S

Today I mostly prospected:

	DISCUSSIONS	
L	DAILY TRACKER	B
	PRESENTATIONS	
	CLIENTS	
	CONTRACTS	
	TRANSACTIONS	

☐ Did not work today; instead, I:

{20 }

S M T W T F S

Today I mostly prospected:

	DISCUSSIONS	
L	DAILY TRACKER	B
	PRESENTATIONS	
	CLIENTS	
	CONTRACTS	
	TRANSACTIONS	

☐ Did not work today; instead, I:

12

November

How could you lower expenses without harming client services? Otherwise, how could you increase GCI *without raising expenses?*

{20 }

{20 }

{20 }

{20 }	{20 }	{20 }
S M T W T F S	S M T W T F S	S M T W T F S
Today I mostly prospected:	Today I mostly prospected:	Today I mostly prospected:
DISCUSSIONS	DISCUSSIONS	DISCUSSIONS
L DAILY TRACKER B	L DAILY TRACKER B	L DAILY TRACKER B
PRESENTATIONS	PRESENTATIONS	PRESENTATIONS
CLIENTS	CLIENTS	CLIENTS
CONTRACTS	CONTRACTS	CONTRACTS
TRANSACTIONS	TRANSACTIONS	TRANSACTIONS
☐ Did not work today; instead, I:	☐ Did not work today; instead, I:	☐ Did not work today; instead, I:

November

13

Are your emotions intertwined with your business?[310]
When things get hot,
how do you keep your cool?[313]

{20 }

{20 }

{20 }

{20 }

S M T W T F S

Today I mostly prospected:

	DISCUSSIONS	
L	DAILY TRACKER	B
	PRESENTATIONS	
	CLIENTS	
	CONTRACTS	
	TRANSACTIONS	

☐ Did not work today; instead, I:

{20 }

S M T W T F S

Today I mostly prospected:

	DISCUSSIONS	
L	DAILY TRACKER	B
	PRESENTATIONS	
	CLIENTS	
	CONTRACTS	
	TRANSACTIONS	

☐ Did not work today; instead, I:

{20 }

S M T W T F S

Today I mostly prospected:

	DISCUSSIONS	
L	DAILY TRACKER	B
	PRESENTATIONS	
	CLIENTS	
	CONTRACTS	
	TRANSACTIONS	

☐ Did not work today; instead, I:

14 November

Recall a recent class or educational session.
What was the number one thing you learned?
How will you implement it into your business?

{20 }

{20 }

{20 }

{20 }

S M T W T F S

Today I mostly prospected:

	DISCUSSIONS	
L	DAILY TRACKER	B
	PRESENTATIONS	
	CLIENTS	
	CONTRACTS	
	TRANSACTIONS	

☐ Did not work today; instead, I:

{20 }

S M T W T F S

Today I mostly prospected:

	DISCUSSIONS	
L	DAILY TRACKER	B
	PRESENTATIONS	
	CLIENTS	
	CONTRACTS	
	TRANSACTIONS	

☐ Did not work today; instead, I:

{20 }

S M T W T F S

Today I mostly prospected:

	DISCUSSIONS	
L	DAILY TRACKER	B
	PRESENTATIONS	
	CLIENTS	
	CONTRACTS	
	TRANSACTIONS	

☐ Did not work today; instead, I:

November

15

Are you falling behind (or surging ahead) on any monthly goals? What's your plan to achieve them all?[XIX] *Adjust your activities now, so you will meet or exceed all.*

{20 } ______________________________

{20 } ______________________________

{20 } ______________________________

{20 }

S M T W T F S

Today I mostly prospected:

L	DAILY TRACKER	B
	DISCUSSIONS	
	PRESENTATIONS	
	CLIENTS	
	CONTRACTS	
	TRANSACTIONS	

☐ Did not work today; instead, I:

{20 }

S M T W T F S

Today I mostly prospected:

L	DAILY TRACKER	B
	DISCUSSIONS	
	PRESENTATIONS	
	CLIENTS	
	CONTRACTS	
	TRANSACTIONS	

☐ Did not work today; instead, I:

{20 }

S M T W T F S

Today I mostly prospected:

L	DAILY TRACKER	B
	DISCUSSIONS	
	PRESENTATIONS	
	CLIENTS	
	CONTRACTS	
	TRANSACTIONS	

☐ Did not work today; instead, I:

16

November

Write an affirmation to soothe your prospecting pains. Otherwise, write one to encourage your enthusiasm.

{20 }

{20 }

{20 }

{20 }

S M T W T F S

Today I mostly prospected:

	DISCUSSIONS	
L	DAILY TRACKER	B
	PRESENTATIONS	
	CLIENTS	
	CONTRACTS	
	TRANSACTIONS	

☐ Did not work today; instead, I:

{20 }

S M T W T F S

Today I mostly prospected:

	DISCUSSIONS	
L	DAILY TRACKER	B
	PRESENTATIONS	
	CLIENTS	
	CONTRACTS	
	TRANSACTIONS	

☐ Did not work today; instead, I:

{20 }

S M T W T F S

Today I mostly prospected:

	DISCUSSIONS	
L	DAILY TRACKER	B
	PRESENTATIONS	
	CLIENTS	
	CONTRACTS	
	TRANSACTIONS	

☐ Did not work today; instead, I:

November

17

Do you preview property before showing to buyers?[223]
Otherwise, how do you save clients' time in the field?

{20 }

{20 }

{20 }

{20 }

S	M	T	W	T	F	S

Today I mostly prospected:

	DISCUSSIONS	
L	DAILY TRACKER	B
	PRESENTATIONS	
	CLIENTS	
	CONTRACTS	
	TRANSACTIONS	

☐ Did not work today; instead, I:

{20 }

S	M	T	W	T	F	S

Today I mostly prospected:

	DISCUSSIONS	
L	DAILY TRACKER	B
	PRESENTATIONS	
	CLIENTS	
	CONTRACTS	
	TRANSACTIONS	

☐ Did not work today; instead, I:

{20 }

S	M	T	W	T	F	S

Today I mostly prospected:

	DISCUSSIONS	
L	DAILY TRACKER	B
	PRESENTATIONS	
	CLIENTS	
	CONTRACTS	
	TRANSACTIONS	

☐ Did not work today; instead, I:

November

The three greatest reasons to hire me are...

{20 }

{20 }

{20 }

{20 }
S M T W T F S
Today I mostly prospected:

	DISCUSSIONS	
L	DAILY TRACKER	B
	PRESENTATIONS	
	CLIENTS	
	CONTRACTS	
	TRANSACTIONS	

☐ Did not work today; instead, I:

{20 }
S M T W T F S
Today I mostly prospected:

	DISCUSSIONS	
L	DAILY TRACKER	B
	PRESENTATIONS	
	CLIENTS	
	CONTRACTS	
	TRANSACTIONS	

☐ Did not work today; instead, I:

{20 }
S M T W T F S
Today I mostly prospected:

	DISCUSSIONS	
L	DAILY TRACKER	B
	PRESENTATIONS	
	CLIENTS	
	CONTRACTS	
	TRANSACTIONS	

☐ Did not work today; instead, I:

November

19

Today is Clean-Up Your Presentations Day.[167]
List three ways your presentations could be improved
(consider scripts, props, delivery,..).

{20 }

{20 }

{20 }

{20 }

S M T W T F S

Today I mostly prospected:

	DISCUSSIONS	
L	DAILY TRACKER	B
	PRESENTATIONS	
	CLIENTS	
	CONTRACTS	
	TRANSACTIONS	

☐ Did not work today; instead, I:

{20 }

S M T W T F S

Today I mostly prospected:

	DISCUSSIONS	
L	DAILY TRACKER	B
	PRESENTATIONS	
	CLIENTS	
	CONTRACTS	
	TRANSACTIONS	

☐ Did not work today; instead, I:

{20 }

S M T W T F S

Today I mostly prospected:

	DISCUSSIONS	
L	DAILY TRACKER	B
	PRESENTATIONS	
	CLIENTS	
	CONTRACTS	
	TRANSACTIONS	

☐ Did not work today; instead, I:

20

November

If your business was a video game,
would you save the princess or are you stuck on a lower level?
Explain yourself.

{20 }

{20 }

{20 }

{20 }	{20 }	{20 }
S M T W T F S	S M T W T F S	S M T W T F S
Today I mostly prospected:	Today I mostly prospected:	Today I mostly prospected:

	DISCUSSIONS	
L	DAILY TRACKER	B
	PRESENTATIONS	
	CLIENTS	
	CONTRACTS	
	TRANSACTIONS	

☐ Did not work today; instead, I:

	DISCUSSIONS	
L	DAILY TRACKER	B
	PRESENTATIONS	
	CLIENTS	
	CONTRACTS	
	TRANSACTIONS	

☐ Did not work today; instead, I:

	DISCUSSIONS	
L	DAILY TRACKER	B
	PRESENTATIONS	
	CLIENTS	
	CONTRACTS	
	TRANSACTIONS	

☐ Did not work today; instead, I:

November

21

Who is your best resource for real estate questions?[038]
How do you return the favor?

{20 }

{20 }

{20 }

{20 }		
S M T W T F S		
Today I mostly prospected:		
	DISCUSSIONS	
L	DAILY TRACKER	B
	PRESENTATIONS	
	CLIENTS	
	CONTRACTS	
	TRANSACTIONS	
☐ Did not work today; instead, I:		

{20 }		
S M T W T F S		
Today I mostly prospected:		
	DISCUSSIONS	
L	DAILY TRACKER	B
	PRESENTATIONS	
	CLIENTS	
	CONTRACTS	
	TRANSACTIONS	
☐ Did not work today; instead, I:		

{20 }		
S M T W T F S		
Today I mostly prospected:		
	DISCUSSIONS	
L	DAILY TRACKER	B
	PRESENTATIONS	
	CLIENTS	
	CONTRACTS	
	TRANSACTIONS	
☐ Did not work today; instead, I:		

22 November

List twenty words that describe your business stats.[x] *Which ones would you like to change?*

{20 }

{20 }

{20 }

{20 }	{20 }	{20 }
S M T W T F S	S M T W T F S	S M T W T F S
Today I mostly prospected:	Today I mostly prospected:	Today I mostly prospected:

L	DAILY TRACKER	B	L	DAILY TRACKER	B	L	DAILY TRACKER	B
	DISCUSSIONS			DISCUSSIONS			DISCUSSIONS	
	PRESENTATIONS			PRESENTATIONS			PRESENTATIONS	
	CLIENTS			CLIENTS			CLIENTS	
	CONTRACTS			CONTRACTS			CONTRACTS	
	TRANSACTIONS			TRANSACTIONS			TRANSACTIONS	

☐ Did not work today; instead, I: ☐ Did not work today; instead, I: ☐ Did not work today; instead, I:

November

23

A funny (real estate related) thing happened recently...

{20 }

{20 }

{20 }

{20 }
S M T W T F S
Today I mostly prospected:

	DISCUSSIONS	
L	DAILY TRACKER	B
	PRESENTATIONS	
	CLIENTS	
	CONTRACTS	
	TRANSACTIONS	

☐ Did not work today; instead, I:

{20 }
S M T W T F S
Today I mostly prospected:

	DISCUSSIONS	
L	DAILY TRACKER	B
	PRESENTATIONS	
	CLIENTS	
	CONTRACTS	
	TRANSACTIONS	

☐ Did not work today; instead, I:

{20 }
S M T W T F S
Today I mostly prospected:

	DISCUSSIONS	
L	DAILY TRACKER	B
	PRESENTATIONS	
	CLIENTS	
	CONTRACTS	
	TRANSACTIONS	

☐ Did not work today; instead, I:

24 November

What is the best advice you've recently received?
Have you implemented it into your life?

{20 }

{20 }

{20 }

{20 }
S M T W T F S
Today I mostly prospected:

	DISCUSSIONS	
L	DAILY TRACKER	B
	PRESENTATIONS	
	CLIENTS	
	CONTRACTS	
	TRANSACTIONS	

☐ Did not work today; instead, I:

{20 }
S M T W T F S
Today I mostly prospected:

	DISCUSSIONS	
L	DAILY TRACKER	B
	PRESENTATIONS	
	CLIENTS	
	CONTRACTS	
	TRANSACTIONS	

☐ Did not work today; instead, I:

{20 }
S M T W T F S
Today I mostly prospected:

	DISCUSSIONS	
L	DAILY TRACKER	B
	PRESENTATIONS	
	CLIENTS	
	CONTRACTS	
	TRANSACTIONS	

☐ Did not work today; instead, I:

November

25

List three things for which you are thankful.

{20 }

{20 }

{20 }

{20 }		
S M T W T F S		
Today I mostly prospected:		
	DISCUSSIONS	
L	DAILY TRACKER	B
	PRESENTATIONS	
	CLIENTS	
	CONTRACTS	
	TRANSACTIONS	
☐ Did not work today; instead, I:		

{20 }		
S M T W T F S		
Today I mostly prospected:		
	DISCUSSIONS	
L	DAILY TRACKER	B
	PRESENTATIONS	
	CLIENTS	
	CONTRACTS	
	TRANSACTIONS	
☐ Did not work today; instead, I:		

{20 }		
S M T W T F S		
Today I mostly prospected:		
	DISCUSSIONS	
L	DAILY TRACKER	B
	PRESENTATIONS	
	CLIENTS	
	CONTRACTS	
	TRANSACTIONS	
☐ Did not work today; instead, I:		

26 November

Recall a recent tough conversation.[215]
How did you perform?
What was the outcome?[214]

{20 }

{20 }

{20 }

{20 }

S M T W T F S

Today I mostly prospected:

L	DISCUSSIONS	B
	DAILY TRACKER	
	PRESENTATIONS	
	CLIENTS	
	CONTRACTS	
	TRANSACTIONS	

☐ Did not work today; instead, I:

{20 }

S M T W T F S

Today I mostly prospected:

L	DISCUSSIONS	B
	DAILY TRACKER	
	PRESENTATIONS	
	CLIENTS	
	CONTRACTS	
	TRANSACTIONS	

☐ Did not work today; instead, I:

{20 }

S M T W T F S

Today I mostly prospected:

L	DISCUSSIONS	B
	DAILY TRACKER	
	PRESENTATIONS	
	CLIENTS	
	CONTRACTS	
	TRANSACTIONS	

☐ Did not work today; instead, I:

November

27

Name one thing that would improve your return on days worked (ROW).[XVI]

{20 }

{20 }

{20 }

{20 }		
S M T W T F S		
Today I mostly prospected:		
	DISCUSSIONS	
L	DAILY TRACKER	B
	PRESENTATIONS	
	CLIENTS	
	CONTRACTS	
	TRANSACTIONS	
☐ Did not work today; instead, I:		

{20 }		
S M T W T F S		
Today I mostly prospected:		
	DISCUSSIONS	
L	DAILY TRACKER	B
	PRESENTATIONS	
	CLIENTS	
	CONTRACTS	
	TRANSACTIONS	
☐ Did not work today; instead, I:		

{20 }		
S M T W T F S		
Today I mostly prospected:		
	DISCUSSIONS	
L	DAILY TRACKER	B
	PRESENTATIONS	
	CLIENTS	
	CONTRACTS	
	TRANSACTIONS	
☐ Did not work today; instead, I:		

28 November

Write a script for this prospect objection:
"I've heard your presentation;
now I need a few days to think things over."

{20 } ____________________

{20 } ____________________

{20 } ____________________

{20 }

S M T W T F S

Today I mostly prospected:

L	DISCUSSIONS	B
	DAILY TRACKER	
	PRESENTATIONS	
	CLIENTS	
	CONTRACTS	
	TRANSACTIONS	

☐ Did not work today; instead, I:

{20 }

S M T W T F S

Today I mostly prospected:

L	DISCUSSIONS	B
	DAILY TRACKER	
	PRESENTATIONS	
	CLIENTS	
	CONTRACTS	
	TRANSACTIONS	

☐ Did not work today; instead, I:

{20 }

S M T W T F S

Today I mostly prospected:

L	DISCUSSIONS	B
	DAILY TRACKER	
	PRESENTATIONS	
	CLIENTS	
	CONTRACTS	
	TRANSACTIONS	

☐ Did not work today; instead, I:

November

29

My grandest achievement this month was...
My plan to repeat this victory is...

{20 }

{20 }

{20 }

{20 }

S M T W T F S

Today I mostly prospected:

L	DAILY TRACKER	B
	DISCUSSIONS	
	PRESENTATIONS	
	CLIENTS	
	CONTRACTS	
	TRANSACTIONS	

☐ Did not work today; instead, I:

{20 }

S M T W T F S

Today I mostly prospected:

L	DAILY TRACKER	B
	DISCUSSIONS	
	PRESENTATIONS	
	CLIENTS	
	CONTRACTS	
	TRANSACTIONS	

☐ Did not work today; instead, I:

{20 }

S M T W T F S

Today I mostly prospected:

L	DAILY TRACKER	B
	DISCUSSIONS	
	PRESENTATIONS	
	CLIENTS	
	CONTRACTS	
	TRANSACTIONS	

☐ Did not work today; instead, I:

30 November

The biggest mistake/misstep I made this month was...
My plan to prevent the same mishap from recurring is...

{20 }

{20 }

{20 }

{20 }

S M T W T F S

Today I mostly prospected:

DISCUSSIONS

L	DAILY TRACKER	B
	PRESENTATIONS	
	CLIENTS	
	CONTRACTS	
	TRANSACTIONS	

☐ Did not work today; instead, I:

{20 }

S M T W T F S

Today I mostly prospected:

DISCUSSIONS

L	DAILY TRACKER	B
	PRESENTATIONS	
	CLIENTS	
	CONTRACTS	
	TRANSACTIONS	

☐ Did not work today; instead, I:

{20 }

S M T W T F S

Today I mostly prospected:

DISCUSSIONS

L	DAILY TRACKER	B
	PRESENTATIONS	
	CLIENTS	
	CONTRACTS	
	TRANSACTIONS	

☐ Did not work today; instead, I:

{20 }

MONTHLY ACTIVITY TRACKER (GOALS→RESULTS)

GOALS	ACTIVITY	WK 1	WK 2	WK 3	WK 4	WK 5	TOTAL RESULTS
	TRANSACTIONS (T)	L B	L B	L B	L B	L B	L B
	NEW CLIENTS (C)	L B	L B	L B	L B	L B	L B
	PRESENTATIONS (P)	L B	L B	L B	L B	L B	L B
	DISCUSSIONS (D)						
	DAYS WORKED (W)						
	DAILY DISCUSSIONS (D/W)	ACTUAL DAILY DISCUSSION AVERAGE				D/W	
$	GCI	$					

{20 }

MONTHLY ACTIVITY TRACKER (GOALS→RESULTS)

GOALS	ACTIVITY	WK 1	WK 2	WK 3	WK 4	WK 5	TOTAL RESULTS
	TRANSACTIONS (T)	L B	L B	L B	L B	L B	L B
	NEW CLIENTS (C)	L B	L B	L B	L B	L B	L B
	PRESENTATIONS (P)	L B	L B	L B	L B	L B	L B
	DISCUSSIONS (D)						
	DAYS WORKED (W)						
	DAILY DISCUSSIONS (D/W)	ACTUAL DAILY DISCUSSION AVERAGE				D/W	
$	GCI	$					

{20 }

MONTHLY ACTIVITY TRACKER (GOALS→RESULTS)

GOALS	ACTIVITY	WK 1	WK 2	WK 3	WK 4	WK 5	TOTAL RESULTS
	TRANSACTIONS (T)	L B	L B	L B	L B	L B	L B
	NEW CLIENTS (C)	L B	L B	L B	L B	L B	L B
	PRESENTATIONS (P)	L B	L B	L B	L B	L B	L B
	DISCUSSIONS (D)						
	DAYS WORKED (W)						
	DAILY DISCUSSIONS (D/W)	ACTUAL DAILY DISCUSSION AVERAGE				D/W	
$	GCI	$					

December

01

Today is Business Plan Day.[XVIII]
Review/revise yours, and contemplate the past/future.
What is your plan to improve upon last month's performance?

{20 }

{20 }

{20 }

{20 }

S M T W T F S

Today I mostly prospected:

	DISCUSSIONS	
L	DAILY TRACKER	B
	PRESENTATIONS	
	CLIENTS	
	CONTRACTS	
	TRANSACTIONS	

☐ Did not work today; instead, I:

{20 }

S M T W T F S

Today I mostly prospected:

	DISCUSSIONS	
L	DAILY TRACKER	B
	PRESENTATIONS	
	CLIENTS	
	CONTRACTS	
	TRANSACTIONS	

☐ Did not work today; instead, I:

{20 }

S M T W T F S

Today I mostly prospected:

	DISCUSSIONS	
L	DAILY TRACKER	B
	PRESENTATIONS	
	CLIENTS	
	CONTRACTS	
	TRANSACTIONS	

☐ Did not work today; instead, I:

02

December

List a good habit you wanna adopt this month. How will you implement and make it a permanent part of your routine? Has last month's habit stuck yet?

{20 }

{20 }

{20 }

{20 }
S M T W T F S
Today I mostly prospected:

	DISCUSSIONS	
L	DAILY TRACKER	B
	PRESENTATIONS	
	CLIENTS	
	CONTRACTS	
	TRANSACTIONS	

☐ Did not work today; instead, I:

{20 }
S M T W T F S
Today I mostly prospected:

	DISCUSSIONS	
L	DAILY TRACKER	B
	PRESENTATIONS	
	CLIENTS	
	CONTRACTS	
	TRANSACTIONS	

☐ Did not work today; instead, I:

{20 }
S M T W T F S
Today I mostly prospected:

	DISCUSSIONS	
L	DAILY TRACKER	B
	PRESENTATIONS	
	CLIENTS	
	CONTRACTS	
	TRANSACTIONS	

☐ Did not work today; instead, I:

December

03

List ten words that describe you.
Which new words on the list are surprising to you?
Which ones should you be sharing with prospects?

{20 }

{20 }

{20 }

{20 }

S M T W T F S

Today I mostly prospected:

L	DISCUSSIONS	B
	DAILY TRACKER	
	PRESENTATIONS	
	CLIENTS	
	CONTRACTS	
	TRANSACTIONS	

☐ Did not work today; instead, I:

{20 }

S M T W T F S

Today I mostly prospected:

L	DISCUSSIONS	B
	DAILY TRACKER	
	PRESENTATIONS	
	CLIENTS	
	CONTRACTS	
	TRANSACTIONS	

☐ Did not work today; instead, I:

{20 }

S M T W T F S

Today I mostly prospected:

L	DISCUSSIONS	B
	DAILY TRACKER	
	PRESENTATIONS	
	CLIENTS	
	CONTRACTS	
	TRANSACTIONS	

☐ Did not work today; instead, I:

04

December

When was the last time you tried something new?
What was the result?
Would you do it again?

{20 }

{20 }

{20 }

{20 }

S M T W T F S

Today I mostly prospected:

	DISCUSSIONS	
L	DAILY TRACKER	B
	PRESENTATIONS	
	CLIENTS	
	CONTRACTS	
	TRANSACTIONS	

☐ Did not work today; instead, I:

{20 }

S M T W T F S

Today I mostly prospected:

	DISCUSSIONS	
L	DAILY TRACKER	B
	PRESENTATIONS	
	CLIENTS	
	CONTRACTS	
	TRANSACTIONS	

☐ Did not work today; instead, I:

{20 }

S M T W T F S

Today I mostly prospected:

	DISCUSSIONS	
L	DAILY TRACKER	B
	PRESENTATIONS	
	CLIENTS	
	CONTRACTS	
	TRANSACTIONS	

☐ Did not work today; instead, I:

December

05

How often do you work during the holiday season?
What has been the result on your wallet/psyche?

{20 }

{20 }

{20 }

{20 }

S M T W T F S

Today I mostly prospected:

	DISCUSSIONS	
L	DAILY TRACKER	B
	PRESENTATIONS	
	CLIENTS	
	CONTRACTS	
	TRANSACTIONS	

☐ Did not work today; instead, I:

{20 }

S M T W T F S

Today I mostly prospected:

	DISCUSSIONS	
L	DAILY TRACKER	B
	PRESENTATIONS	
	CLIENTS	
	CONTRACTS	
	TRANSACTIONS	

☐ Did not work today; instead, I:

{20 }

S M T W T F S

Today I mostly prospected:

	DISCUSSIONS	
L	DAILY TRACKER	B
	PRESENTATIONS	
	CLIENTS	
	CONTRACTS	
	TRANSACTIONS	

☐ Did not work today; instead, I:

06 December

Write a script for this objection from a listing agent: "Get real. I won't take this low-ball offer to my seller. Your buyer needs to be serious."

{20 }

{20 }

{20 }

{20 }
S M T W T F S
Today I mostly prospected:

L	DAILY TRACKER	B
	DISCUSSIONS	
	PRESENTATIONS	
	CLIENTS	
	CONTRACTS	
	TRANSACTIONS	

☐ Did not work today; instead, I:

{20 }
S M T W T F S
Today I mostly prospected:

L	DAILY TRACKER	B
	DISCUSSIONS	
	PRESENTATIONS	
	CLIENTS	
	CONTRACTS	
	TRANSACTIONS	

☐ Did not work today; instead, I:

{20 }
S M T W T F S
Today I mostly prospected:

L	DAILY TRACKER	B
	DISCUSSIONS	
	PRESENTATIONS	
	CLIENTS	
	CONTRACTS	
	TRANSACTIONS	

☐ Did not work today; instead, I:

December

07

Name your biggest advocates (those who send you referrals)?
How do you show your gratitude?
How could you find more advocates?

{20 }

{20 }

{20 }

{20 }

S M T W T F S

Today I mostly prospected:

	DISCUSSIONS	
L	DAILY TRACKER	B
	PRESENTATIONS	
	CLIENTS	
	CONTRACTS	
	TRANSACTIONS	

☐ Did not work today; instead, I:

{20 }

S M T W T F S

Today I mostly prospected:

	DISCUSSIONS	
L	DAILY TRACKER	B
	PRESENTATIONS	
	CLIENTS	
	CONTRACTS	
	TRANSACTIONS	

☐ Did not work today; instead, I:

{20 }

S M T W T F S

Today I mostly prospected:

	DISCUSSIONS	
L	DAILY TRACKER	B
	PRESENTATIONS	
	CLIENTS	
	CONTRACTS	
	TRANSACTIONS	

☐ Did not work today; instead, I:

08

December

Are you a listing slut?[190]
Or are you a choosy agent?
Justify your position with a new script.

{20 }

{20 }

{20 }

{20 }		
S M T W T F S		
Today I mostly prospected:		
	DISCUSSIONS	
L	DAILY TRACKER	B
	PRESENTATIONS	
	CLIENTS	
	CONTRACTS	
	TRANSACTIONS	
☐ Did not work today; instead, I:		

{20 }		
S M T W T F S		
Today I mostly prospected:		
	DISCUSSIONS	
L	DAILY TRACKER	B
	PRESENTATIONS	
	CLIENTS	
	CONTRACTS	
	TRANSACTIONS	
☐ Did not work today; instead, I:		

{20 }		
S M T W T F S		
Today I mostly prospected:		
	DISCUSSIONS	
L	DAILY TRACKER	B
	PRESENTATIONS	
	CLIENTS	
	CONTRACTS	
	TRANSACTIONS	
☐ Did not work today; instead, I:		

December

09

Recall a recent good deed done.
What was it? How did it make you feel?
How did the recipient react?

{20 }

{20 }

{20 }

{20 }

S M T W T F S

Today I mostly prospected:

	DISCUSSIONS	
L	DAILY TRACKER	B
	PRESENTATIONS	
	CLIENTS	
	CONTRACTS	
	TRANSACTIONS	

☐ Did not work today; instead, I:

{20 }

S M T W T F S

Today I mostly prospected:

	DISCUSSIONS	
L	DAILY TRACKER	B
	PRESENTATIONS	
	CLIENTS	
	CONTRACTS	
	TRANSACTIONS	

☐ Did not work today; instead, I:

{20 }

S M T W T F S

Today I mostly prospected:

	DISCUSSIONS	
L	DAILY TRACKER	B
	PRESENTATIONS	
	CLIENTS	
	CONTRACTS	
	TRANSACTIONS	

☐ Did not work today; instead, I:

10 December

Name one thing that would improve your contract turnover rate (KTR).[XVI]

{20 }

{20 }

{20 }

{20 }

S M T W T F S

Today I mostly prospected:

	DISCUSSIONS	
L	DAILY TRACKER	B
	PRESENTATIONS	
	CLIENTS	
	CONTRACTS	
	TRANSACTIONS	

☐ Did not work today; instead, I:

{20 }

S M T W T F S

Today I mostly prospected:

	DISCUSSIONS	
L	DAILY TRACKER	B
	PRESENTATIONS	
	CLIENTS	
	CONTRACTS	
	TRANSACTIONS	

☐ Did not work today; instead, I:

{20 }

S M T W T F S

Today I mostly prospected:

	DISCUSSIONS	
L	DAILY TRACKER	B
	PRESENTATIONS	
	CLIENTS	
	CONTRACTS	
	TRANSACTIONS	

☐ Did not work today; instead, I:

December

11

Are your listings winning the real estate beauty contest?[229] *What could you do to raise the eyebrows of buyers far and wide?*

{20 }

{20 }

{20 }

{20 }		
S M T W T F S		
Today I mostly prospected:		
	DISCUSSIONS	
L	DAILY TRACKER	B
	PRESENTATIONS	
	CLIENTS	
	CONTRACTS	
	TRANSACTIONS	
☐ Did not work today; instead, I:		

{20 }		
S M T W T F S		
Today I mostly prospected:		
	DISCUSSIONS	
L	DAILY TRACKER	B
	PRESENTATIONS	
	CLIENTS	
	CONTRACTS	
	TRANSACTIONS	
☐ Did not work today; instead, I:		

{20 }		
S M T W T F S		
Today I mostly prospected:		
	DISCUSSIONS	
L	DAILY TRACKER	B
	PRESENTATIONS	
	CLIENTS	
	CONTRACTS	
	TRANSACTIONS	
☐ Did not work today; instead, I:		

12

December

How could you increase GCI without adding time to your day? List three ways and a plan to implement.

{20 } ______________________________

{20 } ______________________________

{20 } ______________________________

{20 }

S M T W T F S

Today I mostly prospected:

L	DISCUSSIONS	B
	DAILY TRACKER	
	PRESENTATIONS	
	CLIENTS	
	CONTRACTS	
	TRANSACTIONS	

☐ Did not work today; instead, I:

{20 }

S M T W T F S

Today I mostly prospected:

L	DISCUSSIONS	B
	DAILY TRACKER	
	PRESENTATIONS	
	CLIENTS	
	CONTRACTS	
	TRANSACTIONS	

☐ Did not work today; instead, I:

{20 }

S M T W T F S

Today I mostly prospected:

L	DISCUSSIONS	B
	DAILY TRACKER	
	PRESENTATIONS	
	CLIENTS	
	CONTRACTS	
	TRANSACTIONS	

☐ Did not work today; instead, I:

December

13

What keeps you motivated to prospect?[300]
What keeps you prospecting
on days you'd rather do something else?

{20 }

{20 }

{20 }

{20 }		
S M T W T F S		
Today I mostly prospected:		
	DISCUSSIONS	
L	DAILY TRACKER	B
	PRESENTATIONS	
	CLIENTS	
	CONTRACTS	
	TRANSACTIONS	
☐ Did not work today; instead, I:		

{20 }		
S M T W T F S		
Today I mostly prospected:		
	DISCUSSIONS	
L	DAILY TRACKER	B
	PRESENTATIONS	
	CLIENTS	
	CONTRACTS	
	TRANSACTIONS	
☐ Did not work today; instead, I:		

{20 }		
S M T W T F S		
Today I mostly prospected:		
	DISCUSSIONS	
L	DAILY TRACKER	B
	PRESENTATIONS	
	CLIENTS	
	CONTRACTS	
	TRANSACTIONS	
☐ Did not work today; instead, I:		

14 December

Are you falling behind (or surging ahead) on any monthly goals?
What's your plan to achieve them all?[XIX]
Adjust your activities now, so you will meet or exceed all.

{20 } ______________________________

{20 } ______________________________

{20 } ______________________________

{20 }

S M T W T F S

Today I mostly prospected:

L	DAILY TRACKER	B
	DISCUSSIONS	
	PRESENTATIONS	
	CLIENTS	
	CONTRACTS	
	TRANSACTIONS	

☐ Did not work today; instead, I:

{20 }

S M T W T F S

Today I mostly prospected:

L	DAILY TRACKER	B
	DISCUSSIONS	
	PRESENTATIONS	
	CLIENTS	
	CONTRACTS	
	TRANSACTIONS	

☐ Did not work today; instead, I:

{20 }

S M T W T F S

Today I mostly prospected:

L	DAILY TRACKER	B
	DISCUSSIONS	
	PRESENTATIONS	
	CLIENTS	
	CONTRACTS	
	TRANSACTIONS	

☐ Did not work today; instead, I:

December

15

What would make your prospecting efforts more efficient?[012]
How could your message reach more prospects in less time?
How could you increase your discussion turnover rate (DTR)?[XVI]

{20 }

{20 }

{20 }

{20 }		
S M T W T F S		
Today I mostly prospected:		
	DISCUSSIONS	
L	DAILY TRACKER	B
	PRESENTATIONS	
	CLIENTS	
	CONTRACTS	
	TRANSACTIONS	
☐ Did not work today; instead, I:		

{20 }		
S M T W T F S		
Today I mostly prospected:		
	DISCUSSIONS	
L	DAILY TRACKER	B
	PRESENTATIONS	
	CLIENTS	
	CONTRACTS	
	TRANSACTIONS	
☐ Did not work today; instead, I:		

{20 }		
S M T W T F S		
Today I mostly prospected:		
	DISCUSSIONS	
L	DAILY TRACKER	B
	PRESENTATIONS	
	CLIENTS	
	CONTRACTS	
	TRANSACTIONS	
☐ Did not work today; instead, I:		

16

December

Where else could you be looking for buyers and sellers? Name three new ways to meet prospects[084] and a plan to implement.

{20 }

{20 }

{20 }

{20 }	{20 }	{20 }
S M T W T F S	S M T W T F S	S M T W T F S
Today I mostly prospected:	Today I mostly prospected:	Today I mostly prospected:
DISCUSSIONS	DISCUSSIONS	DISCUSSIONS
L · DAILY TRACKER · B	L · DAILY TRACKER · B	L · DAILY TRACKER · B
PRESENTATIONS	PRESENTATIONS	PRESENTATIONS
CLIENTS	CLIENTS	CLIENTS
CONTRACTS	CONTRACTS	CONTRACTS
TRANSACTIONS	TRANSACTIONS	TRANSACTIONS
☐ Did not work today; instead, I:	☐ Did not work today; instead, I:	☐ Did not work today; instead, I:

December

17

Name one thing that would improve the effectiveness of your presentations.[168]

{20 }

{20 }

{20 }

{20 }
S M T W T F S
Today I mostly prospected:
DISCUSSIONS
L · DAILY TRACKER · B
PRESENTATIONS
CLIENTS
CONTRACTS
TRANSACTIONS
☐ Did not work today; instead, I:

{20 }
S M T W T F S
Today I mostly prospected:
DISCUSSIONS
L · DAILY TRACKER · B
PRESENTATIONS
CLIENTS
CONTRACTS
TRANSACTIONS
☐ Did not work today; instead, I:

{20 }
S M T W T F S
Today I mostly prospected:
DISCUSSIONS
L · DAILY TRACKER · B
PRESENTATIONS
CLIENTS
CONTRACTS
TRANSACTIONS
☐ Did not work today; instead, I:

December

Winter has dawned, and the new year approaches.
What will be your resolution?[078]
Who can you call for a referral?

{20 }

{20 }

{20 }

{20 }
S M T W T F S
Today I mostly prospected:

	DISCUSSIONS	
L	DAILY TRACKER	B
	PRESENTATIONS	
	CLIENTS	
	CONTRACTS	
	TRANSACTIONS	

☐ Did not work today; instead, I:

{20 }
S M T W T F S
Today I mostly prospected:

	DISCUSSIONS	
L	DAILY TRACKER	B
	PRESENTATIONS	
	CLIENTS	
	CONTRACTS	
	TRANSACTIONS	

☐ Did not work today; instead, I:

{20 }
S M T W T F S
Today I mostly prospected:

	DISCUSSIONS	
L	DAILY TRACKER	B
	PRESENTATIONS	
	CLIENTS	
	CONTRACTS	
	TRANSACTIONS	

☐ Did not work today; instead, I:

December

19

How does the holiday season make you feel?
Describe your favorite tradition.

{20 }

{20 }

{20 }

{20 }

S M T W T F S

Today I mostly prospected:

	DISCUSSIONS	
L	DAILY TRACKER	B
	PRESENTATIONS	
	CLIENTS	
	CONTRACTS	
	TRANSACTIONS	

☐ Did not work today; instead, I:

{20 }

S M T W T F S

Today I mostly prospected:

	DISCUSSIONS	
L	DAILY TRACKER	B
	PRESENTATIONS	
	CLIENTS	
	CONTRACTS	
	TRANSACTIONS	

☐ Did not work today; instead, I:

{20 }

S M T W T F S

Today I mostly prospected:

	DISCUSSIONS	
L	DAILY TRACKER	B
	PRESENTATIONS	
	CLIENTS	
	CONTRACTS	
	TRANSACTIONS	

☐ Did not work today; instead, I:

20 December

List twenty words that describe your hopes for the future.

{20 }

{20 }

{20 }

{20 }
S M T W T F S
Today I mostly prospected:

	DISCUSSIONS	
L	DAILY TRACKER	B
	PRESENTATIONS	
	CLIENTS	
	CONTRACTS	
	TRANSACTIONS	

☐ Did not work today; instead, I:

{20 }
S M T W T F S
Today I mostly prospected:

	DISCUSSIONS	
L	DAILY TRACKER	B
	PRESENTATIONS	
	CLIENTS	
	CONTRACTS	
	TRANSACTIONS	

☐ Did not work today; instead, I:

{20 }
S M T W T F S
Today I mostly prospected:

	DISCUSSIONS	
L	DAILY TRACKER	B
	PRESENTATIONS	
	CLIENTS	
	CONTRACTS	
	TRANSACTIONS	

☐ Did not work today; instead, I:

December

21

Today is Bacon Day.
Write about a guilty pleasure/favorite pastime?
Might you find prospects hidden in the same niche?

{20 }

{20 }

{20 }

{20 }

S M T W T F S

Today I mostly prospected:

	DISCUSSIONS	
L	DAILY TRACKER	B
	PRESENTATIONS	
	CLIENTS	
	CONTRACTS	
	TRANSACTIONS	

☐ Did not work today; instead, I:

{20 }

S M T W T F S

Today I mostly prospected:

	DISCUSSIONS	
L	DAILY TRACKER	B
	PRESENTATIONS	
	CLIENTS	
	CONTRACTS	
	TRANSACTIONS	

☐ Did not work today; instead, I:

{20 }

S M T W T F S

Today I mostly prospected:

	DISCUSSIONS	
L	DAILY TRACKER	B
	PRESENTATIONS	
	CLIENTS	
	CONTRACTS	
	TRANSACTIONS	

☐ Did not work today; instead, I:

22 December

Today is Clean-Up Your Business Day.
List three systems that need improvement.[070]
How can you be more effective/efficient?

{20 }

{20 }

{20 }

{20 }	{20 }	{20 }
S M T W T F S	S M T W T F S	S M T W T F S
Today I mostly prospected:	Today I mostly prospected:	Today I mostly prospected:
DISCUSSIONS	DISCUSSIONS	DISCUSSIONS
L · DAILY TRACKER · B	L · DAILY TRACKER · B	L · DAILY TRACKER · B
PRESENTATIONS	PRESENTATIONS	PRESENTATIONS
CLIENTS	CLIENTS	CLIENTS
CONTRACTS	CONTRACTS	CONTRACTS
TRANSACTIONS	TRANSACTIONS	TRANSACTIONS
☐ Did not work today; instead, I:	☐ Did not work today; instead, I:	☐ Did not work today; instead, I:

December

23

How will your business be different this time next year?
Be specific.

{20 }

{20 }

{20 }

{20 }

S M T W T F S

Today I mostly prospected:

	DISCUSSIONS	
L	DAILY TRACKER	B
	PRESENTATIONS	
	CLIENTS	
	CONTRACTS	
	TRANSACTIONS	

☐ Did not work today; instead, I:

{20 }

S M T W T F S

Today I mostly prospected:

	DISCUSSIONS	
L	DAILY TRACKER	B
	PRESENTATIONS	
	CLIENTS	
	CONTRACTS	
	TRANSACTIONS	

☐ Did not work today; instead, I:

{20 }

S M T W T F S

Today I mostly prospected:

	DISCUSSIONS	
L	DAILY TRACKER	B
	PRESENTATIONS	
	CLIENTS	
	CONTRACTS	
	TRANSACTIONS	

☐ Did not work today; instead, I:

24 December

What was the largest commission check you earned this year?
What was the smallest?
Which transaction meant the most to you? Why?

{20 }

{20 }

{20 }

{20 }

S M T W T F S

Today I mostly prospected:

L	DAILY TRACKER	B
	DISCUSSIONS	
	PRESENTATIONS	
	CLIENTS	
	CONTRACTS	
	TRANSACTIONS	

☐ Did not work today; instead, I:

{20 }

S M T W T F S

Today I mostly prospected:

L	DAILY TRACKER	B
	DISCUSSIONS	
	PRESENTATIONS	
	CLIENTS	
	CONTRACTS	
	TRANSACTIONS	

☐ Did not work today; instead, I:

{20 }

S M T W T F S

Today I mostly prospected:

L	DAILY TRACKER	B
	DISCUSSIONS	
	PRESENTATIONS	
	CLIENTS	
	CONTRACTS	
	TRANSACTIONS	

☐ Did not work today; instead, I:

December

25

Today is Christmas Day.
Do you give closing gifts to clients?[307]
Do you always give the same gift, or customize it to each client?

{20 } ______

{20 } ______

{20 } ______

{20 }	{20 }	{20 }
S M T W T F S	S M T W T F S	S M T W T F S
Today I mostly prospected:	Today I mostly prospected:	Today I mostly prospected:

	DISCUSSIONS	
L	DAILY TRACKER	B
	PRESENTATIONS	
	CLIENTS	
	CONTRACTS	
	TRANSACTIONS	

☐ Did not work today; instead, I:

	DISCUSSIONS	
L	DAILY TRACKER	B
	PRESENTATIONS	
	CLIENTS	
	CONTRACTS	
	TRANSACTIONS	

☐ Did not work today; instead, I:

	DISCUSSIONS	
L	DAILY TRACKER	B
	PRESENTATIONS	
	CLIENTS	
	CONTRACTS	
	TRANSACTIONS	

☐ Did not work today; instead, I:

December

Write a script for this prospect objection:
"You're too new for me (or you don't sell enough in my area), so I need to hire someone else."

{20 }

{20 }

{20 }

{20 }	{20 }	{20 }
S M T W T F S	S M T W T F S	S M T W T F S
Today I mostly prospected:	Today I mostly prospected:	Today I mostly prospected:

	DISCUSSIONS	
L	DAILY TRACKER	B
	PRESENTATIONS	
	CLIENTS	
	CONTRACTS	
	TRANSACTIONS	

	DISCUSSIONS	
L	DAILY TRACKER	B
	PRESENTATIONS	
	CLIENTS	
	CONTRACTS	
	TRANSACTIONS	

	DISCUSSIONS	
L	DAILY TRACKER	B
	PRESENTATIONS	
	CLIENTS	
	CONTRACTS	
	TRANSACTIONS	

☐ Did not work today; instead, I:

☐ Did not work today; instead, I:

☐ Did not work today; instead, I:

December

27

Summarize this past year with one word, then explain yourself.

{20 }

{20 }

{20 }

{20 }

S M T W T F S

Today I mostly prospected:

	DISCUSSIONS	
L	DAILY TRACKER	B
	PRESENTATIONS	
	CLIENTS	
	CONTRACTS	
	TRANSACTIONS	

☐ Did not work today; instead, I:

{20 }

S M T W T F S

Today I mostly prospected:

	DISCUSSIONS	
L	DAILY TRACKER	B
	PRESENTATIONS	
	CLIENTS	
	CONTRACTS	
	TRANSACTIONS	

☐ Did not work today; instead, I:

{20 }

S M T W T F S

Today I mostly prospected:

	DISCUSSIONS	
L	DAILY TRACKER	B
	PRESENTATIONS	
	CLIENTS	
	CONTRACTS	
	TRANSACTIONS	

☐ Did not work today; instead, I:

December

My grandest achievement this month was...
My plan to repeat this victory is...

{20 }

{20 }

{20 }

{20 }

S M T W T F S

Today I mostly prospected:

	DISCUSSIONS	
L	DAILY TRACKER	B
	PRESENTATIONS	
	CLIENTS	
	CONTRACTS	
	TRANSACTIONS	

☐ Did not work today; instead, I:

{20 }

S M T W T F S

Today I mostly prospected:

	DISCUSSIONS	
L	DAILY TRACKER	B
	PRESENTATIONS	
	CLIENTS	
	CONTRACTS	
	TRANSACTIONS	

☐ Did not work today; instead, I:

{20 }

S M T W T F S

Today I mostly prospected:

	DISCUSSIONS	
L	DAILY TRACKER	B
	PRESENTATIONS	
	CLIENTS	
	CONTRACTS	
	TRANSACTIONS	

☐ Did not work today; instead, I:

December

29

The biggest mistake/misstep I made this month was...
My plan to prevent the same mishap from recurring is...

{20 }

{20 }

{20 }

{20 }

S M T W T F S

Today I mostly prospected:

L	DAILY TRACKER	B
	DISCUSSIONS	
	PRESENTATIONS	
	CLIENTS	
	CONTRACTS	
	TRANSACTIONS	

☐ Did not work today; instead, I:

{20 }

S M T W T F S

Today I mostly prospected:

L	DAILY TRACKER	B
	DISCUSSIONS	
	PRESENTATIONS	
	CLIENTS	
	CONTRACTS	
	TRANSACTIONS	

☐ Did not work today; instead, I:

{20 }

S M T W T F S

Today I mostly prospected:

L	DAILY TRACKER	B
	DISCUSSIONS	
	PRESENTATIONS	
	CLIENTS	
	CONTRACTS	
	TRANSACTIONS	

☐ Did not work today; instead, I:

30 December

Summarize the last three months with one word.
Given the opportunity, would you take a do-over?
Which parts would you like to forget?.. never forget?

{20 }

{20 }

{20 }

{20 }

S M T W T F S

Today I mostly prospected:

L	DAILY TRACKER	B
	DISCUSSIONS	
	PRESENTATIONS	
	CLIENTS	
	CONTRACTS	
	TRANSACTIONS	

☐ Did not work today; instead, I:

{20 }

S M T W T F S

Today I mostly prospected:

L	DAILY TRACKER	B
	DISCUSSIONS	
	PRESENTATIONS	
	CLIENTS	
	CONTRACTS	
	TRANSACTIONS	

☐ Did not work today; instead, I:

{20 }

S M T W T F S

Today I mostly prospected:

L	DAILY TRACKER	B
	DISCUSSIONS	
	PRESENTATIONS	
	CLIENTS	
	CONTRACTS	
	TRANSACTIONS	

☐ Did not work today; instead, I:

December

31

How do you plan to ring-in the new year?
Recall your fondest memory of the year.

{20 }

{20 }

{20 }

{20 }

S M T W T F S

Today I mostly prospected:

	DISCUSSIONS	
L	DAILY TRACKER	B
	PRESENTATIONS	
	CLIENTS	
	CONTRACTS	
	TRANSACTIONS	

☐ Did not work today; instead, I:

{20 }

S M T W T F S

Today I mostly prospected:

	DISCUSSIONS	
L	DAILY TRACKER	B
	PRESENTATIONS	
	CLIENTS	
	CONTRACTS	
	TRANSACTIONS	

☐ Did not work today; instead, I:

{20 }

S M T W T F S

Today I mostly prospected:

	DISCUSSIONS	
L	DAILY TRACKER	B
	PRESENTATIONS	
	CLIENTS	
	CONTRACTS	
	TRANSACTIONS	

☐ Did not work today; instead, I:

ACTIVITY LOG

JANUARY

DISCUSSIONS (D)	PRESENTATIONS (P)	CLIENTS (C)	CONTRACTS (K)	TRANSACTIONS (T)
#D; Δ | #	#LP; Δ | #	#LC; Δ | #	#LK; Δ | #	#LT; Δ | #
DAYS WORKED (W)	#BP; Δ | #	#BC; Δ | #	#BK; Δ | #	#BT; Δ | #
#W; Δ | #	#P; Δ | #	#C; Δ | #	#K; Δ | #	#T; Δ | #

FEBRUARY

DISCUSSIONS (D)	PRESENTATIONS (P)	CLIENTS (C)	CONTRACTS (K)	TRANSACTIONS (T)
#D; Δ | #	#LP; Δ | #	#LC; Δ | #	#LK; Δ | #	#LT; Δ | #
DAYS WORKED (W)	#BP; Δ | #	#BC; Δ | #	#BK; Δ | #	#BT; Δ | #
#W; Δ | #	#P; Δ | #	#C; Δ | #	#K; Δ | #	#T; Δ | #

MARCH

DISCUSSIONS (D)	PRESENTATIONS (P)	CLIENTS (C)	CONTRACTS (K)	TRANSACTIONS (T)
#D; Δ | #	#LP; Δ | #	#LC; Δ | #	#LK; Δ | #	#LT; Δ | #
DAYS WORKED (W)	#BP; Δ | #	#BC; Δ | #	#BK; Δ | #	#BT; Δ | #
#W; Δ | #	#P; Δ | #	#C; Δ | #	#K; Δ | #	#T; Δ | #

QUARTER 01

DISCUSSIONS (D)	PRESENTATIONS (P)	CLIENTS (C)	CONTRACTS (K)	TRANSACTIONS (T)
#D; Δ | #	#LP; Δ | #	#LC; Δ | #	#LK; Δ | #	#LT; Δ | #
DAYS WORKED (W)	#BP; Δ | #	#BC; Δ | #	#BK; Δ | #	#BT; Δ | #
#W; Δ | #	#P; Δ | #	#C; Δ | #	#K; Δ | #	#T; Δ | #

QUARTERLY TRANSACTION DATA

GROSS COMMISSION INCOME (GCI)	DAYS ON MARKET (DOM)
LGCI $; Δ | $	LDOM DAYS; Δ | DAYS
BGCI $; Δ | $	BDOM DAYS; Δ | DAYS
GCI $; Δ | $	DOM DAYS; Δ | DAYS
SALES VOLUME (V)	**ORIGINAL PRICE VOLUME (OPV)**
LV $; Δ | $	LOPV $; Δ | $
BV $; Δ | $	BOPV $; Δ | $
V $; Δ | $	OPV $; Δ | $

MARKET COMPARISON

	#TRANSACTIONS	Δ	AVERAGE TRANS. PRICE (ATP)	AVG. LDOM	SP/LP
METRO		|	$; Δ | $		%
MACRO #1		|	$; Δ | $		%
MACRO #2		|	$; Δ | $		%
MACRO #3		|	$; Δ | $		%
PERSONAL		|	$; Δ | $		%

During Quarter 01, I mostly prospected:	1	2	3

CONVERSION RATIOS & TURNOVER RATES

	CONVERSION RATIOS		TURNOVER	Δ	L TURNOVER	Δ	B TURNOVER	Δ
DISCUSSIONS TO PRESENTATIONS	$\frac{\#D}{\#P}$ =	D:P	DTR $\frac{\#P}{\#D}$ = %	%	$\frac{\#LP}{\#D}$ = %	%	$\frac{\#BP}{\#D}$ = %	%
PRESENTATIONS TO CLIENTS	$\frac{\#P}{\#C}$ =	P:C	PTR $\frac{\#C}{\#P}$ = %	%	$\frac{\#LC}{\#LP}$ = %	%	$\frac{\#BC}{\#BP}$ = %	%
CLIENTS TO TRANSACTIONS	$\frac{\#C}{\#T}$ =	T:C	CTR $\frac{\#T}{\#C}$ = %	%	$\frac{\#LT}{\#LC}$ = %	%	$\frac{\#BT}{\#BC}$ = %	%
CONTRACTS TO TRANSACTIONS	$\frac{\#K}{\#T}$ =	K:T	KTR $\frac{\#T}{\#K}$ = %	%	$\frac{\#LT}{\#LK}$ = %	%	$\frac{\#BT}{\#BK}$ = %	%

METRICS

AVERAGE COMMISSION RATE (ACR)	AVERAGE TRANSACTION PRICE (ATP)	CLIENT TURNOVER RATE (CTR)
$\frac{GCI}{V}$ = %; Δ | %	$\frac{V}{T}$ = $; Δ | $	$\frac{T}{C}$ = %; Δ | %
RETURN ON PRESENTATIONS (ROP)	**RETURN ON TRANSACTIONS (ROT)**	**RETURN ON CLIENTS (ROC)**
$\frac{GCI}{P}$ = $; Δ | $	$\frac{GCI}{T}$ = $; Δ | $	$\frac{GCI}{C}$ = $; Δ | $
AVG. LIST DAYS ON MKT (AVG. LDOM)	**SALES PRICE TO LIST PRICE (SP/LP)**	**RETURN ON DAYS WORKED (ROW)**
$\frac{LDOM}{LT}$ = DAYS; Δ | DAYS	$\frac{LV}{LOPV}$ = %; Δ | %	$\frac{GCI}{W}$ = $; Δ | $

LEVERAGE LOG

Be mindful of Buyer, Listing, and Overall figures when applying these formulas.[XVII]

$$\frac{GCI}{V} \times \frac{V}{T} \times \frac{T}{C} = \frac{GCI}{C} \qquad \frac{GCI}{T} - \frac{GCI}{C}$$

QUARTER 01	AVERAGE COMMISSION RATE	AVERAGE TRANSACTION PRICE	CLIENT TURNOVER RATE	RETURN ON CLIENTS	LOST OPPORTUNITY DIFFERENTIAL
LISTINGS	%	$	%	$	$
BUYERS	%	$	%	$	$
OVERALL	%	$	%	$	$

BUSINESS PLAN (FOR EACH MONTH OF QUARTER 02)

STEP	CALCULATION	QUARTER 01 STATS	QUARTER 02 GOALS	
1	ANNUAL GCI GOAL	$	ANNUAL GCI GOAL	$
2	− GCI EARNED TO DATE	− $	REMAINING GCI GOAL	$
3	÷ MONTHS REMAINING	÷ 9 MONTHS	MONTHLY GCI GOAL	$
4	÷ ACR	÷ %	MONTHLY SALES VOLUME GOAL	$
5	÷ ATP	÷ $	MONTHLY TRANSACTIONS GOAL	#T
6	÷ CTR	÷ %	MONTHLY NEW CLIENTS GOAL	#C
7	÷ PTR	÷ %	MONTHLY PRESENTATIONS GOAL	#P
8	÷ DTR	÷ %	MONTHLY DISCUSSIONS GOAL	#D
9	÷ WORKING DAYS/MTH	÷ DAYS	DAILY DISCUSSIONS GOAL	#D/W

ACTIVITY LOG

APRIL

DISCUSSIONS (D)	PRESENTATIONS (P)	CLIENTS (C)	CONTRACTS (K)	TRANSACTIONS (T)
#D; Δ | #	#LP; Δ | #	#LC; Δ | #	#LK; Δ | #	#LT; Δ | #
DAYS WORKED (W)	#BP; Δ | #	#BC; Δ | #	#BK; Δ | #	#BT; Δ | #
#W; Δ | #	#P; Δ | #	#C; Δ | #	#K; Δ | #	#T; Δ | #

MAY

DISCUSSIONS (D)	PRESENTATIONS (P)	CLIENTS (C)	CONTRACTS (K)	TRANSACTIONS (T)
#D; Δ | #	#LP; Δ | #	#LC; Δ | #	#LK; Δ | #	#LT; Δ | #
DAYS WORKED (W)	#BP; Δ | #	#BC; Δ | #	#BK; Δ | #	#BT; Δ | #
#W; Δ | #	#P; Δ | #	#C; Δ | #	#K; Δ | #	#T; Δ | #

JUNE

DISCUSSIONS (D)	PRESENTATIONS (P)	CLIENTS (C)	CONTRACTS (K)	TRANSACTIONS (T)
#D; Δ | #	#LP; Δ | #	#LC; Δ | #	#LK; Δ | #	#LT; Δ | #
DAYS WORKED (W)	#BP; Δ | #	#BC; Δ | #	#BK; Δ | #	#BT; Δ | #
#W; Δ | #	#P; Δ | #	#C; Δ | #	#K; Δ | #	#T; Δ | #

QUARTER 02

DISCUSSIONS (D)	PRESENTATIONS (P)	CLIENTS (C)	CONTRACTS (K)	TRANSACTIONS (T)
#D; Δ | #	#LP; Δ | #	#LC; Δ | #	#LK; Δ | #	#LT; Δ | #
DAYS WORKED (W)	#BP; Δ | #	#BC; Δ | #	#BK; Δ | #	#BT; Δ | #
#W; Δ | #	#P; Δ | #	#C; Δ | #	#K; Δ | #	#T; Δ | #

QUARTERLY TRANSACTION DATA

GROSS COMMISSION INCOME (GCI)	DAYS ON MARKET (DOM)
LGCI $; Δ | $	LDOM DAYS; Δ | DAYS
BGCI $; Δ | $	BDOM DAYS; Δ | DAYS
GCI $; Δ | $	DOM DAYS; Δ | DAYS
SALES VOLUME (V)	**ORIGINAL PRICE VOLUME (OPV)**
LV $; Δ | $	LOPV $; Δ | $
BV $; Δ | $	BOPV $; Δ | $
V $; Δ | $	OPV $; Δ | $

MARKET COMPARISON

	#TRANSACTIONS	Δ	AVERAGE TRANS. PRICE (ATP)	AVG. LDOM	SP/LP
METRO		|	$; Δ | $		%
MACRO #1		|	$; Δ | $		%
MACRO #2		|	$; Δ | $		%
MACRO #3		|	$; Δ | $		%
PERSONAL		|	$; Δ | $		%

During Quarter 02, I mostly prospected:	1	2	3

CONVERSION RATIOS & TURNOVER RATES

	CONVERSION RATIOS		TURNOVER		Δ	L TURNOVER	Δ	B TURNOVER	Δ
DISCUSSIONS TO PRESENTATIONS	$\frac{\#D}{\#P}$ =	D:P	DTR	$\frac{\#P}{\#D}$ = %	%	$\frac{\#LP}{\#D}$ = %	%	$\frac{\#BP}{\#D}$ = %	%
PRESENTATIONS TO CLIENTS	$\frac{\#P}{\#C}$ =	P:C	PTR	$\frac{\#C}{\#P}$ = %	%	$\frac{\#LC}{\#LP}$ = %	%	$\frac{\#BC}{\#BP}$ = %	%
CLIENTS TO TRANSACTIONS	$\frac{\#C}{\#T}$ =	T:C	CTR	$\frac{\#T}{\#C}$ = %	%	$\frac{\#LT}{\#LC}$ = %	%	$\frac{\#BT}{\#BC}$ = %	%
CONTRACTS TO TRANSACTIONS	$\frac{\#K}{\#T}$ =	K:T	KTR	$\frac{\#T}{\#K}$ = %	%	$\frac{\#LT}{\#LK}$ = %	%	$\frac{\#BT}{\#BK}$ = %	%

METRICS

AVERAGE COMMISSION RATE (ACR)	AVERAGE TRANSACTION PRICE (ATP)	CLIENT TURNOVER RATE (CTR)
$\frac{GCI}{V}$ = %; Δ | %	$\frac{V}{T}$ = $; Δ | $	$\frac{T}{C}$ = %; Δ | %
RETURN ON PRESENTATIONS (ROP)	**RETURN ON TRANSACTIONS (ROT)**	**RETURN ON CLIENTS (ROC)**
$\frac{GCI}{P}$ = $; Δ | $	$\frac{GCI}{T}$ = $; Δ | $	$\frac{GCI}{C}$ = $; Δ | $
AVG. LIST DAYS ON MKT (AVG. LDOM)	**SALES PRICE TO LIST PRICE (SP/LP)**	**RETURN ON DAYS WORKED (ROW)**
$\frac{LDOM}{LT}$ = DAYS; Δ | DAYS	$\frac{LV}{LOPV}$ = %; Δ | %	$\frac{GCI}{W}$ = $; Δ | $

LEVERAGE LOG

Be mindful of Buyer, Listing, and Overall figures when applying these formulas. XVII		$\frac{GCI}{V}$ ×	$\frac{V}{T}$ ×	$\frac{T}{C}$ =	$\frac{GCI}{C}$	$\frac{GCI}{T} - \frac{GCI}{C}$
		AVERAGE COMMISSION RATE	AVERAGE TRANSACTION PRICE	CLIENT TURNOVER RATE	RETURN ON CLIENTS	LOST OPPORTUNITY DIFFERENTIAL
QUARTER 02	LISTINGS	%	$	%	$	$
	BUYERS	%	$	%	$	$
	OVERALL	%	$	%	$	$

BUSINESS PLAN (FOR EACH MONTH OF QUARTER 03)

STEP	CALCULATION	QUARTER 02 STATS	QUARTER 03 GOALS	
1	ANNUAL GCI GOAL	$	ANNUAL GCI GOAL	$
2	− GCI EARNED TO DATE	− $	REMAINING GCI GOAL	$
3	÷ MONTHS REMAINING	÷ 6 MONTHS	MONTHLY GCI GOAL	$
4	÷ ACR	÷ %	MONTHLY SALES VOLUME GOAL	$
5	÷ ATP	÷ $	MONTHLY TRANSACTIONS GOAL	#T
6	÷ CTR	÷ %	MONTHLY NEW CLIENTS GOAL	#C
7	÷ PTR	÷ %	MONTHLY PRESENTATIONS GOAL	#P
8	÷ DTR	÷ %	MONTHLY DISCUSSIONS GOAL	#D
9	÷ WORKING DAYS/MTH	÷ DAYS	DAILY DISCUSSIONS GOAL	#D/W

ACTIVITY LOG

JULY

DISCUSSIONS (D)	PRESENTATIONS (P)	CLIENTS (C)	CONTRACTS (K)	TRANSACTIONS (T)
#D; Δ | #	#LP; Δ | #	#LC; Δ | #	#LK; Δ | #	#LT; Δ | #
DAYS WORKED (W)	#BP; Δ | #	#BC; Δ | #	#BK; Δ | #	#BT; Δ | #
#W; Δ | #	#P; Δ | #	#C; Δ | #	#K; Δ | #	#T; Δ | #

AUGUST

DISCUSSIONS (D)	PRESENTATIONS (P)	CLIENTS (C)	CONTRACTS (K)	TRANSACTIONS (T)
#D; Δ | #	#LP; Δ | #	#LC; Δ | #	#LK; Δ | #	#LT; Δ | #
DAYS WORKED (W)	#BP; Δ | #	#BC; Δ | #	#BK; Δ | #	#BT; Δ | #
#W; Δ | #	#P; Δ | #	#C; Δ | #	#K; Δ | #	#T; Δ | #

SEPTEMBER

DISCUSSIONS (D)	PRESENTATIONS (P)	CLIENTS (C)	CONTRACTS (K)	TRANSACTIONS (T)
#D; Δ | #	#LP; Δ | #	#LC; Δ | #	#LK; Δ | #	#LT; Δ | #
DAYS WORKED (W)	#BP; Δ | #	#BC; Δ | #	#BK; Δ | #	#BT; Δ | #
#W; Δ | #	#P; Δ | #	#C; Δ | #	#K; Δ | #	#T; Δ | #

QUARTER 03

DISCUSSIONS (D)	PRESENTATIONS (P)	CLIENTS (C)	CONTRACTS (K)	TRANSACTIONS (T)
#D; Δ | #	#LP; Δ | #	#LC; Δ | #	#LK; Δ | #	#LT; Δ | #
DAYS WORKED (W)	#BP; Δ | #	#BC; Δ | #	#BK; Δ | #	#BT; Δ | #
#W; Δ | #	#P; Δ | #	#C; Δ | #	#K; Δ | #	#T; Δ | #

QUARTERLY TRANSACTION DATA

GROSS COMMISSION INCOME (GCI)	DAYS ON MARKET (DOM)
LGCI $; Δ | $	LDOM DAYS; Δ | DAYS
BGCI $; Δ | $	BDOM DAYS; Δ | DAYS
GCI $; Δ | $	DOM DAYS; Δ | DAYS
SALES VOLUME (V)	**ORIGINAL PRICE VOLUME (OPV)**
LV $; Δ | $	LOPV $; Δ | $
BV $; Δ | $	BOPV $; Δ | $
V $; Δ | $	OPV $; Δ | $

MARKET COMPARISON

	#TRANSACTIONS	Δ	AVERAGE TRANS. PRICE (ATP)	AVG. LDOM	SP/LP
METRO		|	$; Δ | $		%
MACRO #1		|	$; Δ | $		%
MACRO #2		|	$; Δ | $		%
MACRO #3		|	$; Δ | $		%
PERSONAL		|	$; Δ | $		%

During Quarter 03, I mostly prospected:	*1*	*2*	*3*

CONVERSION RATIOS & TURNOVER RATES

	CONVERSION RATIOS		TURNOVER	Δ	L TURNOVER	Δ	B TURNOVER	Δ
DISCUSSIONS TO PRESENTATIONS	#D / #P = D:P	DTR	#P / #D = %	%	#LP / #D = %	%	#BP / #D = %	%
PRESENTATIONS TO CLIENTS	#P / #C = P:C	PTR	#C / #P = %	%	#LC / #LP = %	%	#BC / #BP = %	%
CLIENTS TO TRANSACTIONS	#C / #T = T:C	CTR	#T / #C = %	%	#LT / #LC = %	%	#BT / #BC = %	%
CONTRACTS TO TRANSACTIONS	#K / #T = K:T	KTR	#T / #K = %	%	#LT / #LK = %	%	#BT / #BK = %	%

METRICS

AVERAGE COMMISSION RATE (ACR)	AVERAGE TRANSACTION PRICE (ATP)	CLIENT TURNOVER RATE (CTR)
GCI / V = %; Δ | %	V / T = $; Δ | $	T / C = %; Δ | %
RETURN ON PRESENTATIONS (ROP)	**RETURN ON TRANSACTIONS (ROT)**	**RETURN ON CLIENTS (ROC)**
GCI / P = $; Δ | $	GCI / T = $; Δ | $	GCI / C = $; Δ | $
AVG. LIST DAYS ON MKT (AVG. LDOM)	**SALES PRICE TO LIST PRICE (SP/LP)**	**RETURN ON DAYS WORKED (ROW)**
LDOM / LT = DAYS; Δ | DAYS	LV / LOPV = %; Δ | %	GCI / W = $; Δ | $

LEVERAGE LOG

Be mindful of Buyer, Listing, and Overall figures when applying these formulas.[XVII]

		GCI / V	× V / T	× T / C	= GCI / C	GCI / T − GCI / C
		AVERAGE COMMISSION RATE	AVERAGE TRANSACTION PRICE	CLIENT TURNOVER RATE	RETURN ON CLIENTS	LOST OPPORTUNITY DIFFERENTIAL
QUARTER 03	LISTINGS	%	$	%	$	$
	BUYERS	%	$	%	$	$
	OVERALL	%	$	%	$	$

BUSINESS PLAN (FOR EACH MONTH OF QUARTER 04)

STEP	CALCULATION	QUARTER 03 STATS	QUARTER 04 GOALS	
1	ANNUAL GCI GOAL	$	ANNUAL GCI GOAL	$
2	− GCI EARNED TO DATE	− $	REMAINING GCI GOAL	$
3	÷ MONTHS REMAINING	÷ 3 MONTHS	MONTHLY GCI GOAL	$
4	÷ ACR	÷ %	MONTHLY SALES VOLUME GOAL	$
5	÷ ATP	÷ $	MONTHLY TRANSACTIONS GOAL	#T
6	÷ CTR	÷ %	MONTHLY NEW CLIENTS GOAL	#C
7	÷ PTR	÷ %	MONTHLY PRESENTATIONS GOAL	#P
8	÷ DTR	÷ %	MONTHLY DISCUSSIONS GOAL	#D
9	÷ WORKING DAYS/MTH	÷ DAYS	DAILY DISCUSSIONS GOAL	#D/W

ACTIVITY LOG

OCTOBER

DISCUSSIONS (D)	PRESENTATIONS (P)	CLIENTS (C)	CONTRACTS (K)	TRANSACTIONS (T)
#D; Δ | #	#LP; Δ | #	#LC; Δ | #	#LK; Δ | #	#LT; Δ | #
DAYS WORKED (W)	#BP; Δ | #	#BC; Δ | #	#BK; Δ | #	#BT; Δ | #
#W; Δ | #	#P; Δ | #	#C; Δ | #	#K; Δ | #	#T; Δ | #

NOVEMBER

DISCUSSIONS (D)	PRESENTATIONS (P)	CLIENTS (C)	CONTRACTS (K)	TRANSACTIONS (T)
#D; Δ | #	#LP; Δ | #	#LC; Δ | #	#LK; Δ | #	#LT; Δ | #
DAYS WORKED (W)	#BP; Δ | #	#BC; Δ | #	#BK; Δ | #	#BT; Δ | #
#W; Δ | #	#P; Δ | #	#C; Δ | #	#K; Δ | #	#T; Δ | #

DECEMBER

DISCUSSIONS (D)	PRESENTATIONS (P)	CLIENTS (C)	CONTRACTS (K)	TRANSACTIONS (T)
#D; Δ | #	#LP; Δ | #	#LC; Δ | #	#LK; Δ | #	#LT; Δ | #
DAYS WORKED (W)	#BP; Δ | #	#BC; Δ | #	#BK; Δ | #	#BT; Δ | #
#W; Δ | #	#P; Δ | #	#C; Δ | #	#K; Δ | #	#T; Δ | #

QUARTER 04

DISCUSSIONS (D)	PRESENTATIONS (P)	CLIENTS (C)	CONTRACTS (K)	TRANSACTIONS (T)
#D; Δ | #	#LP; Δ | #	#LC; Δ | #	#LK; Δ | #	#LT; Δ | #
DAYS WORKED (W)	#BP; Δ | #	#BC; Δ | #	#BK; Δ | #	#BT; Δ | #
#W; Δ | #	#P; Δ | #	#C; Δ | #	#K; Δ | #	#T; Δ | #

QUARTERLY TRANSACTION DATA

GROSS COMMISSION INCOME (GCI)	DAYS ON MARKET (DOM)
LGCI $; Δ | $	LDOM DAYS; Δ | DAYS
BGCI $; Δ | $	BDOM DAYS; Δ | DAYS
GCI $; Δ | $	DOM DAYS; Δ | DAYS
SALES VOLUME (V)	**ORIGINAL PRICE VOLUME (OPV)**
LV $; Δ | $	LOPV $; Δ | $
BV $; Δ | $	BOPV $; Δ | $
V $; Δ | $	OPV $; Δ | $

MARKET COMPARISON

	#TRANSACTIONS	Δ	AVERAGE TRANS. PRICE (ATP)	AVG. LDOM	SP/LP
METRO		|	$; Δ | $		%
MACRO #1		|	$; Δ | $		%
MACRO #2		|	$; Δ | $		%
MACRO #3		|	$; Δ | $		%
PERSONAL		|	$; Δ | $		%

During Quarter 04, I mostly prospected:	*1*	*2*	*3*

CONVERSION RATIOS & TURNOVER RATES

	CONVERSION RATIOS		TURNOVER	Δ	L TURNOVER	Δ	B TURNOVER	Δ
DISCUSSIONS TO PRESENTATIONS	#D / #P =	D:P	DTR: #P / #D = %	%	#LP / #D = %	%	#BP / #D = %	%
PRESENTATIONS TO CLIENTS	#P / #C =	P:C	PTR: #C / #P = %	%	#LC / #LP = %	%	#BC / #BP = %	%
CLIENTS TO TRANSACTIONS	#C / #T =	T:C	CTR: #T / #C = %	%	#LT / #LC = %	%	#BT / #BC = %	%
CONTRACTS TO TRANSACTIONS	#K / #T =	K:T	KTR: #T / #K = %	%	#LT / #LK = %	%	#BT / #BK = %	%

METRICS

AVERAGE COMMISSION RATE (ACR)	AVERAGE TRANSACTION PRICE (ATP)	CLIENT TURNOVER RATE (CTR)
GCI / V = %; Δ | %	V / T = $; Δ | $	T / C = %; Δ | %
RETURN ON PRESENTATIONS (ROP)	**RETURN ON TRANSACTIONS (ROT)**	**RETURN ON CLIENTS (ROC)**
GCI / P = $; Δ | $	GCI / T = $; Δ | $	GCI / C = $; Δ | $
AVG. LIST DAYS ON MKT (AVG. LDOM)	**SALES PRICE TO LIST PRICE (SP/LP)**	**RETURN ON DAYS WORKED (ROW)**
LDOM / LT = DAYS; Δ | DAYS	LV / LOPV = %; Δ | %	GCI / W = $; Δ | $

LEVERAGE LOG

Be mindful of Buyer, Listing, and Overall figures when applying these formulas.[XVII]		GCI / V	× V / T	× T / C	= GCI / C	GCI / T − GCI / C
		AVERAGE COMMISSION RATE	AVERAGE TRANSACTION PRICE	CLIENT TURNOVER RATE	RETURN ON CLIENTS	LOST OPPORTUNITY DIFFERENTIAL
QUARTER 04	LISTINGS	%	$	%	$	$
	BUYERS	%	$	%	$	$
	OVERALL	%	$	%	$	$

BUSINESS PLAN (FOR EACH MONTH OF QUARTER 01)

STEP	CALCULATION	QUARTER 04 STATS	QUARTER 01 GOALS	
1	ANNUAL GCI GOAL	$	ANNUAL GCI GOAL	$
2	− GCI EARNED TO DATE	− $ ZERO	REMAINING GCI GOAL	$
3	÷ MONTHS REMAINING	÷ 12 MONTHS	MONTHLY GCI GOAL	$
4	÷ ACR	÷ %	MONTHLY SALES VOLUME GOAL	$
5	÷ ATP	÷ $	MONTHLY TRANSACTIONS GOAL	#T
6	÷ CTR	÷ %	MONTHLY NEW CLIENTS GOAL	#C
7	÷ PTR	÷ %	MONTHLY PRESENTATIONS GOAL	#P
8	÷ DTR	÷ %	MONTHLY DISCUSSIONS GOAL	#D
9	÷ WORKING DAYS/MTH	÷ DAYS	DAILY DISCUSSIONS GOAL	#D/W

insert annual goal for next year now (STEP 1)

ANNUAL ACTIVITY LOG

DISCUSSIONS (D)	PRESENTATIONS (P)	CLIENTS (C)	CONTRACTS (K)	TRANSACTIONS (T)
#D; Δ | #	#LP; Δ | #	#LC; Δ | #	#LK; Δ | #	#LT; Δ | #
DAYS WORKED (W)	#BP; Δ | #	#BC; Δ | #	#BK; Δ | #	#BT; Δ | #
#W; Δ | #	#P; Δ | #	#C; Δ | #	#K; Δ | #	#T; Δ | #

ANNUAL TRANSACTION DATA

GROSS COMMISSION INCOME (GCI)	DAYS ON MARKET (DOM)
LGCI $; Δ | $	LDOM DAYS; Δ | DAYS
BGCI $; Δ | $	BDOM DAYS; Δ | DAYS
GCI $; Δ | $	DOM DAYS; Δ | DAYS
SALES VOLUME (V)	**ORIGINAL PRICE VOLUME (OPV)**
LV $; Δ | $	LOPV $; Δ | $
BV $; Δ | $	BOPV $; Δ | $
V $; Δ | $	OPV $; Δ | $

CLIENTS FROM LISTINGS (L→C)

JAN	FEB	MAR	APR	MAY	JUN	JUL	AUG	SEP	OCT	NOV	DEC
TOTAL (L→C) = ; Δ |				AVG. (L→C) PER MONTH = ; Δ |							

DATABASE (Db)			OUTBOUND REFERRALS (R)		
#MEMBERS EXISTING			REFERRALS SENT (R)	#R : Δ |	#
#NEW MEMBERS	+	Δ |	REFERRAL TRANS. (RT)	#RT : Δ |	#
#MEMBERS PURGED	-	Δ |	REFERRAL GCI (RGCI)	$: Δ | $	
#Db	=	Δ |	REFERRALS FROM DATABASE (Db→R): Δ |		
CLIENTS FROM DATABASE (Db→C): Δ |					

DATABASE & REFERRAL METRICS

RETURN ON REFERRALS (ROR)	AVG. REFERRAL COMMISSION (ARC)	REFERRAL TURNOVER RATE (RTR)
$\frac{RGCI}{R}$ = $; Δ | $	$\frac{RGCI}{RT}$ = $; Δ | $	$\frac{RT}{R}$ = %; Δ | %
MEMBERS PER REFERRAL (MPR)	**MEMBERS PER CLIENT (MPC)**	**RETURN PER MEMBER (RPM)**
$\frac{Db}{R}$ = Db:R; Δ | Db:R	$\frac{Db}{C}$ = Db:C; Δ | Db:C	$\frac{GCI}{Db}$ = $; Δ | $
DATABASE LEVERAGE RATE (DbLR)	**LISTING LEVERAGE RATE (LLR)**	**TRANS. PER REFERRAL TRANS. (T/RT)**
$\frac{Db \to C}{C}$ = %; Δ | %	$\frac{L \to C}{C}$ = %; Δ | %	$\frac{LT+BT}{RT}$ = T:RT; Δ | T:RT

MARKET COMPARISON

	#TRANSACTIONS	Δ	AVERAGE TRANS. PRICE (ATP)	AVG. LDOM	SP/LP
METRO		|	$; Δ | $		%
MACRO		|	$; Δ | $		%
PERSONAL		|	$; Δ | $		%

During this year, I mostly prospected:	1	2	3

CONVERSION RATIOS & TURNOVER RATES

	CONVERSION RATIOS		TURNOVER	Δ	L TURNOVER	Δ	B TURNOVER	Δ
DISCUSSIONS TO PRESENTATIONS	$\frac{\#D}{\#P}$ =	D:P	DTR $\frac{\#P}{\#D}$ = %	%	$\frac{\#LP}{\#D}$ = %	%	$\frac{\#BP}{\#D}$ = %	%
PRESENTATIONS TO CLIENTS	$\frac{\#P}{\#C}$ =	P:C	PTR $\frac{\#C}{\#P}$ = %	%	$\frac{\#LC}{\#LP}$ = %	%	$\frac{\#BC}{\#BP}$ = %	%
CLIENTS TO TRANSACTIONS	$\frac{\#C}{\#T}$ =	T:C	CTR $\frac{\#T}{\#C}$ = %	%	$\frac{\#LT}{\#LC}$ = %	%	$\frac{\#BT}{\#BC}$ = %	%
CONTRACTS TO TRANSACTIONS	$\frac{\#K}{\#T}$ =	K:T	KTR $\frac{\#T}{\#K}$ = %	%	$\frac{\#LT}{\#LK}$ = %	%	$\frac{\#BT}{\#BK}$ = %	%

METRICS

AVERAGE COMMISSION RATE (ACR)	AVERAGE TRANSACTION PRICE (ATP)	CLIENT TURNOVER RATE (CTR)
$\frac{GCI}{V}$ = %; Δ | %	$\frac{V}{T}$ = $; Δ | $	$\frac{T}{C}$ = %; Δ | %
RETURN ON PRESENTATIONS (ROP)	**RETURN ON TRANSACTIONS (ROT)**	**RETURN ON CLIENTS (ROC)**
$\frac{GCI}{P}$ = $; Δ | $	$\frac{GCI}{T}$ = $; Δ | $	$\frac{GCI}{C}$ = $; Δ | $
AVG. LIST DAYS ON MKT (AVG. LDOM)	**SALES PRICE TO LIST PRICE (SP/LP)**	**RETURN ON DAYS WORKED (ROW)**
$\frac{LDOM}{LT}$ = DAYS; Δ | DAYS	$\frac{LV}{LOPV}$ = %; Δ | %	$\frac{GCI}{W}$ = $; Δ | $

LEVERAGE LOG

Be mindful of Buyer, Listing, and Overall figures when applying these formulas.[XVII]

	$\frac{GCI}{V}$ ×	$\frac{V}{T}$ ×	$\frac{T}{C}$ =	$\frac{GCI}{C}$	$\frac{GCI}{T} - \frac{GCI}{C}$
	AVERAGE COMMISSION RATE	AVERAGE TRANSACTION PRICE	CLIENT TURNOVER RATE	RETURN ON CLIENTS	LOST OPPORTUNITY DIFFERENTIAL
ANNUAL LISTINGS	%	$	%	$	$
ANNUAL BUYERS	%	$	%	$	$
ANNUAL OVERALL	%	$	%	$	$

INCOME STATEMENT

FOR MONTHS ENDED 31 DECEMBER

INCOME		EXPENSE	
LGCI	$	BROKER FEES	$
BGCI	$	EDUCATION	$
RGCI	$	SERVICES	$
OTHER	$	SUPPLIES	$
SOLD EQUIP.	$	EQUIPMENT	$
	$	STAFF	$
TOTAL INCOME	$	TOTAL EXPENSE	$

TOTAL INCOME - TOTAL EXPENSE = NET INCOME: $; Δ | $

ACTIVITY LOG

JANUARY

DISCUSSIONS (D)	PRESENTATIONS (P)	CLIENTS (C)	CONTRACTS (K)	TRANSACTIONS (T)
#D; Δ | #	#LP; Δ | #	#LC; Δ | #	#LK; Δ | #	#LT; Δ | #
DAYS WORKED (W)	#BP; Δ | #	#BC; Δ | #	#BK; Δ | #	#BT; Δ | #
#W; Δ | #	#P; Δ | #	#C; Δ | #	#K; Δ | #	#T; Δ | #

FEBRUARY

DISCUSSIONS (D)	PRESENTATIONS (P)	CLIENTS (C)	CONTRACTS (K)	TRANSACTIONS (T)
#D; Δ | #	#LP; Δ | #	#LC; Δ | #	#LK; Δ | #	#LT; Δ | #
DAYS WORKED (W)	#BP; Δ | #	#BC; Δ | #	#BK; Δ | #	#BT; Δ | #
#W; Δ | #	#P; Δ | #	#C; Δ | #	#K; Δ | #	#T; Δ | #

MARCH

DISCUSSIONS (D)	PRESENTATIONS (P)	CLIENTS (C)	CONTRACTS (K)	TRANSACTIONS (T)
#D; Δ | #	#LP; Δ | #	#LC; Δ | #	#LK; Δ | #	#LT; Δ | #
DAYS WORKED (W)	#BP; Δ | #	#BC; Δ | #	#BK; Δ | #	#BT; Δ | #
#W; Δ | #	#P; Δ | #	#C; Δ | #	#K; Δ | #	#T; Δ | #

QUARTER 01

DISCUSSIONS (D)	PRESENTATIONS (P)	CLIENTS (C)	CONTRACTS (K)	TRANSACTIONS (T)
#D; Δ | #	#LP; Δ | #	#LC; Δ | #	#LK; Δ | #	#LT; Δ | #
DAYS WORKED (W)	#BP; Δ | #	#BC; Δ | #	#BK; Δ | #	#BT; Δ | #
#W; Δ | #	#P; Δ | #	#C; Δ | #	#K; Δ | #	#T; Δ | #

QUARTERLY TRANSACTION DATA

GROSS COMMISSION INCOME (GCI)	DAYS ON MARKET (DOM)
LGCI $; Δ | $	LDOM DAYS; Δ | DAYS
BGCI $; Δ | $	BDOM DAYS; Δ | DAYS
GCI $; Δ | $	DOM DAYS; Δ | DAYS
SALES VOLUME (V)	**ORIGINAL PRICE VOLUME (OPV)**
LV $; Δ | $	LOPV $; Δ | $
BV $; Δ | $	BOPV $; Δ | $
V $; Δ | $	OPV $; Δ | $

MARKET COMPARISON

	#TRANSACTIONS	Δ	AVERAGE TRANS. PRICE (ATP)	AVG. LDOM	SP/LP
METRO		|	$; Δ | $		%
MACRO #1		|	$; Δ | $		%
MACRO #2		|	$; Δ | $		%
MACRO #3		|	$; Δ | $		%
PERSONAL		|	$; Δ | $		%

During Quarter 01, I mostly prospected:	*1*	*2*	*3*

CONVERSION RATIOS & TURNOVER RATES

	CONVERSION RATIOS		TURNOVER	Δ	L TURNOVER	Δ	B TURNOVER	Δ
DISCUSSIONS TO PRESENTATIONS	#D / #P =	D:P	DTR: #P / #D = %	| %	#LP / #D = %	| %	#BP / #D = %	| %
PRESENTATIONS TO CLIENTS	#P / #C =	P:C	PTR: #C / #P = %	| %	#LC / #LP = %	| %	#BC / #BP = %	| %
CLIENTS TO TRANSACTIONS	#C / #T =	T:C	CTR: #T / #C = %	| %	#LT / #LC = %	| %	#BT / #BC = %	| %
CONTRACTS TO TRANSACTIONS	#K / #T =	K:T	KTR: #T / #K = %	| %	#LT / #LK = %	| %	#BT / #BK = %	| %

METRICS

AVERAGE COMMISSION RATE (ACR)	AVERAGE TRANSACTION PRICE (ATP)	CLIENT TURNOVER RATE (CTR)
GCI / V = %; Δ | %	V / T = $; Δ | $	T / C = %; Δ | %
RETURN ON PRESENTATIONS (ROP)	RETURN ON TRANSACTIONS (ROT)	RETURN ON CLIENTS (ROC)
GCI / P = $; Δ | $	GCI / T = $; Δ | $	GCI / C = $; Δ | $
AVG. LIST DAYS ON MKT (AVG. LDOM)	SALES PRICE TO LIST PRICE (SP/LP)	RETURN ON DAYS WORKED (ROW)
LDOM / LT = DAYS; Δ | DAYS	LV / LOPV = %; Δ | %	GCI / W = $; Δ | $

LEVERAGE LOG

Be mindful of Buyer, Listing, and Overall figures when applying these formulas.[XVII]	GCI / V ×	V / T ×	T / C =	GCI / C	GCI / T − GCI / C
	AVERAGE COMMISSION RATE	AVERAGE TRANSACTION PRICE	CLIENT TURNOVER RATE	RETURN ON CLIENTS	LOST OPPORTUNITY DIFFERENTIAL
QUARTER 01 — LISTINGS	%	$	%	$	$
QUARTER 01 — BUYERS	%	$	%	$	$
QUARTER 01 — OVERALL	%	$	%	$	$

BUSINESS PLAN (FOR EACH MONTH OF QUARTER 02)

STEP	CALCULATION	QUARTER 01 STATS	QUARTER 02 GOALS	
1	ANNUAL GCI GOAL	$	ANNUAL GCI GOAL	$
2	− GCI EARNED TO DATE	− $	REMAINING GCI GOAL	$
3	÷ MONTHS REMAINING	÷ 9 MONTHS	MONTHLY GCI GOAL	$
4	÷ ACR	÷ %	MONTHLY SALES VOLUME GOAL	$
5	÷ ATP	÷ $	MONTHLY TRANSACTIONS GOAL	#T
6	÷ CTR	÷ %	MONTHLY NEW CLIENTS GOAL	#C
7	÷ PTR	÷ %	MONTHLY PRESENTATIONS GOAL	#P
8	÷ DTR	÷ %	MONTHLY DISCUSSIONS GOAL	#D
9	÷ WORKING DAYS/MTH	÷ DAYS	DAILY DISCUSSIONS GOAL	#D/W

ACTIVITY LOG

APRIL

DISCUSSIONS (D)	PRESENTATIONS (P)	CLIENTS (C)	CONTRACTS (K)	TRANSACTIONS (T)
#D; Δ | #	#LP; Δ | #	#LC; Δ | #	#LK; Δ | #	#LT; Δ | #
DAYS WORKED (W)	#BP; Δ | #	#BC; Δ | #	#BK; Δ | #	#BT; Δ | #
#W; Δ | #	#P; Δ | #	#C; Δ | #	#K; Δ | #	#T; Δ | #

MAY

DISCUSSIONS (D)	PRESENTATIONS (P)	CLIENTS (C)	CONTRACTS (K)	TRANSACTIONS (T)
#D; Δ | #	#LP; Δ | #	#LC; Δ | #	#LK; Δ | #	#LT; Δ | #
DAYS WORKED (W)	#BP; Δ | #	#BC; Δ | #	#BK; Δ | #	#BT; Δ | #
#W; Δ | #	#P; Δ | #	#C; Δ | #	#K; Δ | #	#T; Δ | #

JUNE

DISCUSSIONS (D)	PRESENTATIONS (P)	CLIENTS (C)	CONTRACTS (K)	TRANSACTIONS (T)
#D; Δ | #	#LP; Δ | #	#LC; Δ | #	#LK; Δ | #	#LT; Δ | #
DAYS WORKED (W)	#BP; Δ | #	#BC; Δ | #	#BK; Δ | #	#BT; Δ | #
#W; Δ | #	#P; Δ | #	#C; Δ | #	#K; Δ | #	#T; Δ | #

QUARTER 02

DISCUSSIONS (D)	PRESENTATIONS (P)	CLIENTS (C)	CONTRACTS (K)	TRANSACTIONS (T)
#D; Δ | #	#LP; Δ | #	#LC; Δ | #	#LK; Δ | #	#LT; Δ | #
DAYS WORKED (W)	#BP; Δ | #	#BC; Δ | #	#BK; Δ | #	#BT; Δ | #
#W; Δ | #	#P; Δ | #	#C; Δ | #	#K; Δ | #	#T; Δ | #

QUARTERLY TRANSACTION DATA

GROSS COMMISSION INCOME (GCI)	DAYS ON MARKET (DOM)
LGCI $; Δ | $	LDOM DAYS; Δ | DAYS
BGCI $; Δ | $	BDOM DAYS; Δ | DAYS
GCI $; Δ | $	DOM DAYS; Δ | DAYS
SALES VOLUME (V)	**ORIGINAL PRICE VOLUME (OPV)**
LV $; Δ | $	LOPV $; Δ | $
BV $; Δ | $	BOPV $; Δ | $
V $; Δ | $	OPV $; Δ | $

MARKET COMPARISON

	#TRANSACTIONS	Δ	AVERAGE TRANS. PRICE (ATP)	AVG. LDOM	SP/LP
METRO			$; Δ | $		%
MACRO #1			$; Δ | $		%
MACRO #2			$; Δ | $		%
MACRO #3			$; Δ | $		%
PERSONAL			$; Δ | $		%

During Quarter 02, I mostly prospected:	*1*	*2*	*3*

CONVERSION RATIOS & TURNOVER RATES

	CONVERSION RATIOS		TURNOVER	Δ	L TURNOVER	Δ	B TURNOVER	Δ
DISCUSSIONS TO PRESENTATIONS	#D / #P =	D:P	DTR: #P / #D = %	%	#LP / #D = %	%	#BP / #D = %	%
PRESENTATIONS TO CLIENTS	#P / #C =	P:C	PTR: #C / #P = %	%	#LC / #LP = %	%	#BC / #BP = %	%
CLIENTS TO TRANSACTIONS	#C / #T =	T:C	CTR: #T / #C = %	%	#LT / #LC = %	%	#BT / #BC = %	%
CONTRACTS TO TRANSACTIONS	#K / #T =	K:T	KTR: #T / #K = %	%	#LT / #LK = %	%	#BT / #BK = %	%

METRICS

AVERAGE COMMISSION RATE (ACR)	AVERAGE TRANSACTION PRICE (ATP)	CLIENT TURNOVER RATE (CTR)
GCI / V = %; Δ | %	V / T = $; Δ | $	T / C = %; Δ | %
RETURN ON PRESENTATIONS (ROP)	**RETURN ON TRANSACTIONS (ROT)**	**RETURN ON CLIENTS (ROC)**
GCI / P = $; Δ | $	GCI / T = $; Δ | $	GCI / C = $; Δ | $
AVG. LIST DAYS ON MKT (AVG. LDOM)	**SALES PRICE TO LIST PRICE (SP/LP)**	**RETURN ON DAYS WORKED (ROW)**
LDOM / LT = DAYS; Δ | DAYS	LV / LOPV = %; Δ | %	GCI / W = $; Δ | $

LEVERAGE LOG

Be mindful of Buyer, Listing, and Overall figures when applying these formulas.[XVII]	GCI / V ×	V / T ×	T / C =	GCI / C	GCI / T − GCI / C
	AVERAGE COMMISSION RATE	AVERAGE TRANSACTION PRICE	CLIENT TURNOVER RATE	RETURN ON CLIENTS	LOST OPPORTUNITY DIFFERENTIAL
QUARTER 02 — LISTINGS	%	$	%	$	$
QUARTER 02 — BUYERS	%	$	%	$	$
QUARTER 02 — OVERALL	%	$	%	$	$

BUSINESS PLAN (FOR EACH MONTH OF QUARTER 03)

STEP	CALCULATION	QUARTER 02 STATS	QUARTER 03 GOALS	
1	ANNUAL GCI GOAL	$	ANNUAL GCI GOAL	$
2	− GCI EARNED TO DATE	− $	REMAINING GCI GOAL	$
3	÷ MONTHS REMAINING	÷ 6 MONTHS	MONTHLY GCI GOAL	$
4	÷ ACR	÷ %	MONTHLY SALES VOLUME GOAL	$
5	÷ ATP	÷ $	MONTHLY TRANSACTIONS GOAL	#T
6	÷ CTR	÷ %	MONTHLY NEW CLIENTS GOAL	#C
7	÷ PTR	÷ %	MONTHLY PRESENTATIONS GOAL	#P
8	÷ DTR	÷ %	MONTHLY DISCUSSIONS GOAL	#D
9	÷ WORKING DAYS/MTH	÷ DAYS	DAILY DISCUSSIONS GOAL	#D/W

ACTIVITY LOG

JULY

DISCUSSIONS (D)	PRESENTATIONS (P)	CLIENTS (C)	CONTRACTS (K)	TRANSACTIONS (T)
#D; Δ | #	#LP; Δ | #	#LC; Δ | #	#LK; Δ | #	#LT; Δ | #
DAYS WORKED (W)	#BP; Δ | #	#BC; Δ | #	#BK; Δ | #	#BT; Δ | #
#W; Δ | #	#P; Δ | #	#C; Δ | #	#K; Δ | #	#T; Δ | #

AUGUST

DISCUSSIONS (D)	PRESENTATIONS (P)	CLIENTS (C)	CONTRACTS (K)	TRANSACTIONS (T)
#D; Δ | #	#LP; Δ | #	#LC; Δ | #	#LK; Δ | #	#LT; Δ | #
DAYS WORKED (W)	#BP; Δ | #	#BC; Δ | #	#BK; Δ | #	#BT; Δ | #
#W; Δ | #	#P; Δ | #	#C; Δ | #	#K; Δ | #	#T; Δ | #

SEPTEMBER

DISCUSSIONS (D)	PRESENTATIONS (P)	CLIENTS (C)	CONTRACTS (K)	TRANSACTIONS (T)
#D; Δ | #	#LP; Δ | #	#LC; Δ | #	#LK; Δ | #	#LT; Δ | #
DAYS WORKED (W)	#BP; Δ | #	#BC; Δ | #	#BK; Δ | #	#BT; Δ | #
#W; Δ | #	#P; Δ | #	#C; Δ | #	#K; Δ | #	#T; Δ | #

QUARTER 03

DISCUSSIONS (D)	PRESENTATIONS (P)	CLIENTS (C)	CONTRACTS (K)	TRANSACTIONS (T)
#D; Δ | #	#LP; Δ | #	#LC; Δ | #	#LK; Δ | #	#LT; Δ | #
DAYS WORKED (W)	#BP; Δ | #	#BC; Δ | #	#BK; Δ | #	#BT; Δ | #
#W; Δ | #	#P; Δ | #	#C; Δ | #	#K; Δ | #	#T; Δ | #

QUARTERLY TRANSACTION DATA

GROSS COMMISSION INCOME (GCI)	DAYS ON MARKET (DOM)
LGCI $; Δ | $	LDOM DAYS; Δ | DAYS
BGCI $; Δ | $	BDOM DAYS; Δ | DAYS
GCI $; Δ | $	DOM DAYS; Δ | DAYS
SALES VOLUME (V)	**ORIGINAL PRICE VOLUME (OPV)**
LV $; Δ | $	LOPV $; Δ | $
BV $; Δ | $	BOPV $; Δ | $
V $; Δ | $	OPV $; Δ | $

MARKET COMPARISON

	#TRANSACTIONS	Δ	AVERAGE TRANS. PRICE (ATP)	AVG. LDOM	SP/LP
METRO		|	$; Δ | $		%
MACRO #1		|	$; Δ | $		%
MACRO #2		|	$; Δ | $		%
MACRO #3		|	$; Δ | $		%
PERSONAL		|	$; Δ | $		%

During Quarter 03, I mostly prospected: 1 2 3

CONVERSION RATIOS & TURNOVER RATES

	CONVERSION RATIOS		TURNOVER	Δ	L TURNOVER	Δ	B TURNOVER	Δ
DISCUSSIONS TO PRESENTATIONS	#D / #P =	D:P	DTR #P / #D = %	%	#LP / #D = %	%	#BP / #D = %	%
PRESENTATIONS TO CLIENTS	#P / #C =	P:C	PTR #C / #P = %	%	#LC / #LP = %	%	#BC / #BP = %	%
CLIENTS TO TRANSACTIONS	#C / #T =	T:C	CTR #T / #C = %	%	#LT / #LC = %	%	#BT / #BC = %	%
CONTRACTS TO TRANSACTIONS	#K / #T =	K:T	KTR #T / #K = %	%	#LT / #LK = %	%	#BT / #BK = %	%

METRICS

AVERAGE COMMISSION RATE (ACR)	AVERAGE TRANSACTION PRICE (ATP)	CLIENT TURNOVER RATE (CTR)
GCI / V = %; Δ | %	V / T = $; Δ | $	T / C = %; Δ | %
RETURN ON PRESENTATIONS (ROP)	**RETURN ON TRANSACTIONS (ROT)**	**RETURN ON CLIENTS (ROC)**
GCI / P = $; Δ | $	GCI / T = $; Δ | $	GCI / C = $; Δ | $
AVG. LIST DAYS ON MKT (AVG. LDOM)	**SALES PRICE TO LIST PRICE (SP/LP)**	**RETURN ON DAYS WORKED (ROW)**
LDOM / LT = DAYS; Δ | DAYS	LV / LOPV = %; Δ | %	GCI / W = $; Δ | $

LEVERAGE LOG

Be mindful of Buyer, Listing, and Overall figures when applying these formulas.[XVII]

		GCI / V ×	V / T ×	T / C =	GCI / C	GCI / T − GCI / C
		AVERAGE COMMISSION RATE	AVERAGE TRANSACTION PRICE	CLIENT TURNOVER RATE	RETURN ON CLIENTS	LOST OPPORTUNITY DIFFERENTIAL
QUARTER 03	LISTINGS	%	$	%	$	$
	BUYERS	%	$	%	$	$
	OVERALL	%	$	%	$	$

BUSINESS PLAN (FOR EACH MONTH OF QUARTER 04)

STEP	CALCULATION	QUARTER 03 STATS	QUARTER 04 GOALS	
1	ANNUAL GCI GOAL	$	ANNUAL GCI GOAL	$
2	− GCI EARNED TO DATE	− $	REMAINING GCI GOAL	$
3	÷ MONTHS REMAINING	÷ 3 MONTHS	MONTHLY GCI GOAL	$
4	÷ ACR	÷ %	MONTHLY SALES VOLUME GOAL	$
5	÷ ATP	÷ $	MONTHLY TRANSACTIONS GOAL	#T
6	÷ CTR	÷ %	MONTHLY NEW CLIENTS GOAL	#C
7	÷ PTR	÷ %	MONTHLY PRESENTATIONS GOAL	#P
8	÷ DTR	÷ %	MONTHLY DISCUSSIONS GOAL	#D
9	÷ WORKING DAYS/MTH	÷ DAYS	DAILY DISCUSSIONS GOAL	#D/W

ACTIVITY LOG

OCTOBER

DISCUSSIONS (D)	PRESENTATIONS (P)	CLIENTS (C)	CONTRACTS (K)	TRANSACTIONS (T)
#D; Δ | #	#LP; Δ | #	#LC; Δ | #	#LK; Δ | #	#LT; Δ | #
DAYS WORKED (W)	#BP; Δ | #	#BC; Δ | #	#BK; Δ | #	#BT; Δ | #
#W; Δ | #	#P; Δ | #	#C; Δ | #	#K; Δ | #	#T; Δ | #

NOVEMBER

DISCUSSIONS (D)	PRESENTATIONS (P)	CLIENTS (C)	CONTRACTS (K)	TRANSACTIONS (T)
#D; Δ | #	#LP; Δ | #	#LC; Δ | #	#LK; Δ | #	#LT; Δ | #
DAYS WORKED (W)	#BP; Δ | #	#BC; Δ | #	#BK; Δ | #	#BT; Δ | #
#W; Δ | #	#P; Δ | #	#C; Δ | #	#K; Δ | #	#T; Δ | #

DECEMBER

DISCUSSIONS (D)	PRESENTATIONS (P)	CLIENTS (C)	CONTRACTS (K)	TRANSACTIONS (T)
#D; Δ | #	#LP; Δ | #	#LC; Δ | #	#LK; Δ | #	#LT; Δ | #
DAYS WORKED (W)	#BP; Δ | #	#BC; Δ | #	#BK; Δ | #	#BT; Δ | #
#W; Δ | #	#P; Δ | #	#C; Δ | #	#K; Δ | #	#T; Δ | #

QUARTER 04

DISCUSSIONS (D)	PRESENTATIONS (P)	CLIENTS (C)	CONTRACTS (K)	TRANSACTIONS (T)
#D; Δ | #	#LP; Δ | #	#LC; Δ | #	#LK; Δ | #	#LT; Δ | #
DAYS WORKED (W)	#BP; Δ | #	#BC; Δ | #	#BK; Δ | #	#BT; Δ | #
#W; Δ | #	#P; Δ | #	#C; Δ | #	#K; Δ | #	#T; Δ | #

QUARTERLY TRANSACTION DATA

GROSS COMMISSION INCOME (GCI)	DAYS ON MARKET (DOM)
LGCI $; Δ | $	LDOM DAYS; Δ | DAYS
BGCI $; Δ | $	BDOM DAYS; Δ | DAYS
GCI $; Δ | $	DOM DAYS; Δ | DAYS

SALES VOLUME (V)	ORIGINAL PRICE VOLUME (OPV)
LV $; Δ | $	LOPV $; Δ | $
BV $; Δ | $	BOPV $; Δ | $
V $; Δ | $	OPV $; Δ | $

MARKET COMPARISON

	#TRANSACTIONS	Δ	AVERAGE TRANS. PRICE (ATP)	AVG. LDOM	SP/LP
METRO		|	$; Δ | $		%
MACRO #1		|	$; Δ | $		%
MACRO #2		|	$; Δ | $		%
MACRO #3		|	$; Δ | $		%
PERSONAL		|	$; Δ | $		%

During Quarter 04, I mostly prospected:	1	2	3

CONVERSION RATIOS & TURNOVER RATES

	CONVERSION RATIOS		TURNOVER		Δ	L TURNOVER	Δ	B TURNOVER	Δ
DISCUSSIONS TO PRESENTATIONS	#D / #P =	D:P	DTR	#P / #D = %	%	#LP / #D = %	%	#BP / #D = %	%
PRESENTATIONS TO CLIENTS	#P / #C =	P:C	PTR	#C / #P = %	%	#LC / #LP = %	%	#BC / #BP = %	%
CLIENTS TO TRANSACTIONS	#C / #T =	T:C	CTR	#T / #C = %	%	#LT / #LC = %	%	#BT / #BC = %	%
CONTRACTS TO TRANSACTIONS	#K / #T =	K:T	KTR	#T / #K = %	%	#LT / #LK = %	%	#BT / #BK = %	%

METRICS

AVERAGE COMMISSION RATE (ACR)	AVERAGE TRANSACTION PRICE (ATP)	CLIENT TURNOVER RATE (CTR)
GCI / V = %; Δ | %	V / T = $; Δ | $	T / C = %; Δ | %
RETURN ON PRESENTATIONS (ROP)	**RETURN ON TRANSACTIONS (ROT)**	**RETURN ON CLIENTS (ROC)**
GCI / P = $; Δ | $	GCI / T = $; Δ | $	GCI / C = $; Δ | $
AVG. LIST DAYS ON MKT (AVG. LDOM)	**SALES PRICE TO LIST PRICE (SP/LP)**	**RETURN ON DAYS WORKED (ROW)**
LDOM / LT = DAYS; Δ | DAYS	LV / LOPV = %; Δ | %	GCI / W = $; Δ | $

LEVERAGE LOG

Be mindful of Buyer, Listing, and Overall figures when applying these formulas.[XVII]

$$\frac{GCI}{V} \times \frac{V}{T} \times \frac{T}{C} = \frac{GCI}{C} \qquad \frac{GCI}{T} - \frac{GCI}{C}$$

QUARTER 04	AVERAGE COMMISSION RATE	AVERAGE TRANSACTION PRICE	CLIENT TURNOVER RATE	RETURN ON CLIENTS	LOST OPPORTUNITY DIFFERENTIAL
LISTINGS	%	$	%	$	$
BUYERS	%	$	%	$	$
OVERALL	%	$	%	$	$

BUSINESS PLAN (FOR EACH MONTH OF QUARTER 01)

STEP	CALCULATION	QUARTER 04 STATS	QUARTER 01 GOALS	
1	ANNUAL GCI GOAL	$	ANNUAL GCI GOAL	$
2	− GCI EARNED TO DATE	− $ ZERO	REMAINING GCI GOAL	$
3	÷ MONTHS REMAINING	÷ 12 MONTHS	MONTHLY GCI GOAL	$
4	÷ ACR	÷ %	MONTHLY SALES VOLUME GOAL	$
5	÷ ATP	÷ $	MONTHLY TRANSACTIONS GOAL	#T
6	÷ CTR	÷ %	MONTHLY NEW CLIENTS GOAL	#C
7	÷ PTR	÷ %	MONTHLY PRESENTATIONS GOAL	#P
8	÷ DTR	÷ %	MONTHLY DISCUSSIONS GOAL	#D
9	÷ WORKING DAYS/MTH	÷ DAYS	DAILY DISCUSSIONS GOAL	#D/W

insert annual goal for next year now (STEP 1)

ANNUAL ACTIVITY LOG

DISCUSSIONS (D)	PRESENTATIONS (P)	CLIENTS (C)	CONTRACTS (K)	TRANSACTIONS (T)
#D; Δ | #	#LP; Δ | #	#LC; Δ | #	#LK; Δ | #	#LT; Δ | #
DAYS WORKED (W)	#BP; Δ | #	#BC; Δ | #	#BK; Δ | #	#BT; Δ | #
#W; Δ | #	#P; Δ | #	#C; Δ | #	#K; Δ | #	#T; Δ | #

ANNUAL TRANSACTION DATA

GROSS COMMISSION INCOME (GCI)	DAYS ON MARKET (DOM)
LGCI $; Δ | $	LDOM DAYS; Δ | DAYS
BGCI $; Δ | $	BDOM DAYS; Δ | DAYS
GCI $; Δ | $	DOM DAYS; Δ | DAYS
SALES VOLUME (V)	**ORIGINAL PRICE VOLUME (OPV)**
LV $; Δ | $	LOPV $; Δ | $
BV $; Δ | $	BOPV $; Δ | $
V $; Δ | $	OPV $; Δ | $

CLIENTS FROM LISTINGS (L→C)

JAN	FEB	MAR	APR	MAY	JUN	JUL	AUG	SEP	OCT	NOV	DEC

TOTAL (L→C) = ; Δ | AVG. (L→C) PER MONTH = ; Δ |

DATABASE (Db)			OUTBOUND REFERRALS (R)	
#MEMBERS EXISTING			REFERRALS SENT (R)	#R Δ | #
#NEW MEMBERS	+	Δ |	REFERRAL TRANS. (RT)	#RT Δ | #
#MEMBERS PURGED	-	Δ |	REFERRAL GCI (RGCI)	$ Δ | $
#Db	=	Δ |	REFERRALS FROM DATABASE (Db→R): Δ |	
CLIENTS FROM DATABASE (Db→C): Δ |				

DATABASE & REFERRAL METRICS

RETURN ON REFERRALS (ROR)	AVG. REFERRAL COMMISSION (ARC)	REFERRAL TURNOVER RATE (RTR)
$\frac{RGCI}{R}$ = $; Δ | $	$\frac{RGCI}{RT}$ = $; Δ | $	$\frac{RT}{R}$ = %; Δ | %
MEMBERS PER REFERRAL (MPR)	**MEMBERS PER CLIENT (MPC)**	**RETURN PER MEMBER (RPM)**
$\frac{Db}{R}$ = Db:R; Δ | Db:R	$\frac{Db}{C}$ = Db:C; Δ | Db:C	$\frac{GCI}{Db}$ = $; Δ | $
DATABASE LEVERAGE RATE (DbLR)	**LISTING LEVERAGE RATE (LLR)**	**TRANS. PER REFERRAL TRANS. (T/RT)**
$\frac{Db \to C}{C}$ = %; Δ | %	$\frac{L \to C}{C}$ = %; Δ | %	$\frac{LT+BT}{RT}$ = T:RT; Δ | T:RT

MARKET COMPARISON

	#TRANSACTIONS	Δ	AVERAGE TRANS. PRICE (ATP)	AVG. LDOM	SP/LP
METRO		|	$; Δ | $		%
MACRO		|	$; Δ | $		%
PERSONAL		|	$; Δ | $		%

During this year, I mostly prospected: 1 2 3

CONVERSION RATIOS & TURNOVER RATES

	CONVERSION RATIOS		TURNOVER		Δ	L TURNOVER	Δ	B TURNOVER	Δ
DISCUSSIONS TO PRESENTATIONS	#D / #P =	D:P	DTR	#P / #D = %	%	#LP / #D = %	%	#BP / #D = %	%
PRESENTATIONS TO CLIENTS	#P / #C =	P:C	PTR	#C / #P = %	%	#LC / #LP = %	%	#BC / #BP = %	%
CLIENTS TO TRANSACTIONS	#C / #T =	T:C	CTR	#T / #C = %	%	#LT / #LC = %	%	#BT / #BC = %	%
CONTRACTS TO TRANSACTIONS	#K / #T =	K:T	KTR	#T / #K = %	%	#LT / #LK = %	%	#BT / #BK = %	%

METRICS

AVERAGE COMMISSION RATE (ACR)	AVERAGE TRANSACTION PRICE (ATP)	CLIENT TURNOVER RATE (CTR)
GCI / V = %; Δ | %	V / T = $; Δ | $	T / C = %; Δ | %
RETURN ON PRESENTATIONS (ROP)	**RETURN ON TRANSACTIONS (ROT)**	**RETURN ON CLIENTS (ROC)**
GCI / P = $; Δ | $	GCI / T = $; Δ | $	GCI / C = $; Δ | $
AVG. LIST DAYS ON MKT (AVG. LDOM)	**SALES PRICE TO LIST PRICE (SP/LP)**	**RETURN ON DAYS WORKED (ROW)**
LDOM / LT = DAYS; Δ | DAYS	LV / LOPV = %; Δ | %	GCI / W = $; Δ | $

LEVERAGE LOG

Be mindful of Buyer, Listing, and Overall figures when applying these formulas.[XVII]

		GCI / V ×	V / T ×	T / C =	GCI / C	GCI / T − GCI / C
		AVERAGE COMMISSION RATE	AVERAGE TRANSACTION PRICE	CLIENT TURNOVER RATE	RETURN ON CLIENTS	LOST OPPORTUNITY DIFFERENTIAL
ANNUAL	LISTINGS	%	$	%	$	$
	BUYERS	%	$	%	$	$
	OVERALL	%	$	%	$	$

INCOME STATEMENT

FOR MONTHS ENDED 31 DECEMBER

INCOME		EXPENSE	
LGCI	$	BROKER FEES	$
BGCI	$	EDUCATION	$
RGCI	$	SERVICES	$
OTHER	$	SUPPLIES	$
SOLD EQUIP.	$	EQUIPMENT	$
	$	STAFF	$
TOTAL INCOME	$	TOTAL EXPENSE	$

TOTAL INCOME - TOTAL EXPENSE = NET INCOME: $; Δ | $

ACTIVITY LOG

JANUARY

DISCUSSIONS (D)	PRESENTATIONS (P)	CLIENTS (C)	CONTRACTS (K)	TRANSACTIONS (T)
#D; Δ | #	#LP; Δ | #	#LC; Δ | #	#LK; Δ | #	#LT; Δ | #
DAYS WORKED (W)	#BP; Δ | #	#BC; Δ | #	#BK; Δ | #	#BT; Δ | #
#W; Δ | #	#P; Δ | #	#C; Δ | #	#K; Δ | #	#T; Δ | #

FEBRUARY

DISCUSSIONS (D)	PRESENTATIONS (P)	CLIENTS (C)	CONTRACTS (K)	TRANSACTIONS (T)
#D; Δ | #	#LP; Δ | #	#LC; Δ | #	#LK; Δ | #	#LT; Δ | #
DAYS WORKED (W)	#BP; Δ | #	#BC; Δ | #	#BK; Δ | #	#BT; Δ | #
#W; Δ | #	#P; Δ | #	#C; Δ | #	#K; Δ | #	#T; Δ | #

MARCH

DISCUSSIONS (D)	PRESENTATIONS (P)	CLIENTS (C)	CONTRACTS (K)	TRANSACTIONS (T)
#D; Δ | #	#LP; Δ | #	#LC; Δ | #	#LK; Δ | #	#LT; Δ | #
DAYS WORKED (W)	#BP; Δ | #	#BC; Δ | #	#BK; Δ | #	#BT; Δ | #
#W; Δ | #	#P; Δ | #	#C; Δ | #	#K; Δ | #	#T; Δ | #

QUARTER 01

DISCUSSIONS (D)	PRESENTATIONS (P)	CLIENTS (C)	CONTRACTS (K)	TRANSACTIONS (T)
#D; Δ | #	#LP; Δ | #	#LC; Δ | #	#LK; Δ | #	#LT; Δ | #
DAYS WORKED (W)	#BP; Δ | #	#BC; Δ | #	#BK; Δ | #	#BT; Δ | #
#W; Δ | #	#P; Δ | #	#C; Δ | #	#K; Δ | #	#T; Δ | #

QUARTERLY TRANSACTION DATA

GROSS COMMISSION INCOME (GCI)	DAYS ON MARKET (DOM)
LGCI $; Δ | $	LDOM DAYS; Δ | DAYS
BGCI $; Δ | $	BDOM DAYS; Δ | DAYS
GCI $; Δ | $	DOM DAYS; Δ | DAYS
SALES VOLUME (V)	**ORIGINAL PRICE VOLUME (OPV)**
LV $; Δ | $	LOPV $; Δ | $
BV $; Δ | $	BOPV $; Δ | $
V $; Δ | $	OPV $; Δ | $

MARKET COMPARISON

	#TRANSACTIONS	Δ	AVERAGE TRANS. PRICE (ATP)	AVG. LDOM	SP/LP
METRO		|	$; Δ | $		%
MACRO #1		|	$; Δ | $		%
MACRO #2		|	$; Δ | $		%
MACRO #3		|	$; Δ | $		%
PERSONAL		|	$; Δ | $		%

During Quarter 01, I mostly prospected:	1	2	3

CONVERSION RATIOS & TURNOVER RATES

	CONVERSION RATIOS		TURNOVER	Δ	L TURNOVER	Δ	B TURNOVER	Δ
DISCUSSIONS TO PRESENTATIONS	$\frac{\#D}{\#P}=$ D:P	DTR	$\frac{\#P}{\#D}=$ %	%	$\frac{\#LP}{\#D}=$ %	%	$\frac{\#BP}{\#D}=$ %	%
PRESENTATIONS TO CLIENTS	$\frac{\#P}{\#C}=$ P:C	PTR	$\frac{\#C}{\#P}=$ %	%	$\frac{\#LC}{\#LP}=$ %	%	$\frac{\#BC}{\#BP}=$ %	%
CLIENTS TO TRANSACTIONS	$\frac{\#C}{\#T}=$ T:C	CTR	$\frac{\#T}{\#C}=$ %	%	$\frac{\#LT}{\#LC}=$ %	%	$\frac{\#BT}{\#BC}=$ %	%
CONTRACTS TO TRANSACTIONS	$\frac{\#K}{\#T}=$ K:T	KTR	$\frac{\#T}{\#K}=$ %	%	$\frac{\#LT}{\#LK}=$ %	%	$\frac{\#BT}{\#BK}=$ %	%

METRICS

AVERAGE COMMISSION RATE (ACR)	AVERAGE TRANSACTION PRICE (ATP)	CLIENT TURNOVER RATE (CTR)
$\frac{GCI}{V}=$ %; Δ | %	$\frac{V}{T}=$ \$; Δ | \$	$\frac{T}{C}=$ %; Δ | %
RETURN ON PRESENTATIONS (ROP)	**RETURN ON TRANSACTIONS (ROT)**	**RETURN ON CLIENTS (ROC)**
$\frac{GCI}{P}=$ \$; Δ | \$	$\frac{GCI}{T}=$ \$; Δ | \$	$\frac{GCI}{C}=$ \$; Δ | \$
AVG. LIST DAYS ON MKT (AVG. LDOM)	**SALES PRICE TO LIST PRICE (SP/LP)**	**RETURN ON DAYS WORKED (ROW)**
$\frac{LDOM}{LT}=$ DAYS; Δ | DAYS	$\frac{LV}{LOPV}=$ %; Δ | %	$\frac{GCI}{W}=$ \$; Δ | \$

LEVERAGE LOG

Be mindful of Buyer, Listing, and Overall figures when applying these formulas. [XVII]	$\frac{GCI}{V}$ ×	$\frac{V}{T}$ ×	$\frac{T}{C}$ =	$\frac{GCI}{C}$	$\frac{GCI}{T}-\frac{GCI}{C}$
	AVERAGE COMMISSION RATE	AVERAGE TRANSACTION PRICE	CLIENT TURNOVER RATE	RETURN ON CLIENTS	LOST OPPORTUNITY DIFFERENTIAL
QUARTER 01 LISTINGS	%	\$	%	\$	\$
QUARTER 01 BUYERS	%	\$	%	\$	\$
QUARTER 01 OVERALL	%	\$	%	\$	\$

BUSINESS PLAN (FOR EACH MONTH OF QUARTER 02)

STEP	CALCULATION	QUARTER 01 STATS	QUARTER 02 GOALS	
1	ANNUAL GCI GOAL	\$	ANNUAL GCI GOAL	\$
2	− GCI EARNED TO DATE	− \$	REMAINING GCI GOAL	\$
3	÷ MONTHS REMAINING	÷ 9 MONTHS	MONTHLY GCI GOAL	\$
4	÷ ACR	÷ %	MONTHLY SALES VOLUME GOAL	\$
5	÷ ATP	÷ \$	MONTHLY TRANSACTIONS GOAL	#T
6	÷ CTR	÷ %	MONTHLY NEW CLIENTS GOAL	#C
7	÷ PTR	÷ %	MONTHLY PRESENTATIONS GOAL	#P
8	÷ DTR	÷ %	MONTHLY DISCUSSIONS GOAL	#D
9	÷ WORKING DAYS/MTH	÷ DAYS	DAILY DISCUSSIONS GOAL	#D/W

ACTIVITY LOG

APRIL

DISCUSSIONS (D)	PRESENTATIONS (P)	CLIENTS (C)	CONTRACTS (K)	TRANSACTIONS (T)
#D; Δ | #	#LP; Δ | #	#LC; Δ | #	#LK; Δ | #	#LT; Δ | #
DAYS WORKED (W)	#BP; Δ | #	#BC; Δ | #	#BK; Δ | #	#BT; Δ | #
#W; Δ | #	#P; Δ | #	#C; Δ | #	#K; Δ | #	#T; Δ | #

MAY

DISCUSSIONS (D)	PRESENTATIONS (P)	CLIENTS (C)	CONTRACTS (K)	TRANSACTIONS (T)
#D; Δ | #	#LP; Δ | #	#LC; Δ | #	#LK; Δ | #	#LT; Δ | #
DAYS WORKED (W)	#BP; Δ | #	#BC; Δ | #	#BK; Δ | #	#BT; Δ | #
#W; Δ | #	#P; Δ | #	#C; Δ | #	#K; Δ | #	#T; Δ | #

JUNE

DISCUSSIONS (D)	PRESENTATIONS (P)	CLIENTS (C)	CONTRACTS (K)	TRANSACTIONS (T)
#D; Δ | #	#LP; Δ | #	#LC; Δ | #	#LK; Δ | #	#LT; Δ | #
DAYS WORKED (W)	#BP; Δ | #	#BC; Δ | #	#BK; Δ | #	#BT; Δ | #
#W; Δ | #	#P; Δ | #	#C; Δ | #	#K; Δ | #	#T; Δ | #

QUARTER 02

DISCUSSIONS (D)	PRESENTATIONS (P)	CLIENTS (C)	CONTRACTS (K)	TRANSACTIONS (T)
#D; Δ | #	#LP; Δ | #	#LC; Δ | #	#LK; Δ | #	#LT; Δ | #
DAYS WORKED (W)	#BP; Δ | #	#BC; Δ | #	#BK; Δ | #	#BT; Δ | #
#W; Δ | #	#P; Δ | #	#C; Δ | #	#K; Δ | #	#T; Δ | #

QUARTERLY TRANSACTION DATA

GROSS COMMISSION INCOME (GCI)	DAYS ON MARKET (DOM)
LGCI $; Δ | $	LDOM DAYS; Δ | DAYS
BGCI $; Δ | $	BDOM DAYS; Δ | DAYS
GCI $; Δ | $	DOM DAYS; Δ | DAYS
SALES VOLUME (V)	**ORIGINAL PRICE VOLUME (OPV)**
LV $; Δ | $	LOPV $; Δ | $
BV $; Δ | $	BOPV $; Δ | $
V $; Δ | $	OPV $; Δ | $

MARKET COMPARISON

	#TRANSACTIONS	Δ	AVERAGE TRANS. PRICE (ATP)	AVG. LDOM	SP/LP
METRO		|	$; Δ | $		%
MACRO #1		|	$; Δ | $		%
MACRO #2		|	$; Δ | $		%
MACRO #3		|	$; Δ | $		%
PERSONAL		|	$; Δ | $		%

During Quarter 02, I mostly prospected:	1	2	3

CONVERSION RATIOS & TURNOVER RATES

	CONVERSION RATIOS		TURNOVER	Δ	L TURNOVER	Δ	B TURNOVER	Δ
DISCUSSIONS TO PRESENTATIONS	#D / #P =	D:P	DTR #P / #D = %	%	#LP / #D = %	%	#BP / #D = %	%
PRESENTATIONS TO CLIENTS	#P / #C =	P:C	PTR #C / #P = %	%	#LC / #LP = %	%	#BC / #BP = %	%
CLIENTS TO TRANSACTIONS	#C / #T =	T:C	CTR #T / #C = %	%	#LT / #LC = %	%	#BT / #BC = %	%
CONTRACTS TO TRANSACTIONS	#K / #T =	K:T	KTR #T / #K = %	%	#LT / #LK = %	%	#BT / #BK = %	%

METRICS

AVERAGE COMMISSION RATE (ACR)	AVERAGE TRANSACTION PRICE (ATP)	CLIENT TURNOVER RATE (CTR)
GCI / V = %; Δ | %	V / T = $; Δ | $	T / C = %; Δ | %
RETURN ON PRESENTATIONS (ROP)	**RETURN ON TRANSACTIONS (ROT)**	**RETURN ON CLIENTS (ROC)**
GCI / P = $; Δ | $	GCI / T = $; Δ | $	GCI / C = $; Δ | $
AVG. LIST DAYS ON MKT (AVG. LDOM)	**SALES PRICE TO LIST PRICE (SP/LP)**	**RETURN ON DAYS WORKED (ROW)**
LDOM / LT = DAYS; Δ | DAYS	LV / LOPV = %; Δ | %	GCI / W = $; Δ | $

LEVERAGE LOG

Be mindful of Buyer, Listing, and Overall figures when applying these formulas.[XVII]

	GCI / V	× V / T	× T / C	= GCI / C	GCI / T − GCI / C
	AVERAGE COMMISSION RATE	AVERAGE TRANSACTION PRICE	CLIENT TURNOVER RATE	RETURN ON CLIENTS	LOST OPPORTUNITY DIFFERENTIAL
QUARTER 02 LISTINGS	%	$	%	$	$
QUARTER 02 BUYERS	%	$	%	$	$
QUARTER 02 OVERALL	%	$	%	$	$

BUSINESS PLAN (FOR EACH MONTH OF QUARTER 03)

STEP	CALCULATION	QUARTER 02 STATS	QUARTER 03 GOALS	
1	ANNUAL GCI GOAL	$	ANNUAL GCI GOAL	$
2	− GCI EARNED TO DATE	− $	REMAINING GCI GOAL	$
3	÷ MONTHS REMAINING	÷ 6 MONTHS	MONTHLY GCI GOAL	$
4	÷ ACR	÷ %	MONTHLY SALES VOLUME GOAL	$
5	÷ ATP	÷ $	MONTHLY TRANSACTIONS GOAL	#T
6	÷ CTR	÷ %	MONTHLY NEW CLIENTS GOAL	#C
7	÷ PTR	÷ %	MONTHLY PRESENTATIONS GOAL	#P
8	÷ DTR	÷ %	MONTHLY DISCUSSIONS GOAL	#D
9	÷ WORKING DAYS/MTH	÷ DAYS	DAILY DISCUSSIONS GOAL	#D/W

ACTIVITY LOG

JULY

DISCUSSIONS (D)	PRESENTATIONS (P)	CLIENTS (C)	CONTRACTS (K)	TRANSACTIONS (T)
#D; Δ | #	#LP; Δ | #	#LC; Δ | #	#LK; Δ | #	#LT; Δ | #
DAYS WORKED (W)	#BP; Δ | #	#BC; Δ | #	#BK; Δ | #	#BT; Δ | #
#W; Δ | #	#P; Δ | #	#C; Δ | #	#K; Δ | #	#T; Δ | #

AUGUST

DISCUSSIONS (D)	PRESENTATIONS (P)	CLIENTS (C)	CONTRACTS (K)	TRANSACTIONS (T)
#D; Δ | #	#LP; Δ | #	#LC; Δ | #	#LK; Δ | #	#LT; Δ | #
DAYS WORKED (W)	#BP; Δ | #	#BC; Δ | #	#BK; Δ | #	#BT; Δ | #
#W; Δ | #	#P; Δ | #	#C; Δ | #	#K; Δ | #	#T; Δ | #

SEPTEMBER

DISCUSSIONS (D)	PRESENTATIONS (P)	CLIENTS (C)	CONTRACTS (K)	TRANSACTIONS (T)
#D; Δ | #	#LP; Δ | #	#LC; Δ | #	#LK; Δ | #	#LT; Δ | #
DAYS WORKED (W)	#BP; Δ | #	#BC; Δ | #	#BK; Δ | #	#BT; Δ | #
#W; Δ | #	#P; Δ | #	#C; Δ | #	#K; Δ | #	#T; Δ | #

QUARTER 03

DISCUSSIONS (D)	PRESENTATIONS (P)	CLIENTS (C)	CONTRACTS (K)	TRANSACTIONS (T)
#D; Δ | #	#LP; Δ | #	#LC; Δ | #	#LK; Δ | #	#LT; Δ | #
DAYS WORKED (W)	#BP; Δ | #	#BC; Δ | #	#BK; Δ | #	#BT; Δ | #
#W; Δ | #	#P; Δ | #	#C; Δ | #	#K; Δ | #	#T; Δ | #

QUARTERLY TRANSACTION DATA

GROSS COMMISSION INCOME (GCI)	DAYS ON MARKET (DOM)
LGCI $; Δ | $	LDOM DAYS; Δ | DAYS
BGCI $; Δ | $	BDOM DAYS; Δ | DAYS
GCI $; Δ | $	DOM DAYS; Δ | DAYS
SALES VOLUME (V)	**ORIGINAL PRICE VOLUME (OPV)**
LV $; Δ | $	LOPV $; Δ | $
BV $; Δ | $	BOPV $; Δ | $
V $; Δ | $	OPV $; Δ | $

MARKET COMPARISON

	#TRANSACTIONS	Δ	AVERAGE TRANS. PRICE (ATP)	AVG. LDOM	SP/LP
METRO		|	$; Δ | $		%
MACRO #1		|	$; Δ | $		%
MACRO #2		|	$; Δ | $		%
MACRO #3		|	$; Δ | $		%
PERSONAL		|	$; Δ | $		%

During Quarter 03, I mostly prospected:	1	2	3

CONVERSION RATIOS & TURNOVER RATES

	CONVERSION RATIOS		TURNOVER	Δ	L TURNOVER	Δ	B TURNOVER	Δ
DISCUSSIONS TO PRESENTATIONS	#D / #P =	D:P	DTR: #P / #D = %	%	#LP / #D = %	%	#BP / #D = %	%
PRESENTATIONS TO CLIENTS	#P / #C =	P:C	PTR: #C / #P = %	%	#LC / #LP = %	%	#BC / #BP = %	%
CLIENTS TO TRANSACTIONS	#C / #T =	T:C	CTR: #T / #C = %	%	#LT / #LC = %	%	#BT / #BC = %	%
CONTRACTS TO TRANSACTIONS	#K / #T =	K:T	KTR: #T / #K = %	%	#LT / #LK = %	%	#BT / #BK = %	%

METRICS

AVERAGE COMMISSION RATE (ACR)	AVERAGE TRANSACTION PRICE (ATP)	CLIENT TURNOVER RATE (CTR)
GCI / V = %; Δ | %	V / T = $; Δ | $	T / C = %; Δ | %
RETURN ON PRESENTATIONS (ROP)	**RETURN ON TRANSACTIONS (ROT)**	**RETURN ON CLIENTS (ROC)**
GCI / P = $; Δ | $	GCI / T = $; Δ | $	GCI / C = $; Δ | $
AVG. LIST DAYS ON MKT (AVG. LDOM)	**SALES PRICE TO LIST PRICE (SP/LP)**	**RETURN ON DAYS WORKED (ROW)**
LDOM / LT = DAYS; Δ | DAYS	LV / LOPV = %; Δ | %	GCI / W = $; Δ | $

LEVERAGE LOG

*Be mindful of Buyer, Listing, and Overall figures when applying these formulas.*XVII

	GCI / V	×	V / T	×	T / C	=	GCI / C	GCI / T − GCI / C
	AVERAGE COMMISSION RATE		AVERAGE TRANSACTION PRICE		CLIENT TURNOVER RATE		RETURN ON CLIENTS	LOST OPPORTUNITY DIFFERENTIAL
QUARTER 03 LISTINGS	%		$		%		$	$
QUARTER 03 BUYERS	%		$		%		$	$
QUARTER 03 OVERALL	%		$		%		$	$

BUSINESS PLAN (FOR EACH MONTH OF QUARTER 04)

STEP	CALCULATION	QUARTER 03 STATS	QUARTER 04 GOALS	
1	ANNUAL GCI GOAL	$	ANNUAL GCI GOAL	$
2	− GCI EARNED TO DATE	− $	REMAINING GCI GOAL	$
3	÷ MONTHS REMAINING	÷ 3 MONTHS	MONTHLY GCI GOAL	$
4	÷ ACR	÷ %	MONTHLY SALES VOLUME GOAL	$
5	÷ ATP	÷ $	MONTHLY TRANSACTIONS GOAL	#T
6	÷ CTR	÷ %	MONTHLY NEW CLIENTS GOAL	#C
7	÷ PTR	÷ %	MONTHLY PRESENTATIONS GOAL	#P
8	÷ DTR	÷ %	MONTHLY DISCUSSIONS GOAL	#D
9	÷ WORKING DAYS/MTH	÷ DAYS	DAILY DISCUSSIONS GOAL	#D/W

ACTIVITY LOG

OCTOBER

DISCUSSIONS (D)	PRESENTATIONS (P)	CLIENTS (C)	CONTRACTS (K)	TRANSACTIONS (T)
#D; Δ | #	#LP; Δ | #	#LC; Δ | #	#LK; Δ | #	#LT; Δ | #
DAYS WORKED (W)	#BP; Δ | #	#BC; Δ | #	#BK; Δ | #	#BT; Δ | #
#W; Δ | #	#P; Δ | #	#C; Δ | #	#K; Δ | #	#T; Δ | #

NOVEMBER

DISCUSSIONS (D)	PRESENTATIONS (P)	CLIENTS (C)	CONTRACTS (K)	TRANSACTIONS (T)
#D; Δ | #	#LP; Δ | #	#LC; Δ | #	#LK; Δ | #	#LT; Δ | #
DAYS WORKED (W)	#BP; Δ | #	#BC; Δ | #	#BK; Δ | #	#BT; Δ | #
#W; Δ | #	#P; Δ | #	#C; Δ | #	#K; Δ | #	#T; Δ | #

DECEMBER

DISCUSSIONS (D)	PRESENTATIONS (P)	CLIENTS (C)	CONTRACTS (K)	TRANSACTIONS (T)
#D; Δ | #	#LP; Δ | #	#LC; Δ | #	#LK; Δ | #	#LT; Δ | #
DAYS WORKED (W)	#BP; Δ | #	#BC; Δ | #	#BK; Δ | #	#BT; Δ | #
#W; Δ | #	#P; Δ | #	#C; Δ | #	#K; Δ | #	#T; Δ | #

QUARTER 04

DISCUSSIONS (D)	PRESENTATIONS (P)	CLIENTS (C)	CONTRACTS (K)	TRANSACTIONS (T)
#D; Δ | #	#LP; Δ | #	#LC; Δ | #	#LK; Δ | #	#LT; Δ | #
DAYS WORKED (W)	#BP; Δ | #	#BC; Δ | #	#BK; Δ | #	#BT; Δ | #
#W; Δ | #	#P; Δ | #	#C; Δ | #	#K; Δ | #	#T; Δ | #

QUARTERLY TRANSACTION DATA

GROSS COMMISSION INCOME (GCI)	DAYS ON MARKET (DOM)
LGCI $; Δ | $	LDOM DAYS; Δ | DAYS
BGCI $; Δ | $	BDOM DAYS; Δ | DAYS
GCI $; Δ | $	DOM DAYS; Δ | DAYS
SALES VOLUME (V)	**ORIGINAL PRICE VOLUME (OPV)**
LV $; Δ | $	LOPV $; Δ | $
BV $; Δ | $	BOPV $; Δ | $
V $; Δ | $	OPV $; Δ | $

MARKET COMPARISON

	#TRANSACTIONS	Δ	AVERAGE TRANS. PRICE (ATP)	AVG. LDOM	SP/LP
METRO		|	$; Δ | $		%
MACRO #1		|	$; Δ | $		%
MACRO #2		|	$; Δ | $		%
MACRO #3		|	$; Δ | $		%
PERSONAL		|	$; Δ | $		%

During Quarter 04, I mostly prospected:	*1*	*2*	*3*

CONVERSION RATIOS & TURNOVER RATES

	CONVERSION RATIOS		TURNOVER	Δ	L TURNOVER	Δ	B TURNOVER	Δ
DISCUSSIONS TO PRESENTATIONS	#D / #P =	D:P	DTR #P / #D = %	%	#LP / #D = %	%	#BP / #D = %	%
PRESENTATIONS TO CLIENTS	#P / #C =	P:C	PTR #C / #P = %	%	#LC / #LP = %	%	#BC / #BP = %	%
CLIENTS TO TRANSACTIONS	#C / #T =	T:C	CTR #T / #C = %	%	#LT / #LC = %	%	#BT / #BC = %	%
CONTRACTS TO TRANSACTIONS	#K / #T =	K:T	KTR #T / #K = %	%	#LT / #LK = %	%	#BT / #BK = %	%

METRICS

AVERAGE COMMISSION RATE (ACR)	AVERAGE TRANSACTION PRICE (ATP)	CLIENT TURNOVER RATE (CTR)
GCI / V = %; Δ | %	V / T = $; Δ | $	T / C = %; Δ | %
RETURN ON PRESENTATIONS (ROP)	**RETURN ON TRANSACTIONS (ROT)**	**RETURN ON CLIENTS (ROC)**
GCI / P = $; Δ | $	GCI / T = $; Δ | $	GCI / C = $; Δ | $
AVG. LIST DAYS ON MKT (AVG. LDOM)	**SALES PRICE TO LIST PRICE (SP/LP)**	**RETURN ON DAYS WORKED (ROW)**
LDOM / LT = DAYS; Δ | DAYS	LV / LOPV = %; Δ | %	GCI / W = $; Δ | $

LEVERAGE LOG

Be mindful of Buyer, Listing, and Overall figures when applying these formulas. XVII

	GCI / V	×	V / T	×	T / C	=	GCI / C	GCI / T − GCI / C
QUARTER 04	AVERAGE COMMISSION RATE		AVERAGE TRANSACTION PRICE		CLIENT TURNOVER RATE		RETURN ON CLIENTS	LOST OPPORTUNITY DIFFERENTIAL
LISTINGS	%		$		%		$	$
BUYERS	%		$		%		$	$
OVERALL	%		$		%		$	$

BUSINESS PLAN (FOR EACH MONTH OF QUARTER 01)

STEP	CALCULATION	QUARTER 04 STATS	QUARTER 01 GOALS	
1	ANNUAL GCI GOAL	$	ANNUAL GCI GOAL	$
2	− GCI EARNED TO DATE	− $ ZERO	REMAINING GCI GOAL	$
3	÷ MONTHS REMAINING	÷ 12 MONTHS	MONTHLY GCI GOAL	$
4	÷ ACR	÷ %	MONTHLY SALES VOLUME GOAL	$
5	÷ ATP	÷ $	MONTHLY TRANSACTIONS GOAL	#T
6	÷ CTR	÷ %	MONTHLY NEW CLIENTS GOAL	#C
7	÷ PTR	÷ %	MONTHLY PRESENTATIONS GOAL	#P
8	÷ DTR	÷ %	MONTHLY DISCUSSIONS GOAL	#D
9	÷ WORKING DAYS/MTH	÷ DAYS	DAILY DISCUSSIONS GOAL	#D/W

insert annual goal for next year now (STEP 1)

ANNUAL ACTIVITY LOG

DISCUSSIONS (D)	PRESENTATIONS (P)	CLIENTS (C)	CONTRACTS (K)	TRANSACTIONS (T)
#D; Δ | #	#LP; Δ | #	#LC; Δ | #	#LK; Δ | #	#LT; Δ | #
DAYS WORKED (W)	#BP; Δ | #	#BC; Δ | #	#BK; Δ | #	#BT; Δ | #
#W; Δ | #	#P; Δ | #	#C; Δ | #	#K; Δ | #	#T; Δ | #

ANNUAL TRANSACTION DATA

GROSS COMMISSION INCOME (GCI)	DAYS ON MARKET (DOM)
LGCI $; Δ | $	LDOM DAYS; Δ | DAYS
BGCI $; Δ | $	BDOM DAYS; Δ | DAYS
GCI $; Δ | $	DOM DAYS; Δ | DAYS
SALES VOLUME (V)	**ORIGINAL PRICE VOLUME (OPV)**
LV $; Δ | $	LOPV $; Δ | $
BV $; Δ | $	BOPV $; Δ | $
V $; Δ | $	OPV $; Δ | $

CLIENTS FROM LISTINGS (L→C)

JAN	FEB	MAR	APR	MAY	JUN	JUL	AUG	SEP	OCT	NOV	DEC

TOTAL (L→C) = ; Δ | AVG. (L→C) PER MONTH = ; Δ |

DATABASE (Db)

#MEMBERS EXISTING		
#NEW MEMBERS	+	Δ |
#MEMBERS PURGED	-	Δ |
#Db	=	Δ |

CLIENTS FROM DATABASE (Db→C): Δ |

OUTBOUND REFERRALS (R)

REFERRALS SENT (R)	#R Δ | #
REFERRAL TRANS. (RT)	#RT Δ | #
REFERRAL GCI (RGCI)	$ Δ | $

REFERRALS FROM DATABASE (Db→R): Δ |

DATABASE & REFERRAL METRICS

RETURN ON REFERRALS (ROR)	AVG. REFERRAL COMMISSION (ARC)	REFERRAL TURNOVER RATE (RTR)
$\frac{RGCI}{R}$ = $; Δ | $	$\frac{RGCI}{RT}$ = $; Δ | $	$\frac{RT}{R}$ = %; Δ | %
MEMBERS PER REFERRAL (MPR)	**MEMBERS PER CLIENT (MPC)**	**RETURN PER MEMBER (RPM)**
$\frac{Db}{R}$ = Db:R; Δ | Db:R	$\frac{Db}{C}$ = Db:C; Δ | Db:C	$\frac{GCI}{Db}$ = $; Δ | $
DATABASE LEVERAGE RATE (DbLR)	**LISTING LEVERAGE RATE (LLR)**	**TRANS. PER REFERRAL TRANS. (T/RT)**
$\frac{Db \rightarrow C}{C}$ = %; Δ | %	$\frac{L \rightarrow C}{C}$ = %; Δ | %	$\frac{LT+BT}{RT}$ = T:RT; Δ | T:RT

MARKET COMPARISON

	#TRANSACTIONS	Δ	AVERAGE TRANS. PRICE (ATP)	AVG. LDOM	SP/LP
METRO		|	$; Δ | $		%
MACRO		|	$; Δ | $		%
PERSONAL		|	$; Δ | $		%

During this year, I mostly prospected: 1 2 3

CONVERSION RATIOS & TURNOVER RATES

	CONVERSION RATIOS		TURNOVER	Δ	L TURNOVER	Δ	B TURNOVER	Δ
DISCUSSIONS TO PRESENTATIONS	#D / #P =	D:P	DTR #P / #D = %	%	#LP / #D = %	%	#BP / #D = %	%
PRESENTATIONS TO CLIENTS	#P / #C =	P:C	PTR #C / #P = %	%	#LC / #LP = %	%	#BC / #BP = %	%
CLIENTS TO TRANSACTIONS	#C / #T =	T:C	CTR #T / #C = %	%	#LT / #LC = %	%	#BT / #BC = %	%
CONTRACTS TO TRANSACTIONS	#K / #T =	K:T	KTR #T / #K = %	%	#LT / #LK = %	%	#BT / #BK = %	%

METRICS

AVERAGE COMMISSION RATE (ACR)	AVERAGE TRANSACTION PRICE (ATP)	CLIENT TURNOVER RATE (CTR)
GCI / V = %; Δ | %	V / T = $; Δ | $	T / C = %; Δ | %
RETURN ON PRESENTATIONS (ROP)	**RETURN ON TRANSACTIONS (ROT)**	**RETURN ON CLIENTS (ROC)**
GCI / P = $; Δ | $	GCI / T = $; Δ | $	GCI / C = $; Δ | $
AVG. LIST DAYS ON MKT (AVG. LDOM)	**SALES PRICE TO LIST PRICE (SP/LP)**	**RETURN ON DAYS WORKED (ROW)**
LDOM / LT = DAYS; Δ | DAYS	LV / LOPV = %; Δ | %	GCI / W = $; Δ | $

LEVERAGE LOG

Be mindful of Buyer, Listing, and Overall figures when applying these formulas. XVII

	GCI / V	× V / T	× T / C	= GCI / C	GCI / T − GCI / C
	AVERAGE COMMISSION RATE	AVERAGE TRANSACTION PRICE	CLIENT TURNOVER RATE	RETURN ON CLIENTS	LOST OPPORTUNITY DIFFERENTIAL
ANNUAL LISTINGS	%	$	%	$	$
ANNUAL BUYERS	%	$	%	$	$
ANNUAL OVERALL	%	$	%	$	$

INCOME STATEMENT

FOR MONTHS ENDED 31 DECEMBER

INCOME		EXPENSE	
LGCI	$	BROKER FEES	$
BGCI	$	EDUCATION	$
RGCI	$	SERVICES	$
OTHER	$	SUPPLIES	$
SOLD EQUIP.	$	EQUIPMENT	$
	$	STAFF	$
TOTAL INCOME	$	TOTAL EXPENSE	$

TOTAL INCOME - TOTAL EXPENSE = NET INCOME: $; Δ | $

YEAR 01 ACTIVITY LOG

DISCUSSIONS (D)	PRESENTATIONS (P)	CLIENTS (C)	CONTRACTS (K)	TRANSACTIONS (T)
#D; Δ | #	#LP; Δ | #	#LC; Δ | #	#LK; Δ | #	#LT; Δ | #
DAYS WORKED (W)	#BP; Δ | #	#BC; Δ | #	#BK; Δ | #	#BT; Δ | #
#W; Δ | #	#P; Δ | #	#C; Δ | #	#K; Δ | #	#T; Δ | #

YEAR 02 ACTIVITY LOG

DISCUSSIONS (D)	PRESENTATIONS (P)	CLIENTS (C)	CONTRACTS (K)	TRANSACTIONS (T)
#D; Δ | #	#LP; Δ | #	#LC; Δ | #	#LK; Δ | #	#LT; Δ | #
DAYS WORKED (W)	#BP; Δ | #	#BC; Δ | #	#BK; Δ | #	#BT; Δ | #
#W; Δ | #	#P; Δ | #	#C; Δ | #	#K; Δ | #	#T; Δ | #

YEAR 03 ACTIVITY LOG

DISCUSSIONS (D)	PRESENTATIONS (P)	CLIENTS (C)	CONTRACTS (K)	TRANSACTIONS (T)
#D; Δ | #	#LP; Δ | #	#LC; Δ | #	#LK; Δ | #	#LT; Δ | #
DAYS WORKED (W)	#BP; Δ | #	#BC; Δ | #	#BK; Δ | #	#BT; Δ | #
#W; Δ | #	#P; Δ | #	#C; Δ | #	#K; Δ | #	#T; Δ | #

TRI-ANNUAL ACTIVITY LOG

DISCUSSIONS (D)	PRESENTATIONS (P)	CLIENTS (C)	CONTRACTS (K)	TRANSACTIONS (T)
#D; Δ | #	#LP; Δ | #	#LC; Δ | #	#LK; Δ | #	#LT; Δ | #
DAYS WORKED (W)	#BP; Δ | #	#BC; Δ | #	#BK; Δ | #	#BT; Δ | #
#W; Δ | #	#P; Δ | #	#C; Δ | #	#K; Δ | #	#T; Δ | #

Over the last three years, I mostly prospected:	*1*	*2*	*3*

TRI-ANNUAL TRANSACTION DATA

GROSS COMMISSION INCOME (GCI)	DAYS ON MARKET (DOM)
LGCI $; Δ | $	LDOM DAYS; Δ | DAYS
BGCI $; Δ | $	BDOM DAYS; Δ | DAYS
GCI $; Δ | $	DOM DAYS; Δ | DAYS

SALES VOLUME (V)	ORIGINAL PRICE VOLUME (OPV)
LV $; Δ | $	LOPV $; Δ | $
BV $; Δ | $	BOPV $; Δ | $
V $; Δ | $	OPV $; Δ | $

DATABASE (Db)			OUTBOUND REFERRALS (R)		
#MEMBERS EXISTING		Δ |	REFERRALS SENT (R)	#R	Δ | #
#NEW MEMBERS	+	Δ |	REFERRAL TRANS. (RT)	#RT	Δ | #
#MEMBERS PURGED	-	Δ |	REFERRAL GCI (RGCI)	$	Δ | $
#Db	=	Δ |	REFERRALS FROM DATABASE (Db→R):		Δ |
CLIENTS FROM DATABASE (Db→C):		Δ |	TOTAL (L→C) =		; Δ |

CONVERSION RATIOS & TURNOVER RATES

	CONVERSION RATIOS		TURNOVER	Δ	L TURNOVER	Δ	B TURNOVER	Δ
DISCUSSIONS TO PRESENTATIONS	#D / #P =	D:P	DTR #P / #D = %	%	#LP / #D = %	%	#BP / #D = %	%
PRESENTATIONS TO CLIENTS	#P / #C =	P:C	PTR #C / #P = %	%	#LC / #LP = %	%	#BC / #BP = %	%
CLIENTS TO TRANSACTIONS	#C / #T =	T:C	CTR #T / #C = %	%	#LT / #LC = %	%	#BT / #BC = %	%
CONTRACTS TO TRANSACTIONS	#K / #T =	K:T	KTR #T / #K = %	%	#LT / #LK = %	%	#BT / #BK = %	%

METRICS

AVERAGE COMMISSION RATE (ACR)	AVERAGE TRANSACTION PRICE (ATP)	CLIENT TURNOVER RATE (CTR)
GCI / V = %; Δ | %	V / T = $; Δ | $	T / C = %; Δ | %
RETURN ON PRESENTATIONS (ROP)	**RETURN ON TRANSACTIONS (ROT)**	**RETURN ON CLIENTS (ROC)**
GCI / P = $; Δ | $	GCI / T = $; Δ | $	GCI / C = $; Δ | $
AVG. LIST DAYS ON MKT (AVG. LDOM)	**SALES PRICE TO LIST PRICE (SP/LP)**	**RETURN ON DAYS WORKED (ROW)**
LDOM / LT = DAYS; Δ | DAYS	LV / LOPV = %; Δ | %	GCI / W = $; Δ | $

LEVERAGE LOG

Be mindful of Buyer, Listing, and Overall figures when applying these formulas.[XVII]

$$\frac{GCI}{V} \times \frac{V}{T} \times \frac{T}{C} = \frac{GCI}{C} \qquad \frac{GCI}{T} - \frac{GCI}{C}$$

TRI-ANNUAL	AVERAGE COMMISSION RATE	AVERAGE TRANSACTION PRICE	CLIENT TURNOVER RATE	RETURN ON CLIENTS	LOST OPPORTUNITY DIFFERENTIAL
LISTINGS	%	$	%	$	$
BUYERS	%	$	%	$	$
OVERALL	%	$	%	$	$

DATABASE & REFERRAL METRICS

RETURN ON REFERRALS (ROR)	AVG. REFERRAL COMMISSION (ARC)	REFERRAL TURNOVER RATE (RTR)
RGCI / R = $; Δ | $	RGCI / RT = $; Δ | $	RT / R = %; Δ | %
MEMBERS PER REFERRAL (MPR)	**MEMBERS PER CLIENT (MPC)**	**RETURN PER MEMBER (RPM)**
Db / R = Db:R; Δ | Db:R	Db / C = Db:C; Δ | Db:C	GCI / Db = $; Δ | $
DATABASE LEVERAGE RATE (DbLR)	**LISTING LEVERAGE RATE (LLR)**	**TRANS. PER REFERRAL TRANS. (T/RT)**
Db→C / C = %; Δ | %	L→C / C = %; Δ | %	LT+BT / RT = T:RT; Δ | T:RT

MARKET COMPARISON

	#TRANSACTIONS	Δ	AVERAGE TRANS. PRICE (ATP)	AVG. LDOM	SP/LP
METRO		|	$; Δ | $		%
MACRO		|	$; Δ | $		%
PERSONAL		|	$; Δ | $		%

OUTBOUND REFERRALS (R)

NO.	REFERRED PARTY	NOTIFIED?	AGENT REFERRED	DATE SENT
1				

L, B, OR BOTH	COMMISH. RATE	ANTICIPATED CLOSE DATE	CLOSED?	RGCI
				$

NO.	REFERRED PARTY	NOTIFIED?	AGENT REFERRED	DATE SENT
2				

L, B, OR BOTH	COMMISH. RATE	ANTICIPATED CLOSE DATE	CLOSED?	RGCI
				$

NO.	REFERRED PARTY	NOTIFIED?	AGENT REFERRED	DATE SENT
3				

L, B, OR BOTH	COMMISH. RATE	ANTICIPATED CLOSE DATE	CLOSED?	RGCI
				$

NO.	REFERRED PARTY	NOTIFIED?	AGENT REFERRED	DATE SENT
4				

L, B, OR BOTH	COMMISH. RATE	ANTICIPATED CLOSE DATE	CLOSED?	RGCI
				$

NO.	REFERRED PARTY	NOTIFIED?	AGENT REFERRED	DATE SENT
5				

L, B, OR BOTH	COMMISH. RATE	ANTICIPATED CLOSE DATE	CLOSED?	RGCI
				$

NO.	REFERRED PARTY	NOTIFIED?	AGENT REFERRED	DATE SENT
6				

L, B, OR BOTH	COMMISH. RATE	ANTICIPATED CLOSE DATE	CLOSED?	RGCI
				$

NO.	REFERRED PARTY	NOTIFIED?	AGENT REFERRED	DATE SENT
7				

L, B, OR BOTH	COMMISH. RATE	ANTICIPATED CLOSE DATE	CLOSED?	RGCI
				$

NO.	REFERRED PARTY	NOTIFIED?	AGENT REFERRED	DATE SENT
8				

L, B, OR BOTH	COMMISH. RATE	ANTICIPATED CLOSE DATE	CLOSED?	RGCI
				$

NO.	REFERRED PARTY	NOTIFIED?	AGENT REFERRED	DATE SENT
9				

L, B, OR BOTH	COMMISH. RATE	ANTICIPATED CLOSE DATE	CLOSED?	RGCI
				$

OUTBOUND REFERRALS (R)

NO.	REFERRED PARTY	NOTIFIED?	AGENT REFERRED	DATE SENT
10				

L, B, OR BOTH	COMMISH. RATE	ANTICIPATED CLOSE DATE	CLOSED?	RGCI
				$

NO.	REFERRED PARTY	NOTIFIED?	AGENT REFERRED	DATE SENT
11				

L, B, OR BOTH	COMMISH. RATE	ANTICIPATED CLOSE DATE	CLOSED?	RGCI
				$

NO.	REFERRED PARTY	NOTIFIED?	AGENT REFERRED	DATE SENT
12				

L, B, OR BOTH	COMMISH. RATE	ANTICIPATED CLOSE DATE	CLOSED?	RGCI
				$

NO.	REFERRED PARTY	NOTIFIED?	AGENT REFERRED	DATE SENT
13				

L, B, OR BOTH	COMMISH. RATE	ANTICIPATED CLOSE DATE	CLOSED?	RGCI
				$

NO.	REFERRED PARTY	NOTIFIED?	AGENT REFERRED	DATE SENT
14				

L, B, OR BOTH	COMMISH. RATE	ANTICIPATED CLOSE DATE	CLOSED?	RGCI
				$

NO.	REFERRED PARTY	NOTIFIED?	AGENT REFERRED	DATE SENT
15				

L, B, OR BOTH	COMMISH. RATE	ANTICIPATED CLOSE DATE	CLOSED?	RGCI
				$

NO.	REFERRED PARTY	NOTIFIED?	AGENT REFERRED	DATE SENT
16				

L, B, OR BOTH	COMMISH. RATE	ANTICIPATED CLOSE DATE	CLOSED?	RGCI
				$

NO.	REFERRED PARTY	NOTIFIED?	AGENT REFERRED	DATE SENT
17				

L, B, OR BOTH	COMMISH. RATE	ANTICIPATED CLOSE DATE	CLOSED?	RGCI
				$

NO.	REFERRED PARTY	NOTIFIED?	AGENT REFERRED	DATE SENT
18				

L, B, OR BOTH	COMMISH. RATE	ANTICIPATED CLOSE DATE	CLOSED?	RGCI
				$

OUTBOUND REFERRALS (R)

NO.	REFERRED PARTY		NOTIFIED?	AGENT REFERRED		DATE SENT
19						
	L, B, OR BOTH	COMMISH. RATE	ANTICIPATED CLOSE DATE		CLOSED?	RGCI
						$

NO.	REFERRED PARTY		NOTIFIED?	AGENT REFERRED		DATE SENT
20						
	L, B, OR BOTH	COMMISH. RATE	ANTICIPATED CLOSE DATE		CLOSED?	RGCI
						$

NO.	REFERRED PARTY		NOTIFIED?	AGENT REFERRED		DATE SENT
21						
	L, B, OR BOTH	COMMISH. RATE	ANTICIPATED CLOSE DATE		CLOSED?	RGCI
						$

NO.	REFERRED PARTY		NOTIFIED?	AGENT REFERRED		DATE SENT
22						
	L, B, OR BOTH	COMMISH. RATE	ANTICIPATED CLOSE DATE		CLOSED?	RGCI
						$

NO.	REFERRED PARTY		NOTIFIED?	AGENT REFERRED		DATE SENT
23						
	L, B, OR BOTH	COMMISH. RATE	ANTICIPATED CLOSE DATE		CLOSED?	RGCI
						$

NO.	REFERRED PARTY		NOTIFIED?	AGENT REFERRED		DATE SENT
24						
	L, B, OR BOTH	COMMISH. RATE	ANTICIPATED CLOSE DATE		CLOSED?	RGCI
						$

NO.	REFERRED PARTY		NOTIFIED?	AGENT REFERRED		DATE SENT
25						
	L, B, OR BOTH	COMMISH. RATE	ANTICIPATED CLOSE DATE		CLOSED?	RGCI
						$

NO.	REFERRED PARTY		NOTIFIED?	AGENT REFERRED		DATE SENT
26						
	L, B, OR BOTH	COMMISH. RATE	ANTICIPATED CLOSE DATE		CLOSED?	RGCI
						$

NO.	REFERRED PARTY		NOTIFIED?	AGENT REFERRED		DATE SENT
27						
	L, B, OR BOTH	COMMISH. RATE	ANTICIPATED CLOSE DATE		CLOSED?	RGCI
						$

OUTBOUND REFERRALS (R)

NO.	REFERRED PARTY	NOTIFIED?	AGENT REFERRED	DATE SENT
28				

L, B, OR BOTH	COMMISH. RATE	ANTICIPATED CLOSE DATE	CLOSED?	RGCI
				$

NO.	REFERRED PARTY	NOTIFIED?	AGENT REFERRED	DATE SENT
29				

L, B, OR BOTH	COMMISH. RATE	ANTICIPATED CLOSE DATE	CLOSED?	RGCI
				$

NO.	REFERRED PARTY	NOTIFIED?	AGENT REFERRED	DATE SENT
30				

L, B, OR BOTH	COMMISH. RATE	ANTICIPATED CLOSE DATE	CLOSED?	RGCI
				$

NO.	REFERRED PARTY	NOTIFIED?	AGENT REFERRED	DATE SENT
31				

L, B, OR BOTH	COMMISH. RATE	ANTICIPATED CLOSE DATE	CLOSED?	RGCI
				$

NO.	REFERRED PARTY	NOTIFIED?	AGENT REFERRED	DATE SENT
32				

L, B, OR BOTH	COMMISH. RATE	ANTICIPATED CLOSE DATE	CLOSED?	RGCI
				$

NO.	REFERRED PARTY	NOTIFIED?	AGENT REFERRED	DATE SENT
33				

L, B, OR BOTH	COMMISH. RATE	ANTICIPATED CLOSE DATE	CLOSED?	RGCI
				$

NO.	REFERRED PARTY	NOTIFIED?	AGENT REFERRED	DATE SENT
34				

L, B, OR BOTH	COMMISH. RATE	ANTICIPATED CLOSE DATE	CLOSED?	RGCI
				$

NO.	REFERRED PARTY	NOTIFIED?	AGENT REFERRED	DATE SENT
35				

L, B, OR BOTH	COMMISH. RATE	ANTICIPATED CLOSE DATE	CLOSED?	RGCI
				$

NO.	REFERRED PARTY	NOTIFIED?	AGENT REFERRED	DATE SENT
36				

L, B, OR BOTH	COMMISH. RATE	ANTICIPATED CLOSE DATE	CLOSED?	RGCI
				$

OUTBOUND REFERRALS (R)

NO.	REFERRED PARTY	NOTIFIED?	AGENT REFERRED	DATE SENT
37				

L, B, OR BOTH	COMMISH. RATE	ANTICIPATED CLOSE DATE	CLOSED?	RGCI
				$

NO.	REFERRED PARTY	NOTIFIED?	AGENT REFERRED	DATE SENT
38				

L, B, OR BOTH	COMMISH. RATE	ANTICIPATED CLOSE DATE	CLOSED?	RGCI
				$

NO.	REFERRED PARTY	NOTIFIED?	AGENT REFERRED	DATE SENT
39				

L, B, OR BOTH	COMMISH. RATE	ANTICIPATED CLOSE DATE	CLOSED?	RGCI
				$

NO.	REFERRED PARTY	NOTIFIED?	AGENT REFERRED	DATE SENT
40				

L, B, OR BOTH	COMMISH. RATE	ANTICIPATED CLOSE DATE	CLOSED?	RGCI
				$

NO.	REFERRED PARTY	NOTIFIED?	AGENT REFERRED	DATE SENT
41				

L, B, OR BOTH	COMMISH. RATE	ANTICIPATED CLOSE DATE	CLOSED?	RGCI
				$

NO.	REFERRED PARTY	NOTIFIED?	AGENT REFERRED	DATE SENT
42				

L, B, OR BOTH	COMMISH. RATE	ANTICIPATED CLOSE DATE	CLOSED?	RGCI
				$

NO.	REFERRED PARTY	NOTIFIED?	AGENT REFERRED	DATE SENT
43				

L, B, OR BOTH	COMMISH. RATE	ANTICIPATED CLOSE DATE	CLOSED?	RGCI
				$

NO.	REFERRED PARTY	NOTIFIED?	AGENT REFERRED	DATE SENT
44				

L, B, OR BOTH	COMMISH. RATE	ANTICIPATED CLOSE DATE	CLOSED?	RGCI
				$

NO.	REFERRED PARTY	NOTIFIED?	AGENT REFERRED	DATE SENT
45				

L, B, OR BOTH	COMMISH. RATE	ANTICIPATED CLOSE DATE	CLOSED?	RGCI
				$

OUTBOUND REFERRALS (R)

NO.	REFERRED PARTY	NOTIFIED?	AGENT REFERRED	DATE SENT
46				
	L, B, OR BOTH	COMMISH. RATE	ANTICIPATED CLOSE DATE	CLOSED?	RGCI
					$

NO.	REFERRED PARTY	NOTIFIED?	AGENT REFERRED	DATE SENT
47				
	L, B, OR BOTH	COMMISH. RATE	ANTICIPATED CLOSE DATE	CLOSED?	RGCI
					$

NO.	REFERRED PARTY	NOTIFIED?	AGENT REFERRED	DATE SENT
48				
	L, B, OR BOTH	COMMISH. RATE	ANTICIPATED CLOSE DATE	CLOSED?	RGCI
					$

NO.	REFERRED PARTY	NOTIFIED?	AGENT REFERRED	DATE SENT
49				
	L, B, OR BOTH	COMMISH. RATE	ANTICIPATED CLOSE DATE	CLOSED?	RGCI
					$

NO.	REFERRED PARTY	NOTIFIED?	AGENT REFERRED	DATE SENT
50				
	L, B, OR BOTH	COMMISH. RATE	ANTICIPATED CLOSE DATE	CLOSED?	RGCI
					$

NO.	REFERRED PARTY	NOTIFIED?	AGENT REFERRED	DATE SENT
51				
	L, B, OR BOTH	COMMISH. RATE	ANTICIPATED CLOSE DATE	CLOSED?	RGCI
					$

NO.	REFERRED PARTY	NOTIFIED?	AGENT REFERRED	DATE SENT
52				
	L, B, OR BOTH	COMMISH. RATE	ANTICIPATED CLOSE DATE	CLOSED?	RGCI
					$

NO.	REFERRED PARTY	NOTIFIED?	AGENT REFERRED	DATE SENT
53				
	L, B, OR BOTH	COMMISH. RATE	ANTICIPATED CLOSE DATE	CLOSED?	RGCI
					$

NO.	REFERRED PARTY	NOTIFIED?	AGENT REFERRED	DATE SENT
54				
	L, B, OR BOTH	COMMISH. RATE	ANTICIPATED CLOSE DATE	CLOSED?	RGCI
					$

OUTBOUND REFERRALS (R)

NO.	REFERRED PARTY	NOTIFIED?	AGENT REFERRED	DATE SENT
55				

L, B, OR BOTH	COMMISH. RATE	ANTICIPATED CLOSE DATE	CLOSED?	RGCI
				$

NO.	REFERRED PARTY	NOTIFIED?	AGENT REFERRED	DATE SENT
56				

L, B, OR BOTH	COMMISH. RATE	ANTICIPATED CLOSE DATE	CLOSED?	RGCI
				$

NO.	REFERRED PARTY	NOTIFIED?	AGENT REFERRED	DATE SENT
57				

L, B, OR BOTH	COMMISH. RATE	ANTICIPATED CLOSE DATE	CLOSED?	RGCI
				$

NO.	REFERRED PARTY	NOTIFIED?	AGENT REFERRED	DATE SENT
58				

L, B, OR BOTH	COMMISH. RATE	ANTICIPATED CLOSE DATE	CLOSED?	RGCI
				$

NO.	REFERRED PARTY	NOTIFIED?	AGENT REFERRED	DATE SENT
59				

L, B, OR BOTH	COMMISH. RATE	ANTICIPATED CLOSE DATE	CLOSED?	RGCI
				$

NO.	REFERRED PARTY	NOTIFIED?	AGENT REFERRED	DATE SENT
60				

L, B, OR BOTH	COMMISH. RATE	ANTICIPATED CLOSE DATE	CLOSED?	RGCI
				$

NO.	REFERRED PARTY	NOTIFIED?	AGENT REFERRED	DATE SENT
61				

L, B, OR BOTH	COMMISH. RATE	ANTICIPATED CLOSE DATE	CLOSED?	RGCI
				$

NO.	REFERRED PARTY	NOTIFIED?	AGENT REFERRED	DATE SENT
62				

L, B, OR BOTH	COMMISH. RATE	ANTICIPATED CLOSE DATE	CLOSED?	RGCI
				$

NO.	REFERRED PARTY	NOTIFIED?	AGENT REFERRED	DATE SENT
63				

L, B, OR BOTH	COMMISH. RATE	ANTICIPATED CLOSE DATE	CLOSED?	RGCI
				$

OUTBOUND REFERRALS (R)

NO.	REFERRED PARTY	NOTIFIED?	AGENT REFERRED	DATE SENT
64				
	L, B, OR BOTH	COMMISH. RATE	ANTICIPATED CLOSE DATE	CLOSED?	RGCI
					$

NO.	REFERRED PARTY	NOTIFIED?	AGENT REFERRED	DATE SENT
65				
	L, B, OR BOTH	COMMISH. RATE	ANTICIPATED CLOSE DATE	CLOSED?	RGCI
					$

NO.	REFERRED PARTY	NOTIFIED?	AGENT REFERRED	DATE SENT
66				
	L, B, OR BOTH	COMMISH. RATE	ANTICIPATED CLOSE DATE	CLOSED?	RGCI
					$

NO.	REFERRED PARTY	NOTIFIED?	AGENT REFERRED	DATE SENT
67				
	L, B, OR BOTH	COMMISH. RATE	ANTICIPATED CLOSE DATE	CLOSED?	RGCI
					$

NO.	REFERRED PARTY	NOTIFIED?	AGENT REFERRED	DATE SENT
68				
	L, B, OR BOTH	COMMISH. RATE	ANTICIPATED CLOSE DATE	CLOSED?	RGCI
					$

NO.	REFERRED PARTY	NOTIFIED?	AGENT REFERRED	DATE SENT
69				
	L, B, OR BOTH	COMMISH. RATE	ANTICIPATED CLOSE DATE	CLOSED?	RGCI
					$

NO.	REFERRED PARTY	NOTIFIED?	AGENT REFERRED	DATE SENT
70				
	L, B, OR BOTH	COMMISH. RATE	ANTICIPATED CLOSE DATE	CLOSED?	RGCI
					$

NO.	REFERRED PARTY	NOTIFIED?	AGENT REFERRED	DATE SENT
71				
	L, B, OR BOTH	COMMISH. RATE	ANTICIPATED CLOSE DATE	CLOSED?	RGCI
					$

NO.	REFERRED PARTY	NOTIFIED?	AGENT REFERRED	DATE SENT
72				
	L, B, OR BOTH	COMMISH. RATE	ANTICIPATED CLOSE DATE	CLOSED?	RGCI
					$

OUTBOUND REFERRALS (R)

NO.	REFERRED PARTY	NOTIFIED?	AGENT REFERRED	DATE SENT
73				

L, B, OR BOTH	COMMISH. RATE	ANTICIPATED CLOSE DATE	CLOSED?	RGCI
				$

NO.	REFERRED PARTY	NOTIFIED?	AGENT REFERRED	DATE SENT
74				

L, B, OR BOTH	COMMISH. RATE	ANTICIPATED CLOSE DATE	CLOSED?	RGCI
				$

NO.	REFERRED PARTY	NOTIFIED?	AGENT REFERRED	DATE SENT
75				

L, B, OR BOTH	COMMISH. RATE	ANTICIPATED CLOSE DATE	CLOSED?	RGCI
				$

NO.	REFERRED PARTY	NOTIFIED?	AGENT REFERRED	DATE SENT
76				

L, B, OR BOTH	COMMISH. RATE	ANTICIPATED CLOSE DATE	CLOSED?	RGCI
				$

NO.	REFERRED PARTY	NOTIFIED?	AGENT REFERRED	DATE SENT
77				

L, B, OR BOTH	COMMISH. RATE	ANTICIPATED CLOSE DATE	CLOSED?	RGCI
				$

NO.	REFERRED PARTY	NOTIFIED?	AGENT REFERRED	DATE SENT
78				

L, B, OR BOTH	COMMISH. RATE	ANTICIPATED CLOSE DATE	CLOSED?	RGCI
				$

NO.	REFERRED PARTY	NOTIFIED?	AGENT REFERRED	DATE SENT
79				

L, B, OR BOTH	COMMISH. RATE	ANTICIPATED CLOSE DATE	CLOSED?	RGCI
				$

NO.	REFERRED PARTY	NOTIFIED?	AGENT REFERRED	DATE SENT
80				

L, B, OR BOTH	COMMISH. RATE	ANTICIPATED CLOSE DATE	CLOSED?	RGCI
				$

NO.	REFERRED PARTY	NOTIFIED?	AGENT REFERRED	DATE SENT
81				

L, B, OR BOTH	COMMISH. RATE	ANTICIPATED CLOSE DATE	CLOSED?	RGCI
				$

OUTBOUND REFERRALS (R)

NO.	REFERRED PARTY	NOTIFIED?	AGENT REFERRED	DATE SENT
82				
	L, B, OR BOTH	COMMISH. RATE	ANTICIPATED CLOSE DATE	CLOSED?	RGCI
					$
NO.	REFERRED PARTY	NOTIFIED?	AGENT REFERRED	DATE SENT
83				
	L, B, OR BOTH	COMMISH. RATE	ANTICIPATED CLOSE DATE	CLOSED?	RGCI
					$
NO.	REFERRED PARTY	NOTIFIED?	AGENT REFERRED	DATE SENT
84				
	L, B, OR BOTH	COMMISH. RATE	ANTICIPATED CLOSE DATE	CLOSED?	RGCI
					$
NO.	REFERRED PARTY	NOTIFIED?	AGENT REFERRED	DATE SENT
85				
	L, B, OR BOTH	COMMISH. RATE	ANTICIPATED CLOSE DATE	CLOSED?	RGCI
					$
NO.	REFERRED PARTY	NOTIFIED?	AGENT REFERRED	DATE SENT
86				
	L, B, OR BOTH	COMMISH. RATE	ANTICIPATED CLOSE DATE	CLOSED?	RGCI
					$
NO.	REFERRED PARTY	NOTIFIED?	AGENT REFERRED	DATE SENT
87				
	L, B, OR BOTH	COMMISH. RATE	ANTICIPATED CLOSE DATE	CLOSED?	RGCI
					$
NO.	REFERRED PARTY	NOTIFIED?	AGENT REFERRED	DATE SENT
88				
	L, B, OR BOTH	COMMISH. RATE	ANTICIPATED CLOSE DATE	CLOSED?	RGCI
					$
NO.	REFERRED PARTY	NOTIFIED?	AGENT REFERRED	DATE SENT
89				
	L, B, OR BOTH	COMMISH. RATE	ANTICIPATED CLOSE DATE	CLOSED?	RGCI
					$
NO.	REFERRED PARTY	NOTIFIED?	AGENT REFERRED	DATE SENT
90				
	L, B, OR BOTH	COMMISH. RATE	ANTICIPATED CLOSE DATE	CLOSED?	RGCI
					$

TRAINING LOG

DATE	TYPE	NAME/TITLE
	☐ CLASS ☐ ONLINE ☐ COACHING ☐ BOOK ☐ OTHER: ☐ CE HOURS:	TOP THING(S) LEARNED
RATING ☆ ☆ ☆ ☆ ☆		

DATE	TYPE	NAME/TITLE
	☐ CLASS ☐ ONLINE ☐ COACHING ☐ BOOK ☐ OTHER: ☐ CE HOURS:	TOP THING(S) LEARNED
RATING ☆ ☆ ☆ ☆ ☆		

DATE	TYPE	NAME/TITLE
	☐ CLASS ☐ ONLINE ☐ COACHING ☐ BOOK ☐ OTHER: ☐ CE HOURS:	TOP THING(S) LEARNED
RATING ☆ ☆ ☆ ☆ ☆		

DATE	TYPE	NAME/TITLE
	☐ CLASS ☐ ONLINE ☐ COACHING ☐ BOOK ☐ OTHER: ☐ CE HOURS:	TOP THING(S) LEARNED
RATING ☆ ☆ ☆ ☆ ☆		

DATE	TYPE	NAME/TITLE
	☐ CLASS ☐ ONLINE ☐ COACHING ☐ BOOK ☐ OTHER: ☐ CE HOURS:	TOP THING(S) LEARNED
RATING ☆ ☆ ☆ ☆ ☆		

DATE	TYPE	NAME/TITLE
	☐ CLASS ☐ ONLINE ☐ COACHING ☐ BOOK ☐ OTHER: ☐ CE HOURS:	TOP THING(S) LEARNED
RATING ☆ ☆ ☆ ☆ ☆		

DATE	TYPE	NAME/TITLE
	☐ CLASS ☐ ONLINE ☐ COACHING ☐ BOOK ☐ OTHER: ☐ CE HOURS:	TOP THING(S) LEARNED
RATING ☆ ☆ ☆ ☆ ☆		

DATE	TYPE	NAME/TITLE
	☐ CLASS ☐ ONLINE ☐ COACHING ☐ BOOK ☐ OTHER: ☐ CE HOURS:	TOP THING(S) LEARNED
RATING ☆ ☆ ☆ ☆ ☆		

DATE	TYPE	NAME/TITLE
	☐ CLASS ☐ ONLINE ☐ COACHING ☐ BOOK ☐ OTHER: ☐ CE HOURS:	TOP THING(S) LEARNED
RATING ☆ ☆ ☆ ☆ ☆		

DATE	TYPE	NAME/TITLE
	☐ CLASS ☐ ONLINE ☐ COACHING ☐ BOOK ☐ OTHER: ☐ CE HOURS:	TOP THING(S) LEARNED
RATING ☆ ☆ ☆ ☆ ☆		

GOOD LEARNIN'

DATE	TYPE	NAME/TITLE
	☐ CLASS ☐ ONLINE ☐ COACHING ☐ BOOK ☐ OTHER: ☐ CE HOURS:	TOP THING(S) LEARNED
RATING ☆ ☆ ☆ ☆ ☆		

DATE	TYPE	NAME/TITLE
	☐ CLASS ☐ ONLINE ☐ COACHING ☐ BOOK ☐ OTHER: ☐ CE HOURS:	TOP THING(S) LEARNED
RATING ☆ ☆ ☆ ☆ ☆		

DATE	TYPE	NAME/TITLE
	☐ CLASS ☐ ONLINE ☐ COACHING ☐ BOOK ☐ OTHER: ☐ CE HOURS:	TOP THING(S) LEARNED
RATING ☆ ☆ ☆ ☆ ☆		

DATE	TYPE	NAME/TITLE
	☐ CLASS ☐ ONLINE ☐ COACHING ☐ BOOK ☐ OTHER: ☐ CE HOURS:	TOP THING(S) LEARNED
RATING ☆ ☆ ☆ ☆ ☆		

DATE	TYPE	NAME/TITLE
	☐ CLASS ☐ ONLINE ☐ COACHING ☐ BOOK ☐ OTHER: ☐ CE HOURS:	TOP THING(S) LEARNED
RATING ☆ ☆ ☆ ☆ ☆		

DATE	TYPE	NAME/TITLE
	☐ CLASS ☐ ONLINE ☐ COACHING ☐ BOOK ☐ OTHER: ☐ CE HOURS:	TOP THING(S) LEARNED
RATING ☆ ☆ ☆ ☆ ☆		

DATE	TYPE	NAME/TITLE
	☐ CLASS ☐ ONLINE ☐ COACHING ☐ BOOK ☐ OTHER: ☐ CE HOURS:	TOP THING(S) LEARNED
RATING ☆ ☆ ☆ ☆ ☆		

DATE	TYPE	NAME/TITLE
	☐ CLASS ☐ ONLINE ☐ COACHING ☐ BOOK ☐ OTHER: ☐ CE HOURS:	TOP THING(S) LEARNED
RATING ☆ ☆ ☆ ☆ ☆		

DATE	TYPE	NAME/TITLE
	☐ CLASS ☐ ONLINE ☐ COACHING ☐ BOOK ☐ OTHER: ☐ CE HOURS:	TOP THING(S) LEARNED
RATING ☆ ☆ ☆ ☆ ☆		

DATE	TYPE	NAME/TITLE
	☐ CLASS ☐ ONLINE ☐ COACHING ☐ BOOK ☐ OTHER: ☐ CE HOURS:	TOP THING(S) LEARNED
RATING ☆ ☆ ☆ ☆ ☆		

TRAINING LOG

DATE	TYPE	NAME/TITLE :
	☐ CLASS ☐ ONLINE ☐ COACHING ☐ BOOK ☐ OTHER: ☐ CE HOURS:	TOP THING(S) LEARNED :
RATING ☆ ☆ ☆ ☆ ☆		

DATE	TYPE	NAME/TITLE :
	☐ CLASS ☐ ONLINE ☐ COACHING ☐ BOOK ☐ OTHER: ☐ CE HOURS:	TOP THING(S) LEARNED :
RATING ☆ ☆ ☆ ☆ ☆		

DATE	TYPE	NAME/TITLE :
	☐ CLASS ☐ ONLINE ☐ COACHING ☐ BOOK ☐ OTHER: ☐ CE HOURS:	TOP THING(S) LEARNED :
RATING ☆ ☆ ☆ ☆ ☆		

DATE	TYPE	NAME/TITLE :
	☐ CLASS ☐ ONLINE ☐ COACHING ☐ BOOK ☐ OTHER: ☐ CE HOURS:	TOP THING(S) LEARNED :
RATING ☆ ☆ ☆ ☆ ☆		

DATE	TYPE	NAME/TITLE :
	☐ CLASS ☐ ONLINE ☐ COACHING ☐ BOOK ☐ OTHER: ☐ CE HOURS:	TOP THING(S) LEARNED :
RATING ☆ ☆ ☆ ☆ ☆		

DATE	TYPE	NAME/TITLE :
	☐ CLASS ☐ ONLINE ☐ COACHING ☐ BOOK ☐ OTHER: ☐ CE HOURS:	TOP THING(S) LEARNED :
RATING ☆ ☆ ☆ ☆ ☆		

DATE	TYPE	NAME/TITLE :
	☐ CLASS ☐ ONLINE ☐ COACHING ☐ BOOK ☐ OTHER: ☐ CE HOURS:	TOP THING(S) LEARNED :
RATING ☆ ☆ ☆ ☆ ☆		

DATE	TYPE	NAME/TITLE :
	☐ CLASS ☐ ONLINE ☐ COACHING ☐ BOOK ☐ OTHER: ☐ CE HOURS:	TOP THING(S) LEARNED :
RATING ☆ ☆ ☆ ☆ ☆		

DATE	TYPE	NAME/TITLE :
	☐ CLASS ☐ ONLINE ☐ COACHING ☐ BOOK ☐ OTHER: ☐ CE HOURS:	TOP THING(S) LEARNED :
RATING ☆ ☆ ☆ ☆ ☆		

DATE	TYPE	NAME/TITLE :
	☐ CLASS ☐ ONLINE ☐ COACHING ☐ BOOK ☐ OTHER: ☐ CE HOURS:	TOP THING(S) LEARNED :
RATING ☆ ☆ ☆ ☆ ☆		

GOOD LEARNIN'

DATE	TYPE	NAME/TITLE
	☐ CLASS ☐ ONLINE ☐ COACHING ☐ BOOK ☐ OTHER: ☐ CE HOURS:	TOP THING(S) LEARNED
RATING ☆ ☆ ☆ ☆ ☆		
DATE	TYPE	NAME/TITLE
	☐ CLASS ☐ ONLINE ☐ COACHING ☐ BOOK ☐ OTHER: ☐ CE HOURS:	TOP THING(S) LEARNED
RATING ☆ ☆ ☆ ☆ ☆		
DATE	TYPE	NAME/TITLE
	☐ CLASS ☐ ONLINE ☐ COACHING ☐ BOOK ☐ OTHER: ☐ CE HOURS:	TOP THING(S) LEARNED
RATING ☆ ☆ ☆ ☆ ☆		
DATE	TYPE	NAME/TITLE
	☐ CLASS ☐ ONLINE ☐ COACHING ☐ BOOK ☐ OTHER: ☐ CE HOURS:	TOP THING(S) LEARNED
RATING ☆ ☆ ☆ ☆ ☆		
DATE	TYPE	NAME/TITLE
	☐ CLASS ☐ ONLINE ☐ COACHING ☐ BOOK ☐ OTHER: ☐ CE HOURS:	TOP THING(S) LEARNED
RATING ☆ ☆ ☆ ☆ ☆		
DATE	TYPE	NAME/TITLE
	☐ CLASS ☐ ONLINE ☐ COACHING ☐ BOOK ☐ OTHER: ☐ CE HOURS:	TOP THING(S) LEARNED
RATING ☆ ☆ ☆ ☆ ☆		
DATE	TYPE	NAME/TITLE
	☐ CLASS ☐ ONLINE ☐ COACHING ☐ BOOK ☐ OTHER: ☐ CE HOURS:	TOP THING(S) LEARNED
RATING ☆ ☆ ☆ ☆ ☆		
DATE	TYPE	NAME/TITLE
	☐ CLASS ☐ ONLINE ☐ COACHING ☐ BOOK ☐ OTHER: ☐ CE HOURS:	TOP THING(S) LEARNED
RATING ☆ ☆ ☆ ☆ ☆		
DATE	TYPE	NAME/TITLE
	☐ CLASS ☐ ONLINE ☐ COACHING ☐ BOOK ☐ OTHER: ☐ CE HOURS:	TOP THING(S) LEARNED
RATING ☆ ☆ ☆ ☆ ☆		
DATE	TYPE	NAME/TITLE
	☐ CLASS ☐ ONLINE ☐ COACHING ☐ BOOK ☐ OTHER: ☐ CE HOURS:	TOP THING(S) LEARNED
RATING ☆ ☆ ☆ ☆ ☆		

TRAINING LOG

DATE	TYPE	NAME/TITLE
	☐ CLASS ☐ ONLINE ☐ COACHING ☐ BOOK ☐ OTHER: ☐ CE HOURS:	TOP THING(S) LEARNED
RATING ☆ ☆ ☆ ☆ ☆		
DATE	TYPE	NAME/TITLE
	☐ CLASS ☐ ONLINE ☐ COACHING ☐ BOOK ☐ OTHER: ☐ CE HOURS:	TOP THING(S) LEARNED
RATING ☆ ☆ ☆ ☆ ☆		
DATE	TYPE	NAME/TITLE
	☐ CLASS ☐ ONLINE ☐ COACHING ☐ BOOK ☐ OTHER: ☐ CE HOURS:	TOP THING(S) LEARNED
RATING ☆ ☆ ☆ ☆ ☆		
DATE	TYPE	NAME/TITLE
	☐ CLASS ☐ ONLINE ☐ COACHING ☐ BOOK ☐ OTHER: ☐ CE HOURS:	TOP THING(S) LEARNED
RATING ☆ ☆ ☆ ☆ ☆		
DATE	TYPE	NAME/TITLE
	☐ CLASS ☐ ONLINE ☐ COACHING ☐ BOOK ☐ OTHER: ☐ CE HOURS:	TOP THING(S) LEARNED
RATING ☆ ☆ ☆ ☆ ☆		
DATE	TYPE	NAME/TITLE
	☐ CLASS ☐ ONLINE ☐ COACHING ☐ BOOK ☐ OTHER: ☐ CE HOURS:	TOP THING(S) LEARNED
RATING ☆ ☆ ☆ ☆ ☆		
DATE	TYPE	NAME/TITLE
	☐ CLASS ☐ ONLINE ☐ COACHING ☐ BOOK ☐ OTHER: ☐ CE HOURS:	TOP THING(S) LEARNED
RATING ☆ ☆ ☆ ☆ ☆		
DATE	TYPE	NAME/TITLE
	☐ CLASS ☐ ONLINE ☐ COACHING ☐ BOOK ☐ OTHER: ☐ CE HOURS:	TOP THING(S) LEARNED
RATING ☆ ☆ ☆ ☆ ☆		
DATE	TYPE	NAME/TITLE
	☐ CLASS ☐ ONLINE ☐ COACHING ☐ BOOK ☐ OTHER: ☐ CE HOURS:	TOP THING(S) LEARNED
RATING ☆ ☆ ☆ ☆ ☆		
DATE	TYPE	NAME/TITLE
	☐ CLASS ☐ ONLINE ☐ COACHING ☐ BOOK ☐ OTHER: ☐ CE HOURS:	TOP THING(S) LEARNED
RATING ☆ ☆ ☆ ☆ ☆		

GOOD LEARNIN'

DATE	TYPE	NAME/TITLE
	☐ CLASS ☐ ONLINE ☐ COACHING ☐ BOOK ☐ OTHER: ☐ CE HOURS:	TOP THING(S) LEARNED
RATING ☆ ☆ ☆ ☆ ☆		

DATE	TYPE	NAME/TITLE
	☐ CLASS ☐ ONLINE ☐ COACHING ☐ BOOK ☐ OTHER: ☐ CE HOURS:	TOP THING(S) LEARNED
RATING ☆ ☆ ☆ ☆ ☆		

DATE	TYPE	NAME/TITLE
	☐ CLASS ☐ ONLINE ☐ COACHING ☐ BOOK ☐ OTHER: ☐ CE HOURS:	TOP THING(S) LEARNED
RATING ☆ ☆ ☆ ☆ ☆		

DATE	TYPE	NAME/TITLE
	☐ CLASS ☐ ONLINE ☐ COACHING ☐ BOOK ☐ OTHER: ☐ CE HOURS:	TOP THING(S) LEARNED
RATING ☆ ☆ ☆ ☆ ☆		

DATE	TYPE	NAME/TITLE
	☐ CLASS ☐ ONLINE ☐ COACHING ☐ BOOK ☐ OTHER: ☐ CE HOURS:	TOP THING(S) LEARNED
RATING ☆ ☆ ☆ ☆ ☆		

DATE	TYPE	NAME/TITLE
	☐ CLASS ☐ ONLINE ☐ COACHING ☐ BOOK ☐ OTHER: ☐ CE HOURS:	TOP THING(S) LEARNED
RATING ☆ ☆ ☆ ☆ ☆		

DATE	TYPE	NAME/TITLE
	☐ CLASS ☐ ONLINE ☐ COACHING ☐ BOOK ☐ OTHER: ☐ CE HOURS:	TOP THING(S) LEARNED
RATING ☆ ☆ ☆ ☆ ☆		

DATE	TYPE	NAME/TITLE
	☐ CLASS ☐ ONLINE ☐ COACHING ☐ BOOK ☐ OTHER: ☐ CE HOURS:	TOP THING(S) LEARNED
RATING ☆ ☆ ☆ ☆ ☆		

DATE	TYPE	NAME/TITLE
	☐ CLASS ☐ ONLINE ☐ COACHING ☐ BOOK ☐ OTHER: ☐ CE HOURS:	TOP THING(S) LEARNED
RATING ☆ ☆ ☆ ☆ ☆		

DATE	TYPE	NAME/TITLE
	☐ CLASS ☐ ONLINE ☐ COACHING ☐ BOOK ☐ OTHER: ☐ CE HOURS:	TOP THING(S) LEARNED
RATING ☆ ☆ ☆ ☆ ☆		

TRAINING LOG

DATE	TYPE	NAME/TITLE
	☐ CLASS ☐ ONLINE ☐ COACHING ☐ BOOK ☐ OTHER: ☐ CE HOURS:	TOP THING(S) LEARNED
RATING ☆ ☆ ☆ ☆ ☆		
DATE	TYPE	NAME/TITLE
	☐ CLASS ☐ ONLINE ☐ COACHING ☐ BOOK ☐ OTHER: ☐ CE HOURS:	TOP THING(S) LEARNED
RATING ☆ ☆ ☆ ☆ ☆		
DATE	TYPE	NAME/TITLE
	☐ CLASS ☐ ONLINE ☐ COACHING ☐ BOOK ☐ OTHER: ☐ CE HOURS:	TOP THING(S) LEARNED
RATING ☆ ☆ ☆ ☆ ☆		
DATE	TYPE	NAME/TITLE
	☐ CLASS ☐ ONLINE ☐ COACHING ☐ BOOK ☐ OTHER: ☐ CE HOURS:	TOP THING(S) LEARNED
RATING ☆ ☆ ☆ ☆ ☆		
DATE	TYPE	NAME/TITLE
	☐ CLASS ☐ ONLINE ☐ COACHING ☐ BOOK ☐ OTHER: ☐ CE HOURS:	TOP THING(S) LEARNED
RATING ☆ ☆ ☆ ☆ ☆		
DATE	TYPE	NAME/TITLE
	☐ CLASS ☐ ONLINE ☐ COACHING ☐ BOOK ☐ OTHER: ☐ CE HOURS:	TOP THING(S) LEARNED
RATING ☆ ☆ ☆ ☆ ☆		
DATE	TYPE	NAME/TITLE
	☐ CLASS ☐ ONLINE ☐ COACHING ☐ BOOK ☐ OTHER: ☐ CE HOURS:	TOP THING(S) LEARNED
RATING ☆ ☆ ☆ ☆ ☆		
DATE	TYPE	NAME/TITLE
	☐ CLASS ☐ ONLINE ☐ COACHING ☐ BOOK ☐ OTHER: ☐ CE HOURS:	TOP THING(S) LEARNED
RATING ☆ ☆ ☆ ☆ ☆		
DATE	TYPE	NAME/TITLE
	☐ CLASS ☐ ONLINE ☐ COACHING ☐ BOOK ☐ OTHER: ☐ CE HOURS:	TOP THING(S) LEARNED
RATING ☆ ☆ ☆ ☆ ☆		
DATE	TYPE	NAME/TITLE
	☐ CLASS ☐ ONLINE ☐ COACHING ☐ BOOK ☐ OTHER: ☐ CE HOURS:	TOP THING(S) LEARNED
RATING ☆ ☆ ☆ ☆ ☆		

GOOD LEARNIN'

DATE	TYPE	NAME/TITLE
	☐ CLASS ☐ ONLINE ☐ COACHING ☐ BOOK ☐ OTHER: ☐ CE HOURS:	TOP THING(S) LEARNED
RATING ☆ ☆ ☆ ☆ ☆		
DATE	TYPE	NAME/TITLE
	☐ CLASS ☐ ONLINE ☐ COACHING ☐ BOOK ☐ OTHER: ☐ CE HOURS:	TOP THING(S) LEARNED
RATING ☆ ☆ ☆ ☆ ☆		
DATE	TYPE	NAME/TITLE
	☐ CLASS ☐ ONLINE ☐ COACHING ☐ BOOK ☐ OTHER: ☐ CE HOURS:	TOP THING(S) LEARNED
RATING ☆ ☆ ☆ ☆ ☆		
DATE	TYPE	NAME/TITLE
	☐ CLASS ☐ ONLINE ☐ COACHING ☐ BOOK ☐ OTHER: ☐ CE HOURS:	TOP THING(S) LEARNED
RATING ☆ ☆ ☆ ☆ ☆		
DATE	TYPE	NAME/TITLE
	☐ CLASS ☐ ONLINE ☐ COACHING ☐ BOOK ☐ OTHER: ☐ CE HOURS:	TOP THING(S) LEARNED
RATING ☆ ☆ ☆ ☆ ☆		
DATE	TYPE	NAME/TITLE
	☐ CLASS ☐ ONLINE ☐ COACHING ☐ BOOK ☐ OTHER: ☐ CE HOURS:	TOP THING(S) LEARNED
RATING ☆ ☆ ☆ ☆ ☆		
DATE	TYPE	NAME/TITLE
	☐ CLASS ☐ ONLINE ☐ COACHING ☐ BOOK ☐ OTHER: ☐ CE HOURS:	TOP THING(S) LEARNED
RATING ☆ ☆ ☆ ☆ ☆		
DATE	TYPE	NAME/TITLE
	☐ CLASS ☐ ONLINE ☐ COACHING ☐ BOOK ☐ OTHER: ☐ CE HOURS:	TOP THING(S) LEARNED
RATING ☆ ☆ ☆ ☆ ☆		
DATE	TYPE	NAME/TITLE
	☐ CLASS ☐ ONLINE ☐ COACHING ☐ BOOK ☐ OTHER: ☐ CE HOURS:	TOP THING(S) LEARNED
RATING ☆ ☆ ☆ ☆ ☆		
DATE	TYPE	NAME/TITLE
	☐ CLASS ☐ ONLINE ☐ COACHING ☐ BOOK ☐ OTHER: ☐ CE HOURS:	TOP THING(S) LEARNED
RATING ☆ ☆ ☆ ☆ ☆		

TRAINING LOG

DATE	TYPE	NAME/TITLE
	☐ CLASS ☐ ONLINE ☐ COACHING ☐ BOOK ☐ OTHER: ☐ CE HOURS:	TOP THING(S) LEARNED
RATING ☆ ☆ ☆ ☆ ☆		

DATE	TYPE	NAME/TITLE
	☐ CLASS ☐ ONLINE ☐ COACHING ☐ BOOK ☐ OTHER: ☐ CE HOURS:	TOP THING(S) LEARNED
RATING ☆ ☆ ☆ ☆ ☆		

DATE	TYPE	NAME/TITLE
	☐ CLASS ☐ ONLINE ☐ COACHING ☐ BOOK ☐ OTHER: ☐ CE HOURS:	TOP THING(S) LEARNED
RATING ☆ ☆ ☆ ☆ ☆		

DATE	TYPE	NAME/TITLE
	☐ CLASS ☐ ONLINE ☐ COACHING ☐ BOOK ☐ OTHER: ☐ CE HOURS:	TOP THING(S) LEARNED
RATING ☆ ☆ ☆ ☆ ☆		

DATE	TYPE	NAME/TITLE
	☐ CLASS ☐ ONLINE ☐ COACHING ☐ BOOK ☐ OTHER: ☐ CE HOURS:	TOP THING(S) LEARNED
RATING ☆ ☆ ☆ ☆ ☆		

DATE	TYPE	NAME/TITLE
	☐ CLASS ☐ ONLINE ☐ COACHING ☐ BOOK ☐ OTHER: ☐ CE HOURS:	TOP THING(S) LEARNED
RATING ☆ ☆ ☆ ☆ ☆		

DATE	TYPE	NAME/TITLE
	☐ CLASS ☐ ONLINE ☐ COACHING ☐ BOOK ☐ OTHER: ☐ CE HOURS:	TOP THING(S) LEARNED
RATING ☆ ☆ ☆ ☆ ☆		

DATE	TYPE	NAME/TITLE
	☐ CLASS ☐ ONLINE ☐ COACHING ☐ BOOK ☐ OTHER: ☐ CE HOURS:	TOP THING(S) LEARNED
RATING ☆ ☆ ☆ ☆ ☆		

DATE	TYPE	NAME/TITLE
	☐ CLASS ☐ ONLINE ☐ COACHING ☐ BOOK ☐ OTHER: ☐ CE HOURS:	TOP THING(S) LEARNED
RATING ☆ ☆ ☆ ☆ ☆		

DATE	TYPE	NAME/TITLE
	☐ CLASS ☐ ONLINE ☐ COACHING ☐ BOOK ☐ OTHER: ☐ CE HOURS:	TOP THING(S) LEARNED
RATING ☆ ☆ ☆ ☆ ☆		

GOOD LEARNIN'

DATE	TYPE	NAME/TITLE
	☐ CLASS ☐ ONLINE ☐ COACHING ☐ BOOK ☐ OTHER: ☐ CE HOURS:	TOP THING(S) LEARNED
RATING ☆ ☆ ☆ ☆ ☆		
DATE	TYPE	NAME/TITLE
	☐ CLASS ☐ ONLINE ☐ COACHING ☐ BOOK ☐ OTHER: ☐ CE HOURS:	TOP THING(S) LEARNED
RATING ☆ ☆ ☆ ☆ ☆		
DATE	TYPE	NAME/TITLE
	☐ CLASS ☐ ONLINE ☐ COACHING ☐ BOOK ☐ OTHER: ☐ CE HOURS:	TOP THING(S) LEARNED
RATING ☆ ☆ ☆ ☆ ☆		
DATE	TYPE	NAME/TITLE
	☐ CLASS ☐ ONLINE ☐ COACHING ☐ BOOK ☐ OTHER: ☐ CE HOURS:	TOP THING(S) LEARNED
RATING ☆ ☆ ☆ ☆ ☆		
DATE	TYPE	NAME/TITLE
	☐ CLASS ☐ ONLINE ☐ COACHING ☐ BOOK ☐ OTHER: ☐ CE HOURS:	TOP THING(S) LEARNED
RATING ☆ ☆ ☆ ☆ ☆		
DATE	TYPE	NAME/TITLE
	☐ CLASS ☐ ONLINE ☐ COACHING ☐ BOOK ☐ OTHER: ☐ CE HOURS:	TOP THING(S) LEARNED
RATING ☆ ☆ ☆ ☆ ☆		
DATE	TYPE	NAME/TITLE
	☐ CLASS ☐ ONLINE ☐ COACHING ☐ BOOK ☐ OTHER: ☐ CE HOURS:	TOP THING(S) LEARNED
RATING ☆ ☆ ☆ ☆ ☆		
DATE	TYPE	NAME/TITLE
	☐ CLASS ☐ ONLINE ☐ COACHING ☐ BOOK ☐ OTHER: ☐ CE HOURS:	TOP THING(S) LEARNED
RATING ☆ ☆ ☆ ☆ ☆		
DATE	TYPE	NAME/TITLE
	☐ CLASS ☐ ONLINE ☐ COACHING ☐ BOOK ☐ OTHER: ☐ CE HOURS:	TOP THING(S) LEARNED
RATING ☆ ☆ ☆ ☆ ☆		
DATE	TYPE	NAME/TITLE
	☐ CLASS ☐ ONLINE ☐ COACHING ☐ BOOK ☐ OTHER: ☐ CE HOURS:	TOP THING(S) LEARNED
RATING ☆ ☆ ☆ ☆ ☆		

Notes

Notes

Notes

Notes

Notes

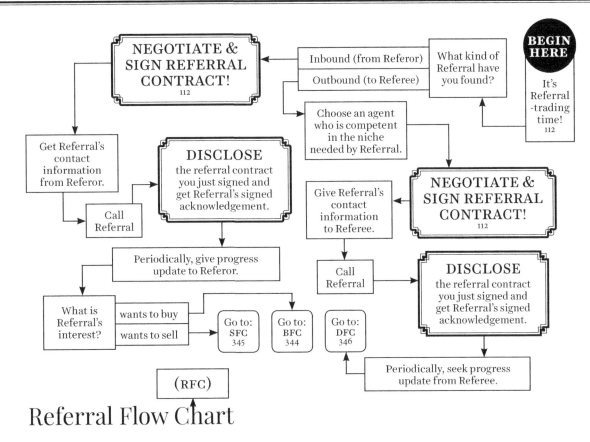

BEGIN HERE

It's Referral -trading time! 112

What kind of Referral have you found?

Inbound (from Referor)

Outbound (to Referee)

NEGOTIATE & SIGN REFERRAL CONTRACT! 112

Get Referral's contact information from Referor.

Call Referral

DISCLOSE the referral contract you just signed and get Referral's signed acknowledgement.

Periodically, give progress update to Referor.

What is Referral's interest?

wants to buy

wants to sell

Go to: SFC 345

Go to: BFC 344

Choose an agent who is competent in the niche needed by Referral.

NEGOTIATE & SIGN REFERRAL CONTRACT! 112

Give Referral's contact information to Referee.

Call Referral

DISCLOSE the referral contract you just signed and get Referral's signed acknowledgement.

Periodically, seek progress update from Referee.

Go to: DFC 346

(RFC)

Referral Flow Chart

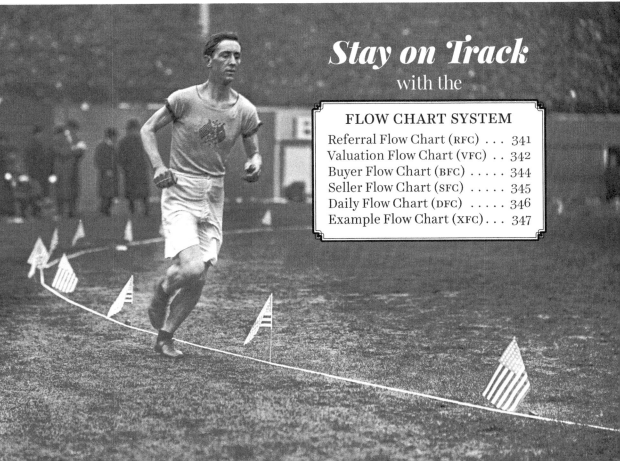

Stay on Track with the

FLOW CHART SYSTEM

Referral Flow Chart (RFC) . . . 341

Valuation Flow Chart (VFC) . . 342

Buyer Flow Chart (BFC) 344

Seller Flow Chart (SFC) 345

Daily Flow Chart (DFC) 346

Example Flow Chart (XFC) . . . 347

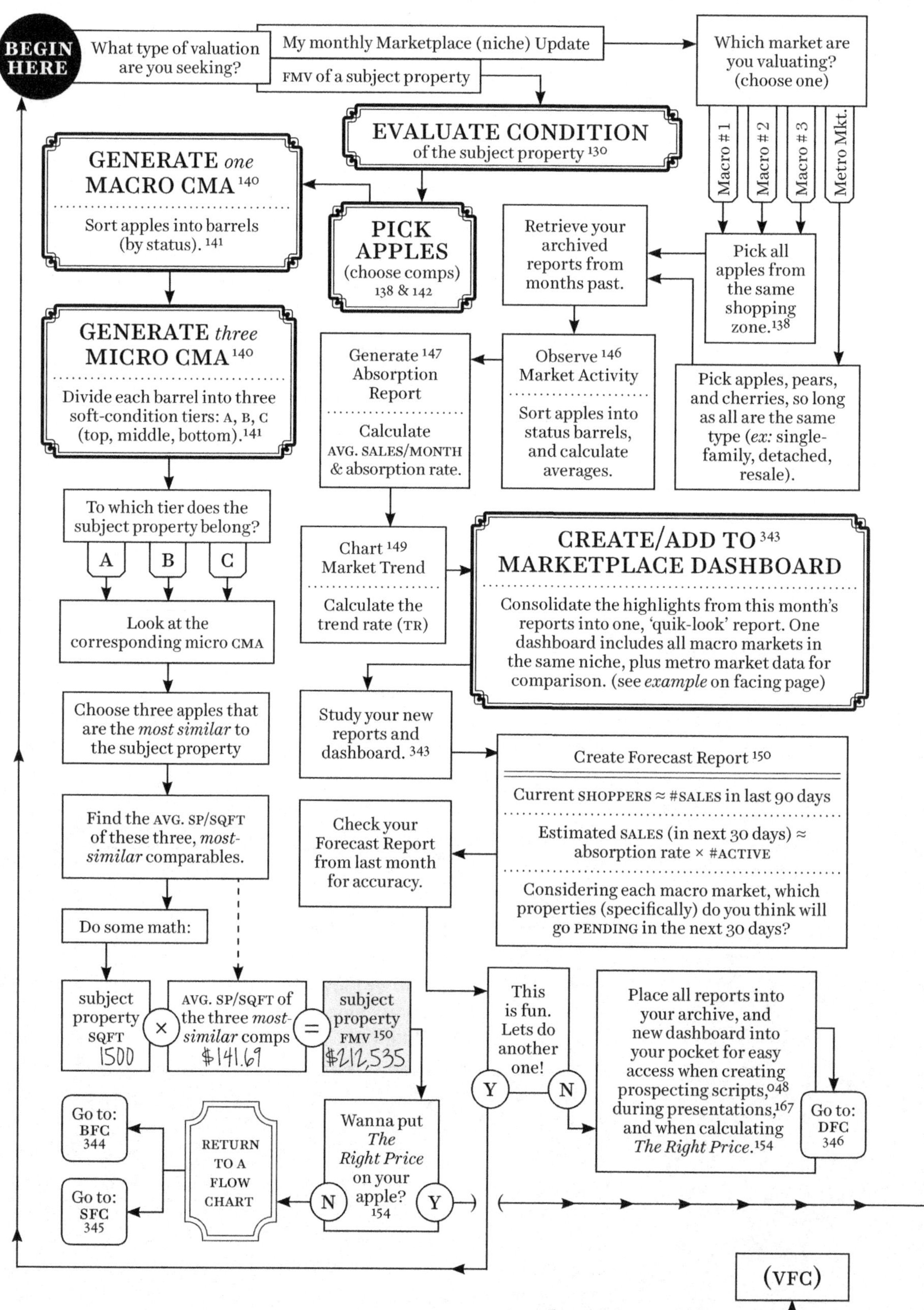
BEGIN HERE
What type of valuation are you seeking?
My monthly Marketplace (niche) Update
FMV of a subject property
Which market are you valuating? (choose one)
Macro # 1
Macro # 2
Macro # 3
Metro Mkt.
EVALUATE CONDITION of the subject property 130
GENERATE one MACRO CMA 140
Sort apples into barrels (by status). 141
PICK APPLES (choose comps) 138 & 142
Retrieve your archived reports from months past.
Pick all apples from the same shopping zone. 138
GENERATE three MICRO CMA 140
Divide each barrel into three soft-condition tiers: A, B, C (top, middle, bottom). 141
Generate 147 Absorption Report
Calculate AVG. SALES/MONTH & absorption rate.
Observe 146 Market Activity
Sort apples into status barrels, and calculate averages.
Pick apples, pears, and cherries, so long as all are the same type (ex: single-family, detached, resale).
To which tier does the subject property belong?
A
B
C
Chart 149 Market Trend
Calculate the trend rate (TR)
CREATE/ADD TO 343 MARKETPLACE DASHBOARD
Consolidate the highlights from this month's reports into one, 'quik-look' report. One dashboard includes all macro markets in the same niche, plus metro market data for comparison. (see example on facing page)
Look at the corresponding micro CMA
Choose three apples that are the most similar to the subject property
Study your new reports and dashboard. 343
Create Forecast Report 150
Current SHOPPERS ≈ #SALES in last 90 days
Estimated SALES (in next 30 days) ≈ absorption rate × #ACTIVE
Considering each macro market, which properties (specifically) do you think will go PENDING in the next 30 days?
Find the AVG. SP/SQFT of these three, most-similar comparables.
Check your Forecast Report from last month for accuracy.
Do some math:
subject property SQFT 1500
×
AVG. SP/SQFT of the three most-similar comps $141.69
=
subject property FMV 150 $212,535
This is fun. Lets do another one!
Y
N
Place all reports into your archive, and new dashboard into your pocket for easy access when creating prospecting scripts, 048 during presentations, 167 and when calculating The Right Price. 154
Go to: DFC 346
Go to: BFC 344
Go to: SFC 345
RETURN TO A FLOW CHART
Wanna put The Right Price on your apple? 154
N
Y

(VFC)

Valuation Flow Chart

MONTHLY MARKETPLACE DASHBOARD

	March	Macro #1	Δ	Macro #2	Δ	Super Macro	Δ	Metro	Δ
from Market Activity Report	#SOLD	28	↑3	30	↓4	156	↑29	25,478	↑3014
	AVG. SOLD PRICE	$238k	↑$2k	$235k	↑0	$241k	↑$1k	$298k	↑$2k
	AVG. DOM	78	↓5	73	↑1	75	↓2	81	↓5
	AVG. SP/LP	96%	—	97%	—	96%	—	94%	—
from Absorp. Report	#ACTIVE	90	↑8	112	↑12	571	↑48	128,456	↑214
	AVG. #SOLD/MTH	25	↑1	26	↑2	138	↑10	23,458	↑451
	MTHS OF INVENTORY	3.6	↓.3	4.3	↑.5	4.1	↓.9	5.5	↓1.4
	ABSORP. RATE	27%	↑3%	23%	↑3%	24%	↑2%	18%	↑4%
Trend Rpt.	TREND RATE (TR)	$0.495/sqft	—	$0.621/sqft	—	$0.524/sqft	—	$0.210/sqft	—

Δ = change since last month; ↑↓ = direction of change

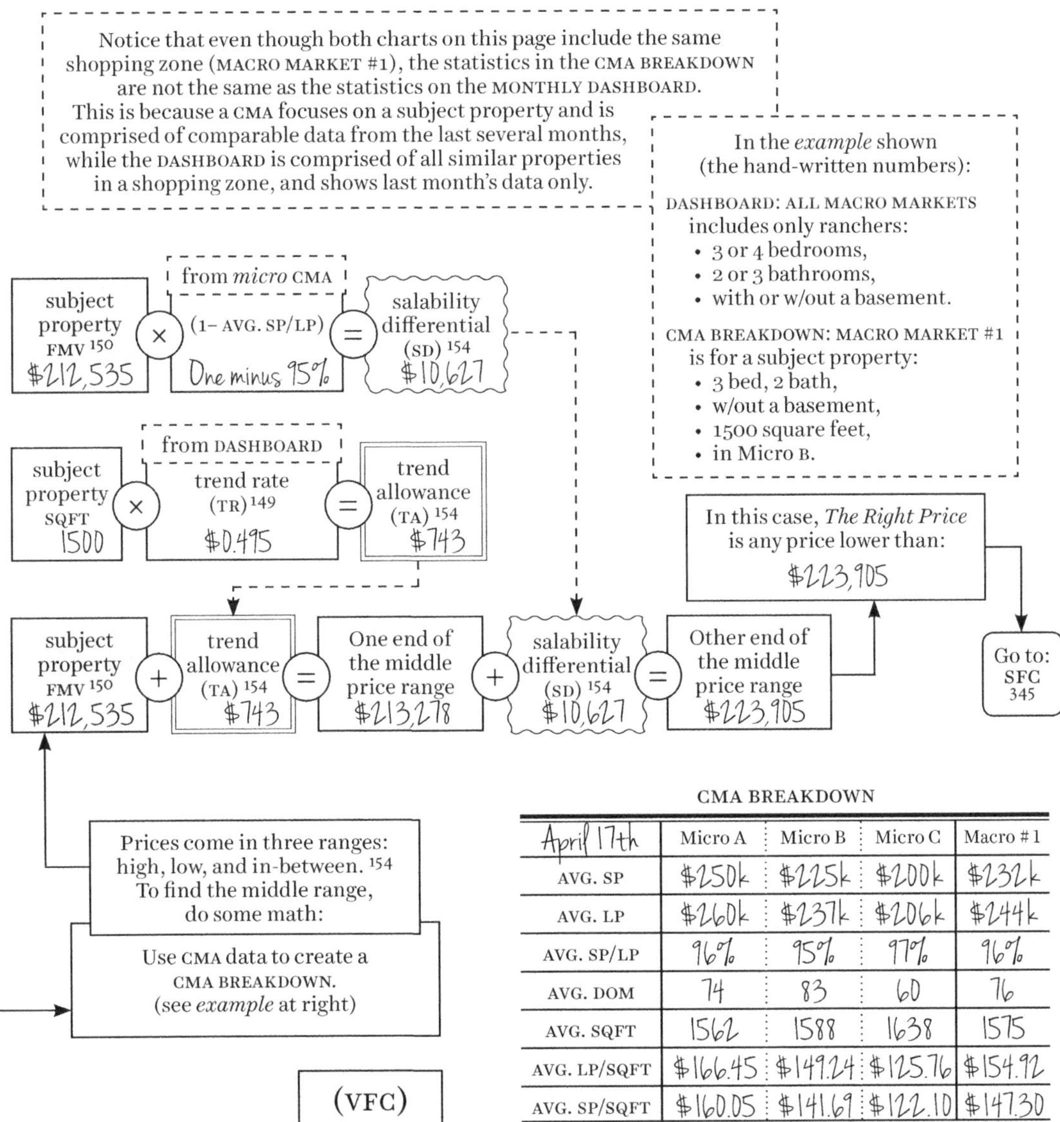

Notice that even though both charts on this page include the same shopping zone (MACRO MARKET #1), the statistics in the CMA BREAKDOWN are not the same as the statistics on the MONTHLY DASHBOARD. This is because a CMA focuses on a subject property and is comprised of comparable data from the last several months, while the DASHBOARD is comprised of all similar properties in a shopping zone, and shows last month's data only.
In the *example* shown (the hand-written numbers):
DASHBOARD: ALL MACRO MARKETS includes only ranchers:
• 3 or 4 bedrooms,
• 2 or 3 bathrooms,
• with or w/out a basement.
CMA BREAKDOWN: MACRO MARKET #1 is for a subject property:
• 3 bed, 2 bath,
• w/out a basement,
• 1500 square feet,
• in Micro B.
subject property FMV 150 $212,535
×
from *micro* CMA
(1– AVG. SP/LP)
One minus 95%
=
salability differential (SD) 154 $10,627
subject property SQFT 1500
×
from DASHBOARD
trend rate (TR) 149
$0.495
=
trend allowance (TA) 154 $743
In this case, *The Right Price* is any price lower than:
$223,905
subject property FMV 150 $212,535
+
trend allowance (TA) 154 $743
=
One end of the middle price range $213,278
+
salability differential (SD) 154 $10,627
=
Other end of the middle price range $223,905
Go to: SFC 345
Prices come in three ranges: high, low, and in-between. 154 To find the middle range, do some math:
Use CMA data to create a CMA BREAKDOWN. (see *example* at right)
(VFC)

CMA BREAKDOWN

April 17th	Micro A	Micro B	Micro C	Macro #1
AVG. SP	$250k	$225k	$200k	$232k
AVG. LP	$260k	$237k	$206k	$244k
AVG. SP/LP	96%	95%	97%	96%
AVG. DOM	74	83	60	76
AVG. SQFT	1562	1588	1638	1575
AVG. LP/SQFT	$166.45	$149.24	$125.76	$154.92
AVG. SP/SQFT	$160.05	$141.69	$122.10	$147.30

Valuation Flow Chart

BEGIN HERE

Congratulations! You found a buyer.

PRE-QUALIFY BUYER! 170

Edit Database 089 & *Wage* 094 *Campaign*

Introduce Buyer to finance coach 179

Y Does Buyer pre-qualify? N

Why not?

not ready to buy now

financial reasons

signed with another agent

Rats!

Edit Database 089 & STOP Campaign

Go to: DFC 346

Will Buyer meet for presentation?

Edit Database 089 & *Wage* 094 *Campaign*

Y Schedule after noon appointment

Presentation begins now? Y N

N Deploy Scripts 051

Are scripts working? Y N

LB

Go to: DFC 346

Set Buyer free 119

Wanna refer Buyer to another agent? 112 N Y

Go to: RFC 341

Negotiate 266 & *Counter-offer* 256

LB

N DoBuyer and Seller agree? Y

Draft offer to amend 260

Amend contract 260

GIVE BUYER PRESENTATION! be thorough 186

Do you want this Buyer as a Client? Y N

N Signed with another? Y

Has Buyer signed exclusive agency with you? N Y

Edit Database 089 & *Wage* 094 *Campaign*

LB

Deploy Scripts 051

Are scripts working? Y N

Y Amend the contract?

Y Terminate the contract?

Does Buyer want to do either of these: N

Does Buyer have a contingency to do so? 252 Y N

SHOW (ANOTHER) PROPERTY! 216

Help Buyer decide 219

Terminate contract 277

Negotiate 266 & *Counter-offer* 256

Prepare Buyer for closing 221

Is today closing day? N Y

Y Has agency expired? N

Does Buyer want to make an offer on this property? Y N

LB

Draft offer to terminate 260

Do Buyer and Seller agree? Y N

Find FMV of subject

Go to: VFC 342

Go to: DFC 346

Edit Database 089 & *Wage* 094 *Campaign*

GO TO CLOSING!

Negotiate 266 & *Counter-offer* 256

Draft offer to purchase 252

Do Buyer and Seller agree? N Y

CREATE P&S CONTRACT! 260

(BFC)

Buyer Flow Chart

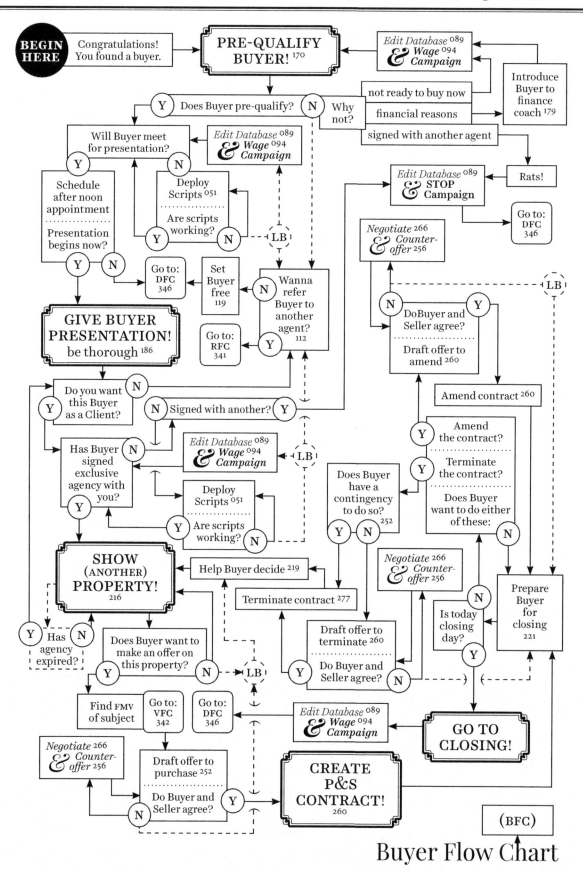

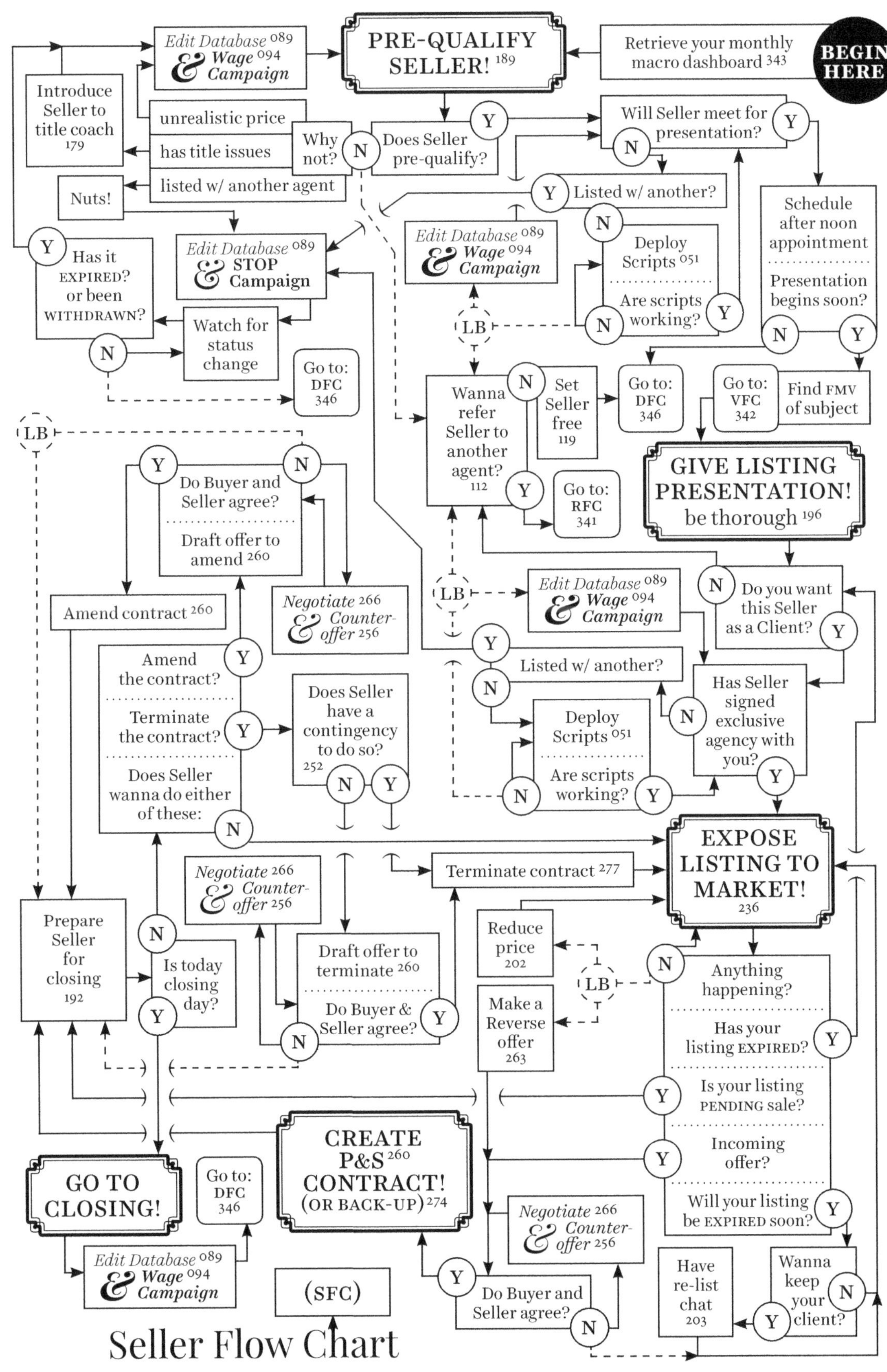

Seller Flow Chart

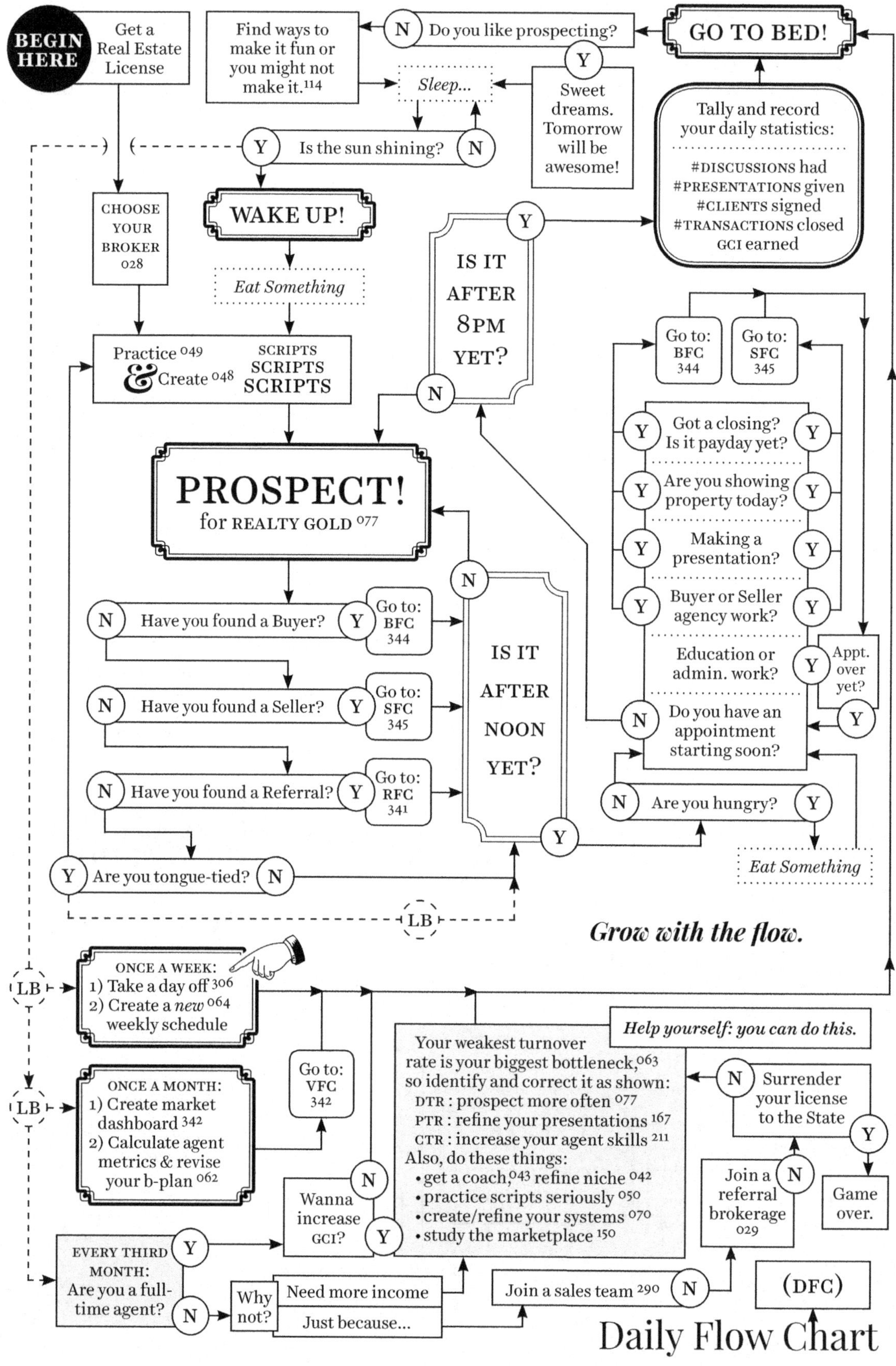
BEGIN HERE
Get a Real Estate License
Find ways to make it fun or you might not make it.114
N
Do you like prospecting?
GO TO BED!
Y
Sleep...
Sweet dreams. Tomorrow will be awesome!
Y
Is the sun shining?
N
Tally and record your daily statistics:
#DISCUSSIONS had
#PRESENTATIONS given
#CLIENTS signed
#TRANSACTIONS closed
GCI earned
CHOOSE YOUR BROKER 028
WAKE UP!
IS IT AFTER 8PM YET?
Eat Something
Practice 049 & Create 048
SCRIPTS SCRIPTS SCRIPTS
Go to: BFC 344
Go to: SFC 345
PROSPECT! for REALTY GOLD 077
Got a closing? Is it payday yet?
Are you showing property today?
Making a presentation?
Buyer or Seller agency work?
Education or admin. work?
Appt. over yet?
Do you have an appointment starting soon?
Have you found a Buyer?
Go to: BFC 344
Have you found a Seller?
Go to: SFC 345
Have you found a Referral?
Go to: RFC 341
IS IT AFTER NOON YET?
Are you hungry?
Eat Something
Are you tongue-tied?
LB
Grow with the flow.
ONCE A WEEK:
1) Take a day off 306
2) Create a new 064 weekly schedule
ONCE A MONTH:
1) Create market dashboard 342
2) Calculate agent metrics & revise your b-plan 062
Go to: VFC 342
Help yourself: you can do this.
Your weakest turnover rate is your biggest bottleneck,063 so identify and correct it as shown:
DTR : prospect more often 077
PTR : refine your presentations 167
CTR : increase your agent skills 211
Also, do these things:
• get a coach,043 refine niche 042
• practice scripts seriously 050
• create/refine your systems 070
• study the marketplace 150
Surrender your license to the State
Game over.
Wanna increase GCI?
Join a referral brokerage 029
EVERY THIRD MONTH: Are you a full-time agent?
Why not?
Need more income
Just because...
Join a sales team 290
(DFC)
Daily Flow Chart

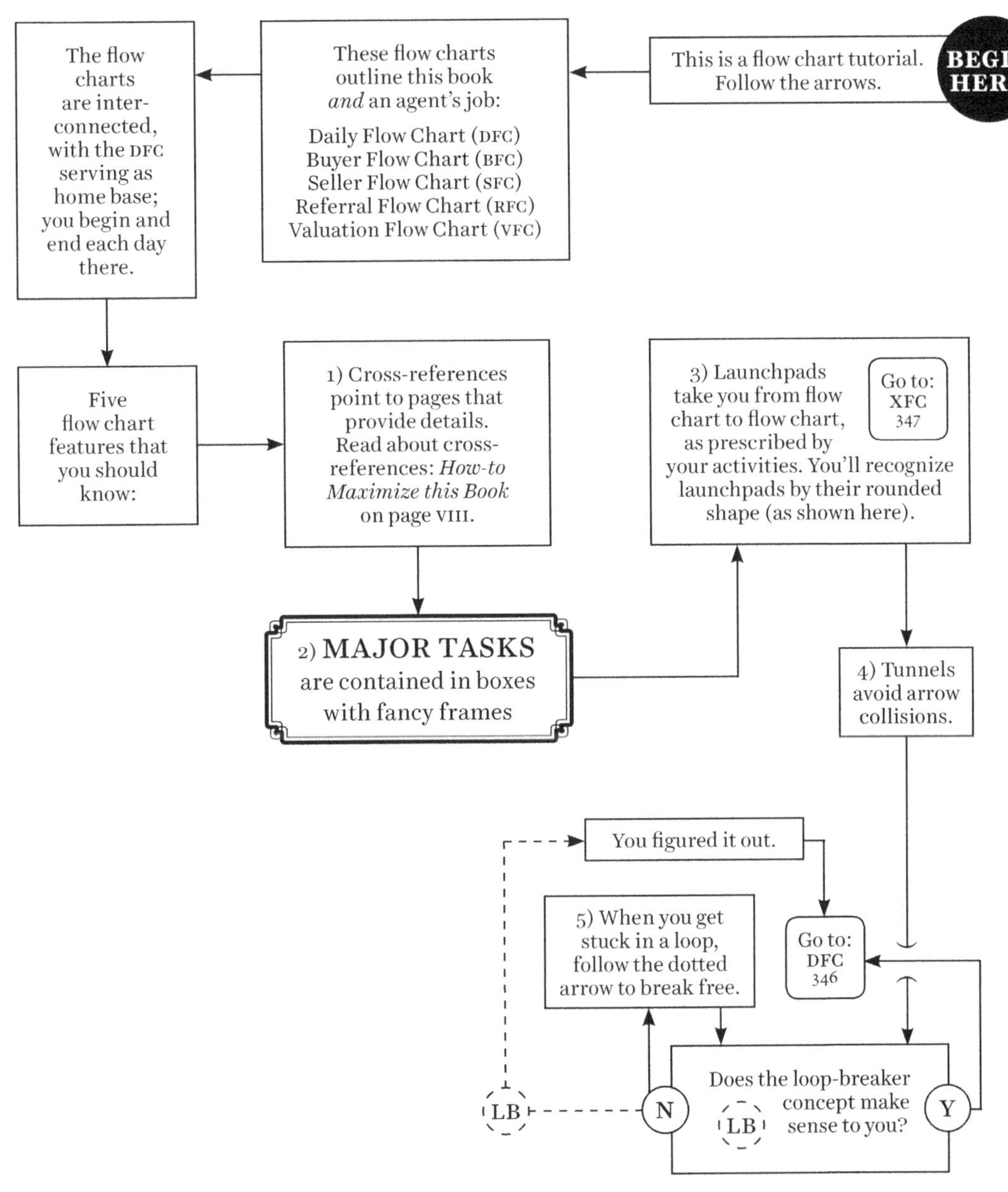

FLOW CHART TIPS

- Fold this page under the book, so the DFC is viewable when prospecting by telephone.[078]
- Rely on these flow charts to shepherd you through this book *and* guide you in the field; they're in the back for your convenience.
- Although each flow chart may seem complicated at first glance, they're really quite simple to read and navigate.

Go on, now—get to know them better.

(XFC)

Example Flow Chart

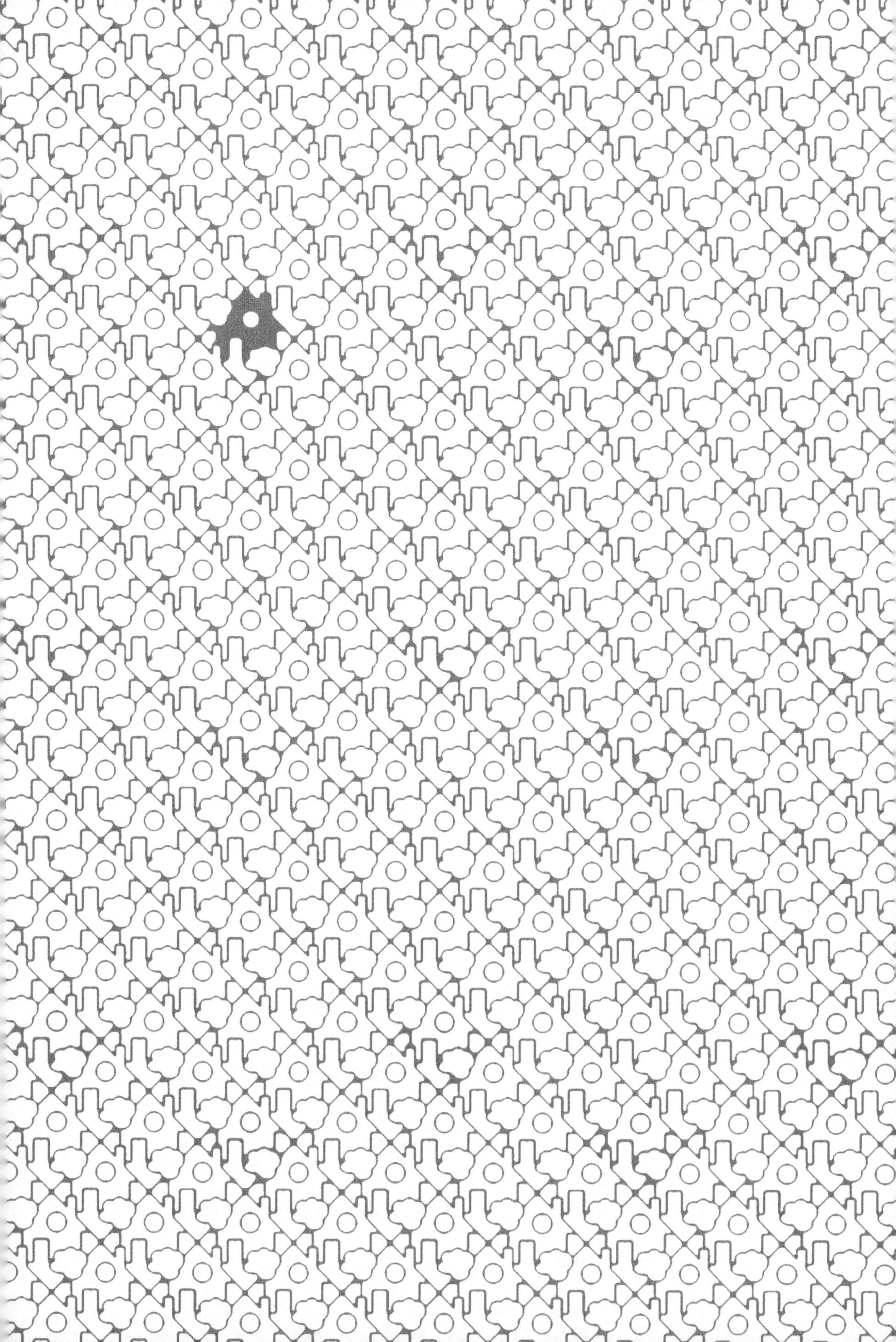

Made in the USA
Columbia, SC
01 February 2019